Grade 7

Glencoe

Georgia Math

Volume **1**

Mc
Graw
Hill
Education

Bothell, WA • Chicago, IL • Columbus, OH • New York, NY

Cover: (tl) Red maple tree (Acer rubrum) on the shore of Lookout Lake in Dade County Georgia, (tr) The most recognizable of all the Georgia state symbols, the Georgia peach, (b) Hurricane Falls, Tallulah Gorge State Park in the town of Tallulah Falls, Georgia.

connectED.mcgraw-hill.com

STEM McGraw-Hill is committed to providing instructional materials in Science, Technology, Engineering, and Mathematics (STEM) that give all students a solid foundation, one that prepares them for college and careers in the 21st century.

Send all inquiries to:
McGraw-Hill Education
STEM Learning Solutions Center
8787 Orion Place
Columbus, OH 43240

ISBN: 978-0-07-665485-7 (*Volume 1*)
MHID: 0-07-665485-0

Printed in the United States of America.

9 10 11 12 QVS 19 18 17 16

Our mission is to provide educational resources that enable students to become the problem solvers of the 21st century and inspire them to explore careers within Science, Technology, Engineering, and Mathematics (STEM) related fields.

CONTENTS IN BRIEF

 Units organized by the Georgia Grade 7 Curriculum Map

GO digital

it's all at connectED.mcgraw-hill.com

Go to the Student Center for your eBook, Resources, Homework, and Messages.

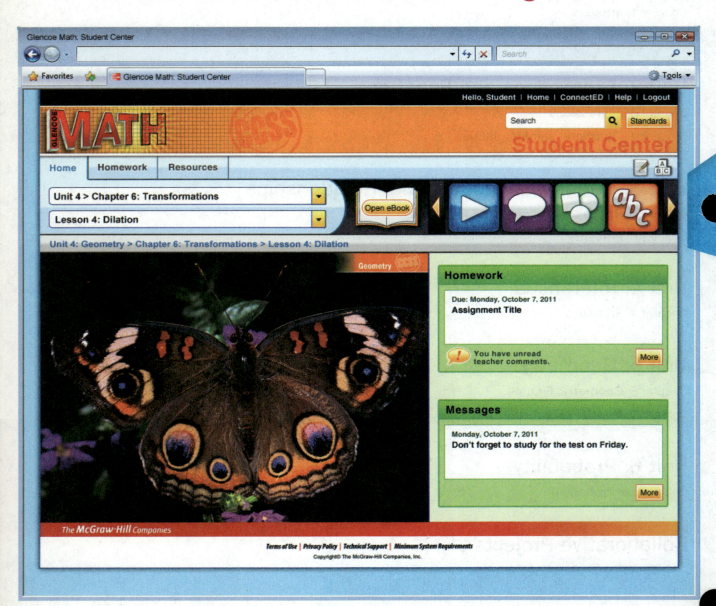

Write your Username [＿＿＿＿＿＿＿＿] ✏ Password [＿＿＿＿＿＿＿＿] ✏

Get your resources online to help you in class and at home.

Vocab

Find activities for building vocabulary.

Watch

Watch animations and videos.

Tutor

See a teacher illustrate examples and problems.

Tools

Explore concepts with virtual manipulatives.

Check

Self-assess your progress.

eHelp

Get targeted homework help.

Masters

Provides practice worksheets.

GO mobile

Scan this QR code with your smart phone* or visit mheonline.com/apps.

*May require quick response code reader app.

Available on the App Store

Chapter 1
Integers

 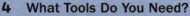
Online Transition Lessons
- Integers and Graphing
- Absolute Value
- Compare and Order Integers
- Graph on the Coordinate Plane
- Polygons on the Coordinate Plane

 Essential Question

WHAT happens when you add, subtract, multiply, and divide integers?

Frank Greenaway/Dorling Kindersley/Getty Images (t)

Chapter 2
Rational Numbers

 Essential Question

WHAT happens when you add, subtract, multiply, and divide fractions?

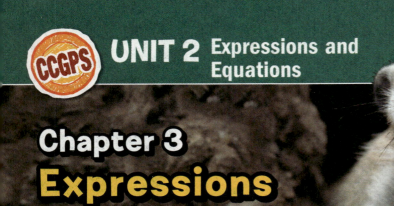

Chapter 3
Expressions

Online Transition Lessons
- **Inquiry Lab:** Equivalent Expressions
- Equivalent Expressions
- **Inquiry Lab:** Write Expressions
- Algebra: Write Expressions

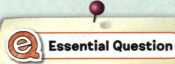

Essential Question

HOW can you use numbers and symbols to represent mathematical ideas?

Chapter 4
Equations and Inequalities

Online Transition Lessons

- **Inquiry Lab:** Inequalities
- Inequalities
- Write and Graph Inequalities
- **Inquiry Lab:** Solve One-Step Inequalities
- Solve One-Step Inequalities

 **Essential Question**

WHAT does it mean to say two quantities are equal?

Chapter 5
Ratios and Proportional Reasoning

 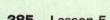
Essential Question

HOW can you show that two objects are proportional?

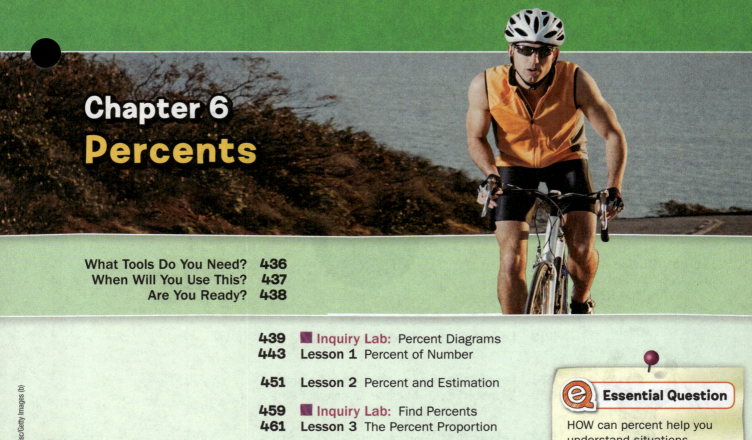

Chapter 6
Percents

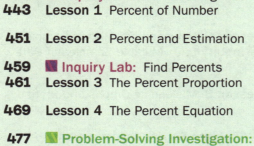

Essential Question

HOW can percent help you
understand situations
involving money?

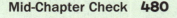

Chapter 7
Statistics

Essential Question

HOW do you know which type of graph to use when displaying data?

Chapter 8
Geometric Figures

Essential Question

HOW does geometry help us describe real-world objects?

Chapter 9
Measure Figures

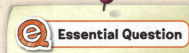

Essential Question

HOW do measurements help you describe real-world objects?

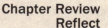

Image Source/Getty Images (t); DLILLC/CORBIS (c); Tim Flach/Stone+/Getty Images (b)

Copyright © The McGraw-Hill Companies, Inc.

UNIT 6 Probability

Chapter 10
Probability

Essential Question

HOW can you predict the outcome of future events?

Georgia Grade 7 Curriculum Map

Georgia Math, Grade 7, focuses on teaching the CCGPS standards in the order of the Georgia Grade 7 Curriculum map.

Unit 1: Operations with Rational Numbers

MCC7.NS 1 Apply and extend previous understandings of addition and subtraction to add and subtract rational numbers; represent addition and subtraction on a horizontal or vertical number line diagram.

MCC7.NS1.a Describe situations in which opposite quantities combine to make 0. For example, a hydrogen atom has 0 charge because its two constituents are oppositely charged.

MCC7.NS1.b Understand $p + q$ as the number located a distance $|q|$ from p, in the positive or negative direction depending on whether q is positive or negative. Show that a number and its opposite have a sum of 0 (are additive inverses). Interpret sums of rational numbers by describing real-world contexts.

MCC7.NS1.c Understand subtraction of rational numbers as adding the additive inverse, $p - q = p + (-q)$. Show that the distance between two rational numbers on the number line is the absolute value of their difference, and apply this principle in real-world context.

MCC7.NS1.d Apply properties of operations as strategies to add and subtract rational numbers.

MCC7.NS 2 Apply and extend previous understandings of multiplication and division and of fractions to multiply and divide rational numbers

MCC7.NS 2.a Understand that multiplication is extended from fractions to rational numbers by requiring that operations continue to satisfy the properties of operations, particularly the distributive property, leading to products such as $(-1)(-1) = 1$ and the rules for multiplying signed numbers. Interpret products of rational numbers by describing real-world contexts.

MCC7.NS 2.b Understand that integers can be divided, provided that the divisor is not zero, and every quotient of integers (with non-zero divisor) is a rational number. If p and q are integers, then $-(p/q) = (-p)/q = p/(-q)$. Interpret quotients of rational numbers by describing real-world contexts.

MCC7.NS 2.c Apply properties of operations as strategies to multiply and divide rational numbers.

MCC7.NS 2.d Convert a rational number to a decimal using long division; know that the decimal form of a rational number terminates in 0s or eventually repeats.

MCC7.NS 3 Solve real-world and mathematical problems involving the four operations with rational numbers.

Real-world problem solving in these chapters also addresses:

MCC7.EE 3 *Solve multi-step real-life and mathematical problems posed with positive and negative rational numbers in any form (whole numbers, fractions, and decimals), using tools strategically. Apply properties of operations to calculate with numbers in any form; convert between forms as appropriate; and assess the reasonableness of answers using mental computation and estimation strategies.*

MCC6.NS.5 *Understand that positive and negative numbers are used together to describe quantities having opposite directions or values (e.g. temperature above/below zero, elevation above/below sea level, debits/credits, positive/negative electric charge);*

use positive and negative numbers to represent quantities in real-world contests, explaining the meaning of 0 in each situation.

MCC6.NS.6 *Understand a rational number as a point on the number line. Extend number line diagrams and coordinate axes familiar from previous grades to represent points on the line and in the plane with negative number coordinates.*

> **MCC6.NS.6a** *Recognize opposite signs of numbers as indicating locations on opposite sides of 0 on the number line; recognize that the opposite of the opposite of a number is the number itself (e.g.,$-(-3) = 3$, and that 0 is its own opposite.*

> **MCC6.NS.6b** *Understand signs of numbers in ordered pairs as indicating locations in quadrants of the coordinate plane; recognize that when two ordered pairs differ only by signs, the locations of the points are related by reflections across one or both axes.*

> **MCC6.NS.6c** *Find and position integers and other rational numbers on a horizontal or vertical number line diagram; find and position pairs of integers and other rational numbers on a coordinate plane.*

MCC6.NS.7 *Understand ordering and absolute value of rational numbers.*

> **MCC6.NS.7a** *Interpret statements of inequality as statements about the relative position of two numbers on a number line diagram.*

> **MCC6.NS.7b** *Write, interpret, and explain statements of order for rational numbers in real-world contexts.*

> **MCC6.NS.7c** *Understand the absolute value of a rational number as its distance from 0 on the number line; interpret absolute value as magnitude for a positive or negative quantity in a real-world situation.*

> **MCC6.NS.7d** *Distinguish comparisons of absolute value from statements about order.*

MCC6.NS.8 *Solve real-world and mathematical problems by graphing points in all four quadrants of the coordinate plane. Include use of coordinates and absolute value to find distances between points with the same first coordinates or the same second coordinates.*

MCC6.G.3 *Draw polygons in the coordinate plane given coordinates for the vertices; use coordinates to find the length of a side joining points with the same first coordinate or the same second coordinate. Apply these techniques in the context of solving real world and mathematical problems.*

Unit 2: Expressions and Equations

MCCS addressed in Unit 2:

MCC7.EE.1 Apply properties of operations as strategies to add, subtract, factor, and expand linear expressions with rational coefficients.

MCC7.EE.2 Understand that rewriting an expression in different forms in a problem context can shed light on the problem and how the quantities in it are related.

MCC7.EE.3 Solve multi step real life and mathematical problems posed with positive and negative rational numbers in any form (whole numbers, fractions, and decimals), using tools strategically. Apply properties of operations as strategies to calculate with numbers in any form; convert between forms as appropriate; and assess the reasonableness of answers using mental computation and estimation strategies.

MCC7.EE.4 Use variables to represent quantities in a real-world or mathematical problem, and construct simple equations and inequalities to solve problems by reasoning about the quantities.

> **7.EE.4a** Solve word problems leading to equations of the form $px + q = r$ and $p(x + q) = r$, where p, q, and r are specific rational numbers. Solve equations of these forms fluently. Compare an algebraic solution to an arithmetic solution, identifying the sequence of the operations used in each approach.

7.EE.4b Solve word problems leading to inequalities of the form $px + q > r$ or $px + q < r$, where p, q, and r are specific rational numbers. Graph the solution set of the inequality and interpret it in the context of the problem.

Additional MCCS incorporated in Unit 2:

MCC7.NS 1 *Apply and extend previous understandings of addition and subtraction to add and subtract rational numbers; represent addition and subtraction on a horizontal or vertical number line diagram.*

MCC7.NS1.a *Describe situations in which opposite quantities combine to make 0. For example, a hydrogen atom has 0 charge because its two constituents are oppositely charged.*

MCC7.NS1.b *Understand $p + q$ as the number located a distance $|q|$ from p, in the positive or negative direction depending on whether q is positive or negative. Show that a number and its opposite have a sum of 0 (are additive inverses). Interpret sums of rational numbers by describing real-world contexts.*

MCC7.NS1.c *Understand subtraction of rational numbers as adding the additive inverse, $p - q = p + (-q)$. Show that the distance between two rational numbers on the number line is the absolute value of their difference, and apply this principle in real-world context.*

MCC7.NS1.d *Apply properties of operations as strategies to add and subtract rational numbers.*

MCC7.NS 2 *Apply and extend previous understandings of multiplication and division and of fractions to multiply and divide rational numbers*

MCC7.NS 2.a *Understand that multiplication is extended from fractions to rational numbers by requiring that operations continue to satisfy the properties of operations, particularly the distributive property, leading to products such as $(-1)(-1) = 1$ and the rules for multiplying signed numbers. Interpret products of rational numbers by describing real-world contexts.*

MCC7.NS 2.b *Understand that integers can be divided, provided that the divisor is not zero, and every quotient of integers (with non-zero divisor) is a rational number. If p and q are integers, then $-(p/q) = (-p)/q = p/(-q)$. Interpret quotients of rational numbers by describing real-world contexts.*

MCC7.NS 2.c *Apply properties of operations as strategies to multiply and divide rational numbers.*

MCC7.NS 2.d *Convert a rational number to a decimal using long division; know that the decimal form of a rational number terminates in 0s or eventually repeats.*

MCC7.NS 3 *Solve real-world and mathematical problems involving the four operations with rational numbers.*

Transition Standards to be addressed:

MCC6.EE.3 *Apply the properties of operations to generate equivalent expressions.*

MCC6.EE.4 *Identify when two expressions are equivalent (i.e., when the two expressions name the same number regardless of which value is substituted into them).*

MCC6.EE.6 *Use variables to represent numbers and write expressions when solving a real-world or mathematical problem; understand that a variable can represent an unknown number, or, depending on the purpose at hand, any number in a specified set.*

MCC6.EE.8 *Write an inequality of the form $x > c$ or $x < c$ to represent a constraint or condition in a real-world or mathematical problem. Recognize that inequalities of the form $x > c$ or $x < c$ have infinitely many solutions; represent solutions of such inequalities on number line diagrams.*

Unit 3: Ratios and Proportional Relationships

MCCS addressed in Unit 3:

MCC7.RP.1 Compute unit rates associated with ratios of fractions, including ratios of lengths, areas and other quantities measured in like or different units.

MCC7.RP.2 Recognize and represent proportional relationships between quantities.

> **MCC7.RP.2a** Decide whether two quantities are in a proportional relationship, e.g., by testing for equivalent ratios in a table or graphing on a coordinate plane and observing whether the graph is a straight line through the origin.

> **MCC7.RP.2b** Identify the constant of proportionality (unit rate) in tables, graphs, equations, diagrams, and verbal descriptions of proportional relationships.

> **MCC7.RP.2c** Represent proportional relationships by equations.

> **MCC7.RP.2d** Explain what a point (x, y) on the graph of a proportional relationship means in terms of the situation, with special attention to the points $(0, 0)$ and $(1, r)$ where r is the unit rate.

MCC7.RP.3 Use proportional relationships to solve multistep ratio and percent problems. Examples: simple interest, tax, markups and markdowns, gratuities and commissions, fees, percent increase and decrease, percent error.

MCC7.G.1 Solve problems involving scale drawings of geometric figures, including computing actual lengths and areas from a scale drawing and reproducing a scale drawing at a different scale.

Additional MCCS incorporated in Unit 3:

MCC7.EE 3 *Solve multi-step real-life and mathematical problems posed with positive and negative rational numbers in any form (whole numbers, fractions, and decimals), using tools strategically. Apply properties of operations to calculate with numbers in any form; convert between forms as appropriate; and assess the reasonableness of answers using mental computation and estimation strategies.*

MCC7.NS 1 *Apply and extend previous understandings of addition and subtraction to add and subtract rational numbers; represent addition and subtraction on a horizontal or vertical number line diagram.*

> **MCC7.NS1.a** *Describe situations in which opposite quantities combine to make 0. For example, a hydrogen atom has 0 charge because its two constituents are oppositely charged.*

> **MCC7.NS1.b** *Understand $p + q$ as the number located a distance $|q|$ from p, in the positive or negative direction depending on whether q is positive or negative. Show that a number and its opposite have a sum of 0 (are additive inverses). Interpret sums of rational numbers by describing real-world contexts.*

> **MCC7.NS1.c** *Understand subtraction of rational numbers as adding the additive inverse, $p - q = p + (-q)$. Show that the distance between two rational numbers on the number line is the absolute value of their difference, and apply this principle in real-world context.*

> **MCC7.NS1.d** *Apply properties of operations as strategies to add and subtract rational numbers.*

MCC7.NS 2. *Apply and extend previous understandings of multiplication and division and of fractions to multiply and divide rational numbers*

> **MCC7.NS 2.a** *Understand that multiplication is extended from fractions to rational numbers by requiring that operations continue to satisfy the properties of operations, particularly the distributive property, leading to products such as $(-1)(-1) = 1$ and the rules for multiplying signed numbers. Interpret products of rational numbers by describing real-world contexts.*

> **MCC7.NS 2.b** *Understand that integers can be divided, provided that the divisor is not zero, and every quotient of integers (with non-zero divisor) is a rational number. If p and q are integers, then $-(p/q) = (-p)/q = p/(-q)$. Interpret quotients of rational numbers by describing real-world contexts.*

MCC7.NS 2.c *Apply properties of operations as strategies to multiply and divide rational numbers.*

MCC7.NS 2.d *Convert a rational number to a decimal using long division; know that the decimal form of a rational number terminates in 0s or eventually repeats.*

MCC7.NS 3 *Solve real-world and mathematical problems involving the four operations with rational numbers.*

Unit 4: Inferences

MCCS addressed in Unit 4:

MCC7.SP.1 Understand that statistics can be used to gain information about a population by examining a sample of the population; generalizations about a population from a sample are valid only if the sample is representative of that population. Understand that random sampling tends to produce representative samples and support valid inferences.

MCC7.SP.2 Use data from a random sample to draw inferences about a population with an unknown characteristic of interest. Generate multiple samples (or simulated samples) of the same size to gauge the variation in estimates or predictions.

MCC7.SP.3 Informally assess the degree of visual overlap of two numerical data distributions with similar variabilities, measuring the difference between the centers by expressing it as a multiple of a measure of variability.

MCC7.SP.4 Use measures of center and measures of variability for numerical data from random samples to draw informal comparative inferences about two populations.

Additional MCCS incorporated in Unit 4:

MCC7.EE 3 *Solve multi-step real-life and mathematical problems posed with positive and negative rational numbers in any form (whole numbers, fractions, and decimals), using tools strategically. Apply properties of operations to calculate with numbers in any form; convert between forms as appropriate; and assess the reasonableness of answers using mental computation and estimation strategies.*

MCC7.NS 1 *Apply and extend previous understandings of addition and subtraction to add and subtract rational numbers; represent addition and subtraction on a horizontal or vertical number line diagram.*

MCC7.NS1.a *Describe situations in which opposite quantities combine to make 0. For example, a hydrogen atom has 0 charge because its two constituents are oppositely charged.*

MCC7.NS1.b *Understand $p + q$ as the number located a distance $|q|$ from p, in the positive or negative direction depending on whether q is positive or negative. Show that a number and its opposite have a sum of 0 (are additive inverses). Interpret sums of rational numbers by describing real-world contexts.*

MCC7.NS1.c *Understand subtraction of rational numbers as adding the additive inverse, $p - q = p + (-q)$. Show that the distance between two rational numbers on the number line is the absolute value of their difference, and apply this principle in real-world context.*

MCC7.NS1.d *Apply properties of operations as strategies to add and subtract rational numbers.*

MCC7.NS 2 *Apply and extend previous understandings of multiplication and division and of fractions to multiply and divide rational numbers*

MCC7.NS 2.a *Understand that multiplication is extended from fractions to rational numbers by requiring that operations continue to satisfy the properties of operations, particularly the distributive property, leading to products such as $(-1)(-1) = 1$ and the rules for multiplying signed numbers. Interpret products of rational numbers by describing real-world contexts.*

MCC7.NS 2.b *Understand that integers can be divided, provided that the divisor is not zero, and every quotient of integers (with non-zero divisor) is a rational number. If p and q are integers, then −(p/q) = (−p)/q = p/(−q). Interpret quotients of rational numbers by describing real-world contexts.*

MCC7.NS 2.c *Apply properties of operations as strategies to multiply and divide rational numbers.*

MCC7.NS 2.d *Convert a rational number to a decimal using long division; know that the decimal form of a rational number terminates in 0s or eventually repeats.*

MCC7.NS 3 *Solve real-world and mathematical problems involving the four operations with rational numbers.*

Unit 5: Geometry

MCCS addressed in Unit 5:

MCC7.G.2 Draw (freehand, with ruler and protractor, and with technology) geometric shapes with given condition. Focus on constructing triangles from three measures of angles or sides, noticing when the conditions determine a unique triangle, more than one triangle, or no triangle.

MCC7.G.3 Describe the two dimensional figures that result from slicing three dimensional figures, as in plane sections of right rectangular prisms and right rectangular pyramids.

MCC7.G.4 Know the formulas for the area and circumference of a circle and use them to solve problems; give an informal derivation of the relationship between the circumference and area of a circle.

MCC7.G.5 Use facts about supplementary, complementary, vertical, and adjacent angles in a multi step problem to write and solve simple equations for an unknown angle in a figure.

MCC7.G.6 Solve real world and mathematical problems involving area, volume and surface area of two and three dimensional objects composed of triangles, quadrilaterals, polygons, cubes, and right prisms.

Additional MCCS incorporated in Unit 5:

MCC7.G.1 *Solve problems involving scale drawings of geometric figures, including computing actual lengths and areas from a scale drawing and reproducing a scale drawing at a different scale.*

Unit 6: Probability

MCCS addressed in Unit 6:

MCC7.SP.5 Understand that the probability of a chance event is a number between 0 and 1 that expresses the likelihood of the event occurring. Larger numbers indicate greater likelihood. A probability near 0 indicates an unlikely event, a probability around 1/2 indicates an event that is neither unlikely nor likely, and a probability near 1 indicates a likely event.

MCC7.SP.6 Approximate the probability of a chance event by collecting data on the chance process that produces it and observing its long run relative frequency, and predict the approximate relative frequency given the probability.

MCC7.SP.7 Develop a probability model and use it to find probabilities of events. Compare probabilities from a model to observed frequencies; if the agreement is not good, explain possible sources of the discrepancy.

> **MCC7.SP.7a** Develop a uniform probability model by assigning equal probability to all outcomes, and use the model to determine probabilities of events.

> **MCC7.SP.7b** Develop a probability model (which may not be uniform) by observing frequencies in data generated from a chance process.

MCC7.SP.8 Find probabilities of compound events using organized lists, tables, tree diagrams, and simulation.

> **MCC7.SP.8a** Understand that, just as with simple events, the probability of a compound event is the fraction of outcomes in the sample space for which the compound event occurs.

> **MCC7.SP.8b** Represent sample spaces for compound events using methods such as organized lists, tables and tree diagrams. For an event described in everyday language (e.g., "rolling double sixes"), identify the outcomes in the sample space which compose the event.

> **MCC7.SP.8c** Design and use a simulation to generate frequencies for compound events.

Unit 7: Show What We Know

MCCS addressed in Unit 8:
ALL

UNIT 1

Operations with Rational Numbers

CCGPS

Essential Question

HOW can mathematical ideas be represented?

Chapter 1
Integers

Negative integers can be used in everyday contexts that involve values below zero. In this chapter, you will add, subtract, multiply, and divide integers.

Chapter 2
Rational Numbers

Every quotient of integers (with non-zero divisor) is a rational number. In this chapter, you will solve multi-step real-life problems by performing operations on rational numbers.

Chapter 1
Integers

Essential Question

WHAT happens when you add, subtract, multiply, and divide integers?

Common Core GPS

Content Standards
MCC7.NS.1, MCC7.NS.1a, MCC7.NS.1b, MCC7.NS.1c, MCC7.NS.1d, MCC7.NS.2, MCC7.NS.2a, MCC7.NS.2b, MCC7.NS.2c, MCC7.NS.3, MCC7.EE.3

Mathematical Practices
1, 2, 3, 4, 5, 6, 7, 8

Math in the Real World

Penguins can stay under water up to 20 minutes at a time, sometimes diving to a depth of −275 feet. The number 20 is a positive integer; −275 is a negative integer.

On the graph below, graph a point at the maximum depth a penguin can dive.

FOLDABLES®
Study Organizer

1 Cut out the correct Foldable from the FL pages in the back of this book.

2 Place your Foldable on the Key Concept page toward the end of this chapter.

3 Use the Foldable throughout this chapter to help you learn about integers.

What Tools Do You Need?

Vocabulary

absolute value	integer	positive integer
additive inverse	negative integer	zero pair
graph	opposites	

Study Skill: Writing Math

Compare and Contrast When you *compare*, you notice how things are alike. When you *contrast*, you notice how they are different. Here are two cell phone plans.

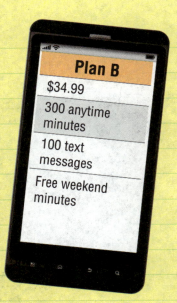

Plan B
$34.99
300 anytime minutes
100 text messages
Free weekend minutes

Plan A
$34.99
200 anytime minutes
200 text messages
Free weekend minutes

Compare and contrast the monthly plans. Make a list of how they are alike and how they are different.

Alike/Compare	Different/Contrast

Try the Quick Check below.
Or, take the Online Readiness Quiz.

Quick Review

Common Core Review MCC5.OA.1, MCC6.NS.6

Example 1

Evaluate 48 ÷ (6 + 2)5.

Follow the order of operations.

$48 \div (6 + 2)5$

$= 48 \div 8 \cdot 5$ Add 6 and 2.

$= 6 \cdot 5$ Divide 48 by 8.

$= 30$ Multiply.

Example 2

Graph and label M(6, 3) on the coordinate plane.

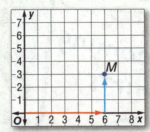

Start from the origin. Point M is located 6 units to the right and 3 units up.

Draw a dot and label the point.

Quick Check

Order of Operations Evaluate each expression.

1. $54 \div (6 + 3) = $ _____

2. $(10 + 50) \div 5 = $ _____

3. $18 + 2(4 - 1) = $ _____

Coordinate Graphing Graph and label each point on the coordinate grid. The first one is done for you.

4. $A(1, 1)$ **5.** $B(2, 8)$

6. $C(8, 1)$ **7.** $D(3, 4)$

8. $E(1, 5)$ **9.** $G(7, 6)$

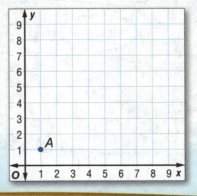

How Did You Do?

Which problems did you answer correctly in the Quick Check? Shade those exercise numbers below.

① ② ③ ④ ⑤ ⑥ ⑦ ⑧ ⑨

Integers and Absolute Value

Lesson 1

What You'll Learn

Scan the lesson. List two headings you would use to make an outline of the lesson.

- _____
  _____
- _____
  _____

Essential Question

WHAT happens when you add, subtract, multiply, and divide integers?

 Vocabulary

integer
negative integer
positive integer
graph
absolute value

 Common Core GPS

Content Standards
Preparation for MCC7.NS.3
Mathematical Practices
1, 3, 4, 5

Vocabulary Start-Up

Numbers like 5 and −8 are called integers. An **integer** is any number from the set {…, −4, −3, −2, −1, 0, 1, 2, 3, 4, …}, where … means *continues without end*.

Complete the graphic organizer.

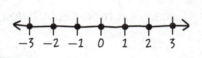

Describe It
_____
_____

Picture It

$-3 \quad -2 \quad -1 \quad 0 \quad 1 \quad 2 \quad 3$

List Some Examples

integer

List Some NonExamples

Awesome halfpipe!

Real-World Link

- The bottom of a snowboarding halfpipe is 5 meters below the top. Circle the integer you would you use to represent this position?

     5   or   −5

- Describe another situation that uses negative integers. _____
  _____

Identify and Graph Integers

Negative integers are integers less than zero. They are written with a − sign.

Positive integers are integers greater than zero. They can be written with a + sign.

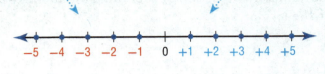

−5 −4 −3 −2 −1 0 +1 +2 +3 +4 +5

Zero is neither negative nor positive.

Integers can be graphed on a number line. To **graph** an integer on the number line, draw a dot on the line at its location.

Examples

Tutor

Write an integer for each situation.

1. **an average temperature of 5 degrees below normal**

Because it represents *below* normal, the integer is −5.

· ·

2. **an average rainfall of 5 inches above normal**

Because it represents *above* normal, the integer is +5 or 5.

Got It? Do these problems to find out.

Show your work.

Write an integer for each situation.

a. 6 degrees above normal

b. 2 inches below normal

a. _____6_____

b. _____−2_____

Example

Tutor

3. **Graph the set of integers {4, −6, 0} on a number line.**

Draw a number line. Then draw a dot at the location of each integer.

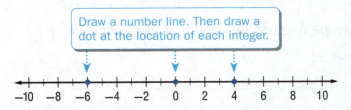

−10 −8 −6 −4 −2 0 2 4 6 8 10

Got It? Do these problems to find out.

Graph each set of integers on a number line.

   c. {−2, 8, −7}   **d.** {−4, 10, −3, 7}

c. _____

d. _____

Absolute Value

 **Key Concept**

Words   The absolute value of a number is the distance between the number and zero on a number line.

| 5 units | 5 units |

```
  ←————————————|————————————→
 −5  −4 −3 −2 −1  0  1  2  3  4  5
```

Examples $|−5| = 5$ $|5| = 5$

On the number line in the Key Concept box, notice that −5 and 5 are each 5 units from 0, even though they are on opposite sides of 0. Numbers that are the same distance from zero on a number line have the same **absolute value**.

Examples

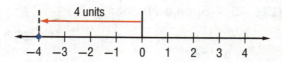 Tutor

Evaluate each expression.

4. $|−4|$

    The graph of −4 is 4 units from 0.

    So, $|−4| = 4$.

```
  ←————————————|
 −4  −3 −2 −1  0  1  2  3  4
```
        4 units

> **Order of Operations**
> The absolute value bars are considered to be a grouping symbol. When evaluating $|−5| − |2|$, evaluate the absolute values before subtracting.

- -

5. $|−5| − |2|$

    $|−5| − |2| = 5 − 2$ $|−5| = 5, |2| = 2$

    So, $|−5| − |2| = 3$.

e. _____

Got It? Do these problems to find out.

f. _____

   e. $|8|$ **f.** $2 + |−3|$ **g.** $|−6| − 5$

g. _____

 Tutor

6. Nick climbs 30 feet up a rock wall and then climbs 22 feet down to a landing area. The number of feet Nick climbs can be represented using the expression $|30| + |-22|$. How many feet does Nick climb?

$|30| + |-22| = 30 + |-22|$ The absolute value of 30 is 30.

$\qquad = 30 + 22$ or 52 The absolute value of -22 is 22. Simplify.

So, Nick climbs 52 feet.

Guided Practice

 Check

Write an integer for each situation. (Examples 1 and 2)

1. a deposit of $16 _____

2. a loss of 11 yards _____

3. 6°F below zero _____

 Show your work.

Evaluate each expression. (Examples 4–6)

4. $|-9| =$ _____

5. $|18| - |-10| =$ _____

6. $|-11| - |-6| =$ _____

7. Graph the set of integers {11, −5, −8} on a number line. (Example 3)

8. **Building on the Essential Question** Why is the absolute value of a number positive? Explain your reasoning. _____

_____

_____

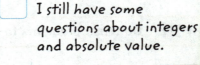

Rate Yourself!

☐ I understand integers and absolute value.

▶▶ Great! You're ready to move on!

☐ I still have some questions about integers and absolute value.

 ▮▮ No Problem! Go online to access a Personal Tutor. Tutor

Independent Practice

Go online for Step-by-Step Solutions

Write an integer for each situation. (Examples 1 and 2)

1. a profit of $9 ____9____

2. a bank withdrawal of $50 __-50__

Show your work.

3. 53°C below zero ___-53___

4. 7 inches more than normal ___7___

Graph each set of integers on a number line. (Example 3)

5 {0, 1, −3}

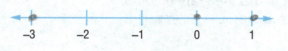

$$-3 \quad -2 \quad -1 \quad 0 \quad 1$$

6. {−5, −1, 10, −9}

$$-10 \; -8 \; -6 \; -4 \; -2 \; 0 \; 2 \; 4 \; 6 \; 8 \; 10$$

Evaluate each expression. (Examples 4 and 5)

7. $|10| =$ ___10___

8. $|-7| - 5 =$ ___2___

9 $1 + |7| =$ ___8___

10. The number of yards a football team moves on the field can be represented using the expression $|8| + |-4|$. How many yards does the football team move? (Example 6)

___12 yards___

11. In golf, scores are often written in relationship to *par*, the average score for a round at a certain course. Write an integer to represent a score that is 7 under par. (Examples 1 and 2)

___-7___

12. A scuba diver descended 10 feet, 8 feet, and 11 feet. The total number of feet can be represented using the expression $|-10| + |-8| + |-11|$. What is the total number of feet the scuba diver descended?

_29ft_

13. **CCGPS** **Use Math Tools** Mr. Chavez spent $199.99 for a new smart phone, $39.99 on a carrying case, and $59.99 on accessories. The expression $|-199.99| + |-39.99| + |-59.99|$ represents the total amount that Mr. Chavez spent. How much did Mr. Chavez spend altogether? Check your answer using estimation.

_299.97_

H.O.T. Problems Higher Order Thinking

14. **CCGPS** **Reason Inductively** If $|x| = 3$, what is the value of x?

_3 & -3_

15. **CCGPS** **Persevere with Problems** Two numbers A and B are graphed on a number line. Is it *always*, *sometimes*, or *never* true that $A - |B| \leq A + B$ and $A > |B|$. Explain.

16. **CCGPS** **Which One Doesn't Belong?** Identify the expression that is not equal to the other three. Explain your reasoning.

$15 - |-5|$	$|-4| + 6$	$-|7 + 3|$	$|-10|$

Georgia Test Practice

17. Which integer represents the temperature shown on the thermometer?

Ⓐ −11°F

Ⓑ −10°F

Ⓒ   10°F

Ⓓ   11°F

Extra Practice

Write an integer for each situation.

18. 2 feet below flood level _−2_

Homework Help ➡ *Because it represents below flood level, the integer is −2.*

19. an elevator goes up 12 floors _____

 Model with Mathematics **Graph each set of integers on a number line.**

20. {3, −7, 6}

−10 −8 −6 −4 −2   0   2   4   6   8   10

21. {−2, −4, −6, −8}

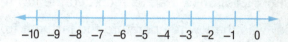
−10 −9 −8 −7 −6 −5 −4 −3 −2 −1   0

Evaluate each expression.

22. |−12| = _____

23. 7 + |4| = _____

24. |−9| + |−5| = _____

25. |−10| ÷ 2 × |5| = _____

26. 12 − |−8| + 7 = _____

27. |27| ÷ 3 − |−4| = _____

28. Jasmine's pet guinea pig gained 8 ounces in one month. Write an integer to describe the amount of weight her pet gained.

_____

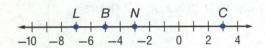

Georgia Test Practice

29. Which point has a coordinate with the greatest absolute value?

A number line showing points L at −7, B at −5, N at −3, and C at 3, marked −10, −8, −6, −4, −2, 0, 2, 4.

- Ⓐ Point *B*
- Ⓒ Point *L*
- Ⓑ Point *C*
- Ⓓ Point *N*

30. Which of the following statements about these real-world situations is *not* true?

- Ⓕ A $100 check deposited in a bank can be represented by +100.
- Ⓖ A loss of 15 yards in a football game can be represented by −15.
- Ⓗ A temperature of 20 below zero can be represented by −20.
- Ⓘ A submarine diving 300 feet under water can be represented by +300.

31. Short Response Rachel recorded the low temperatures for one week in the table. On which day was the low temperature the farthest from 0°F? _____

Low Temperatures							
Day	Sunday	Monday	Tuesday	Wednesday	Thursday	Friday	Saturday
Temperature (°F)	2	−6	4	−8	2	0	−1

CCGPS Common Core Review

Write the ordered pair corresponding to each point graphed at the right. Then state the quadrant or axis location of each point. MCC6.NS.6

32. *J* _____

33. *K* _____

34. *L* _____

35. *M* _____

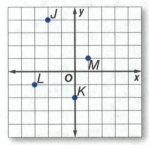

Graph and label each point on the coordinate plane. MCC6.NS.6c

36. *A*(2, 4)

37. *B*(−3, 1)

38. *C*(2, 0)

39. *D*(−3, −3)

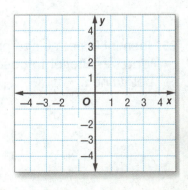

WHEN is the sum of two integers a negative number?

CCGPS Content Standards
MCC7.NS.1,
MCC7.NS.3

Mathematical Practices
1, 3, 7

Football In football, forward progress is represented by a positive integer. Losing yardage is represented by a negative integer. On the first play, a team lost 5 yards. On the second play, the team lost 2 yards. What was the team's total yardage on the two plays? Find out in Investigation 1.

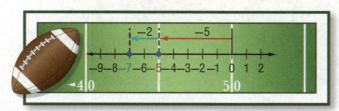

Investigation 1

Watch Tools

Use counters to find the total yardage.

Step 1   Use negative integers to represent the yards lost on each play.

$$\boxed{} + \boxed{}$$

a loss of 5 yards   a loss of 2 yards

Step 2   Combine a set of 5 negative counters and a set of 2 negative counters.

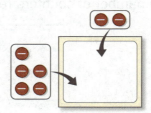

Step 3   There is a total of $\boxed{}$ negative counters.

So, $-5 + (-2) = \boxed{}$. The team lost a total of $\boxed{}$ yards

on the first two plays.

The following two properties are important when modeling operations with integers.

- When one positive counter is paired with one negative counter, the result is called a **zero pair**. The value of a zero pair is 0.

- You can add or remove zero pairs from a mat because adding or removing zero does not change the value of the counters on the mat.

Investigation 2

Use counters to find −4 + 2.

Step 1   Combine ☐ negative counters with ☐ positive counters.

Step 2   Remove all zero pairs.

Step 3   Find the number of counters remaining.

There are ☐ negative counters remaining.

So, −4 + 2 = ☐ .

Work with a partner. Find each sum. Show your work using drawings.

1. $5 + 6 =$ _____

2. $-3 + (-5) =$ _____

3. $-5 + (-4) =$ _____

4. $7 + 3 =$ _____

5. $-6 + 5 =$ _____

6. $-2 + 7 =$ _____

7. $8 + (-3) =$ _____

8. $3 + (-6) =$ _____

Work with a partner to complete the table. The first one is done for you.

	Addition Expression	Sum	Sign of Addend with Greater Absolute Value	Sign of Sum
	5 + (−2)	3	Positive	Positive
9.	−6 + 2			
10.	7 + (−12)			
11.	−4 + 9			
12.	−12 + 20			
13.	15 + (−18)			

14. **CCGPS** **Identify Structure** Write two addition sentences where the sum is positive. In each sentence, one addend should be positive and the other negative.

_____

15. Write two addition sentences where the sum is negative. In each sentence, one addend should be positive and the other negative.

_____

16. Write two addition sentences where the sum is zero. Describe the numbers.

_____

_____

17. **CCGPS** **Justify Conclusions** A contestant scores −100 points in the first round, −250 points in the second round, and 500 points in the third round. Find the contestant's total number of points. Explain your reasoning.

_____

_____

18. **Inquiry** WHEN is the sum of two integers a negative number?

_____

_____

Add Integers

What You'll Learn

Scan the lesson. List two headings you would use to make an outline of the lesson.

- _____
- _____

 Essential Question

WHAT happens when you add, subtract, multiply, and divide integers?

 Vocabulary

opposites
additive inverse

CCGPS **Common Core GPS**

Content Standards
MCC7.NS.1, MCC7.NS.1a, MCC7.NS.1b, MCC7.NS.1d, MCC7.NS.3, MCC7.EE.3

Mathematical Practices
1, 3, 4, 7

Vocabulary Start-Up

Integers like 2 and −2 are called **opposites** because they are the same distance from 0, but on opposite sides. Complete the graphic organizer about opposites.

Picture It

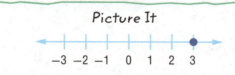

−3 −2 −1 0 1 2 3

Real-World Example	Math Example

Two integers that are opposites are also called **additive inverses**. The Additive Inverse Property states that the sum of any number and its additive inverse is zero. You can show 2 + (−2) on a number line.

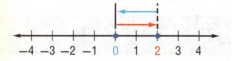

−4 −3 −2 −1 0 1 2 3 4

Start at zero.
Move 2 units to the right to show 2.
Then move 2 units to the left to show −2.

So, 2 + (−2) = ☐.

Real-World Link

The temperature outside is −5°. Name the temperature that would make the sum of the two temperatures 0°. ☐

Add Integers with the Same Sign

Words To add integers with the same sign, add their absolute values. The sum is:

- positive if both integers are positive.
- negative if both integers are negative.

Examples $7 + 4 = 11$ $-7 + (-4) = -11$

Work Zone

Examples

1. **Find $-3 + (-2)$.**

Start at 0. Move 3 units down to show -3.

From there, move 2 units down to show -2.

So, $-3 + (-2) = -5$.

 Show your work.

2. **Find $-26 + (-17)$.**

$-26 + (-17) = -43$ Both integers are negative, so the sum is negative.

Got It? Do these problems to find out.

a. _____

b. _____

c. _____

   a. $-5 + (-7)$ **b.** $-10 + (-4)$ **c.** $-14 + (-16)$

Key Concept

Add Integers with Different Signs

Words To add integers with different signs, subtract their absolute values. The sum is:

- positive if the positive integer's absolute value is greater.
- negative if the negative integer's absolute value is greater.

Examples $9 + (-4) = 5$ $-9 + 4 = -5$

When you add integers with different signs, start at zero. Move right for positive integers. Move left for negative integers. So, the sum of $p + q$ is located a distance $|q|$ from p.

Examples

 Watch | Tutor

3. Find $5 + (-3)$.

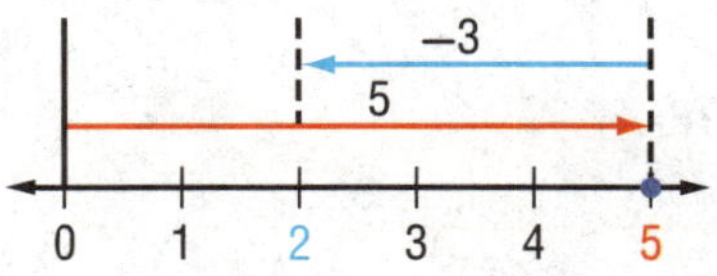

4. Find $-3 + 2$.

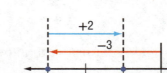

So, $5 + (-3) = 2$.

So, $-3 + 2 = -1$.

> **Got It?** Do these problems to find out.
>
> **d.** $6 + (-7)$ **e.** $-15 + 19$

Examples

Tutor

5. Find $7 + (-7)$.

$7 + (-7) = 0$ Subtract absolute values; $7 - 7 = 0$. 7 and (-7) are opposites. The sum of any number and its opposite is always zero.

6. Find $-8 + 3$.

$-8 + 3 = -5$ Subtract absolute values; $8 - 3 = 5$. Since -8 has the greater absolute value, the sum is negative.

7. Find $2 + (-15) + (-2)$.

$2 + (-15) + (-2) = 2 + (-2) + (-15)$ Commutative Property ($+$)

$= [2 + (-2)] + (-15)$ Associative Property ($+$)

$= 0 + (-15)$ Additive Inverse Property

$= -15$ Additive Identity Property

> **Got It?** Do these problems to find out.
>
> **f.** $10 + (-12)$ **g.** $-13 + 18$ **h.** $(-14) + (-6) + 6$

Right margin notes:

Show your work. →

d. _____

e. _____

Commutative Properties
$a + b = b + a$
$a \cdot b = b \cdot a$

Associative Properties
$a + (b + c) = (a + b) + c$
$a \cdot (b \cdot c) = (a \cdot b) \cdot c$

Identity Properties
$a + 0 = a$
$a \cdot 1 = a$

f. _____

g. _____

h. _____

Example

Tutor

8. A roller coaster starts at point *A*. It goes up 20 feet, down 32 feet, and then up 16 feet to point *B*. Write an addition sentence to find the height at point *B* in relation to point *A*. Then find the sum and explain its meaning.

$$20 + (-32) + 16 = 20 + 16 + (-32) \qquad \text{Commutative Property (+)}$$
$$= 36 + (-32) \qquad 20 + 16 = 36$$
$$= 4 \qquad \text{Subtract absolute values.}$$

Point *B* is 4 feet higher than point *A*.

Got It? Do this problem to find out.

i. The temperature is −3°. An hour later, it drops 6° and 2 hours later, it rises 4°. Write an addition expression to describe this situation. Then find the sum and explain its meaning.

Show your work.

i. _____

Guided Practice

Check ✓

Add. (Examples 1–7)

1. −6 + (−8) = _____

2. −3 + 10 = _____

3. −8 + (−4) + 12 = _____

Show your work.

4. Sofia owes her brother $25. She gives her brother the $18 she earned dog-sitting. Write an addition expression to describe this situation. Then find the sum and explain its meaning. (Example 8) _____

_____

5. 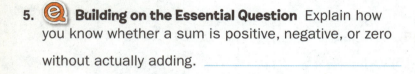 **Building on the Essential Question** Explain how you know whether a sum is positive, negative, or zero without actually adding. _____

_____

_____

_____

_____

Rate Yourself!

How confident are you about adding integers? Check the box that applies.

☐ ☐ ☐ ☐ ☐

For more help, go online to access a Personal Tutor.

Tutor

FOLDABLES Time to update your Foldable!

Perry Mastrovito/CORBIS   Copyright © The McGraw-Hill Companies, Inc.

Independent Practice

Go online for Step-by-Step Solutions

Add. (Examples 1–7)

1. $-22 + (-16) =$ _____ -38

$$\begin{array}{r} 22 \\ +16 \\ \hline -38 \end{array}$$

2. $-10 + (-15) =$ _____ -25

$$\begin{array}{r} -10 \\ +15 \\ \hline -25 \end{array}$$

3. $6 + 10 =$ _____ 16

4. $21 + (-21) + (-4) =$ _____ -4

$$21 + (-25)$$
$$-4$$

5. $-17 + 20 + (-3) =$ _____ 0

$$-17 + 17$$
$$0$$

6. $-34 + 25 + (-25) =$ _____ -34

$$-34 + 0$$

7. $4 + 5 =$ _____ 9

8. $-15 + 8 =$ _____ -7

$$\begin{array}{r} 15 \\ -8 \\ \hline 7 \end{array}$$

9. $7 + (-11) =$ _____ -4

10. Financial Literacy Stephanie has $152 in the bank. She withdraws $20. Then she deposits $84. Write an addition expression to represent this situation. Then find the sum and explain its meaning. (Example 8)

$152 - 20 + 84 = 216$

11. CCGPS **Model with Mathematics** Find the total profit or loss for each color of T-shirt. Green = $1   White = $3   Black = $1

12. **CCGPS Reason Abstractly** Lena deposits and withdraws money from a bank account. The table shows her transactions for March. Write an addition expression to describe her transactions. Then find the sum and explain its meaning.

March	
Week	Transaction
1	deposit $300
2	withdraw $50
3	withdraw $75
4	deposit $225

$300 + (-50) + (-75) + 225$
$300 + (-125) + 225$
$175 + 225$
400

H.O.T. Problems Higher Order Thinking

13. **CCGPS Model with Mathematics** Describe two situations in which opposite quantities combine to make zero.

$-10 + 10 = 0$
$-9999 + 9999 = 0$

14. **CCGPS Identify Structure** Name the property illustrated by the following.

   a. $x + (-x) = 0$ ___additive inverse___

   b. $x + (-y) = -y + x$ ___comutative property___

CCGPS Model with Mathematics Simplify.

15. $8 + (-8) + a$ ___a___   16. $x + (-5) + 1$ ___-4 + x___   17. $-9 + m + (-6)$ ___-15 + m___
   $x + -4$

Georgia Test Practice

18. Which of the following expressions is represented by the number line below?

   Ⓐ $-4 + 3$ Ⓒ $3 + (-7)$
   Ⓑ $-4 + 7$ Ⓓ $0 + (-7)$

Extra Practice

Add.

19. $18 + (-5) =$ ___13___

$18 + (-5) = 18 - 5$
$\quad\quad\quad = 13$

Homework Help

20. $-19 + 24 =$ ___5___

$-19 + 24 = 24 + (-19)$
$\quad\quad\quad = 24 - 19$
$\quad\quad\quad = 5$

21. $13 + (-19) =$ _____

22. $14 + (-6) =$ _____

23. $15 + 9 + (-9) =$ _____

24. $-4 + 12 + (-9) =$ _____

25. $-16 + 16 + 22 =$ _____

26. $25 + 3 + (-25) =$ _____

27. $7 + (-19) + (-7) =$ _____

CCGPS Justify Conclusions Write an addition expression to describe each situation. Then find each sum and explain its meaning.

28. Ronnie receives $40 for his birthday. Then he spends $15 at the movies.

_____

29. A quarterback is sacked for a loss of 5 yards. On the next play, his team loses 15 yards. Then the team gains 12 yards on the third play.

_____

_____

30. A pelican starts at 60 feet above sea level. It descends 60 feet to catch a fish.

_____

31. At 8 A.M., the temperature was 3°F below zero. By 1 P.M., the temperature rose 14°F and by 10 P.M., dropped 12°F. What was the temperature at 10 P.M?

- Ⓐ 5°F above zero
- Ⓑ 5°F below zero
- Ⓒ 1°F above zero
- Ⓓ 1°F below zero

32. What is the value of $-8 + 7 + (-3)$?

- Ⓕ −18
- Ⓖ −4
- Ⓗ 2
- Ⓘ 18

33. **Short Response** Write an addition sentence to represent the number line below. _____

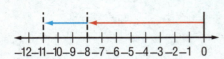

Write an integer for each situation. MCC6.NS.5

34. a bank deposit of $75 _____

35. a loss of 8 pounds _____

36. 13° below zero _____

37. a gain of 4 yards _____

38. spending $12 _____

39. a gain of 5 hours _____

Inquiry HOW is the subtraction of integers related to the addition of integers?

CCGPS Content Standards
MCC7.NS.1,
MCC7.NS.1c,
MCC7.NS.3
Mathematical Practices
1, 2, 3, 7

Dolphins A dolphin swims 6 meters below the surface of the ocean. Then it jumps to a height of 5 meters above the surface of the water. Determine the difference between the two distances.

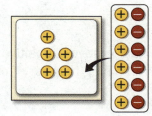

Investigation 1

Watch ▶ Tools

Use counters to find 5 − (−6), the difference between the distances.

$$5 - (-6)$$

the number of positive counters placed on the mat

the number of negative counters that need removed from the mat

Step 1 Place 5 positive counters on the mat. Remove 6 negative counters. However, there are 0 negative counters.

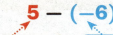

Step 2 Add ☐ zero pairs to the mat.

Step 3 Now you can remove ☐ negative counters. Count the remaining positive counters.

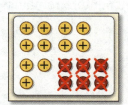

So, 5 − (−6) = ☐. The difference between the distances is ☐ meters.

Investigation 2

Use counters to find −6 − (−3).

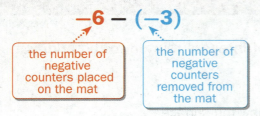

−6 − (−3)

the number of negative counters placed on the mat

the number of negative counters removed from the mat

Step 1 Place 6 negative counters on the mat.

Step 2 Remove 3 negative counters.

There are ☐ negative counters remaining. So, −6 − (−3) = ☐.

Investigation 3

Use counters to find −5 − 1.

Step 1 Place ☐ negative counters on the mat. You need to remove 1 positive counter. However, there are 0 positive counters.

Step 2 Add 1 zero pair to the mat.

Step 3 Now you can remove 1 positive counter. Find the remaining number of counters.

There are ☐ negative counters remaining.

So, −5 − 1 = ☐.

Check Use addition.   −6 + 1 $\overset{?}{=}$ −5

−5 = −5 ✔

Collaborate

Work with a partner. Find each difference. Show your work using drawings.

1. $7 - 6 =$ _____

Show your work.

2. $5 - (-3) =$ _____

3. $6 - (-2) =$ _____

4. $5 - 8 =$ _____

5. $-7 - (-2) =$ _____

6. $-7 - 3 =$ _____

7. $-5 - (-7) =$ _____

8. $-2 - (-9) =$ _____

 **Analyze**

Work with a partner. Circle an expression that is equal to the expression in the first column. The first one is done for you.

	$-3 - 1$	$-3 + 1$	$\boxed{-3 + (-1)}$	$-3 - (-1)$
9.	$-2 - 9$	$-2 - (-9)$	$-2 + 9$	$-2 + (-9)$
10.	$-8 - 4$	$-8 + 4$	$-8 + (-4)$	$-8 - (-4)$
11.	$6 - (-2)$	$6 + 2$	$6 - 2$	$6 + (-2)$
12.	$5 - (-7)$	$5 - 7$	$5 + (-7)$	$5 + 7$
13.	$-1 - (-3)$	$-1 - 3$	$-1 + 3$	$-1 + (-3)$
14.	$-3 - (-8)$	$-3 + 8$	$-3 - 8$	$-3 + (-8)$

15. **CCGPS Identify Structure** Write a subtraction sentence where the difference is positive. Use a positive and a negative integer.

_____

16. Write a subtraction sentence where the difference is negative. Use a positive and a negative integer.

_____

 Reflect

17. **CCGPS Reason Abstractly** Jake owes his sister $3. She decides to "take away" his debt. That is, he does not have to pay her back. Write a subtraction sentence for this situation.

_____

18. **Inquiry** HOW is the subtraction of integers related to the addition of integers?

_____

_____

Subtract Integers

What You'll Learn

Scan the lesson. List two real-world scenarios in which you would subtract integers.

- _____
- _____

Essential Question

WHAT happens when you add, subtract, multiply, and divide integers?

CCGPS Common Core GPS

Content Standards
MCC7.NS.1, MCC7.NS.1c, MCC7.NS.1d, MCC7.NS.3

Mathematical Practices
1, 2, 3, 4, 5, 6, 7

Real-World Link

Diving The platform on a diving board is 3 meters high. The actions of a diver climbing up to the diving board platform and diving 1 meter below the water's surface are shown on the number line at the right.

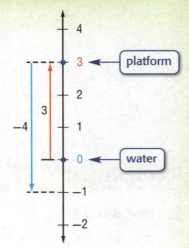

The diver's actions can be represented by the subtraction equation $3 - 4 = -1$.

1. Write a related addition sentence for the subtraction sentence.

   _____

2. Use a number line to find $1 - 5$. Then write a related addition sentence for the subtraction sentence.

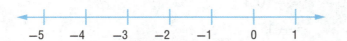

Difference: _____   Addition Sentence: _____

Subtract Integers

Words	To subtract an integer, add its additive inverse.
Symbols	$p - q = p + (-q)$
Examples	$4 - 9 = 4 + (-9) = -5$ $7 - (-10) = 7 + (10) = 17$

When you subtract 7, the result is the same as adding its additive inverse, -7.

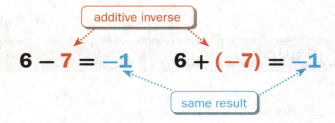

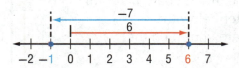

Examples

1. **Find $8 - 13$.**

$$8 - 13 = 8 + (-13) \quad \text{To subtract 13, add } -13.$$
$$= -5 \quad \text{Simplify.}$$

Check by adding $-5 + 13 \overset{?}{=} 8$
$$8 = 8 \checkmark$$

2. **Find $-10 - 7$.**

$$-10 - 7 = -10 + (-7) \quad \text{To subtract 7, add } -7.$$
$$= -17 \quad \text{Simplify.}$$

Check by adding $-17 + 7 \overset{?}{=} -10$
$$-10 = -10 \checkmark$$

Show your work.

a. _____

b. _____

Got It? Do these problems to find out.

 a. $6 - 12$ **b.** $-20 - 15$ **c.** $-22 - 26$

c. _____

Examples

Tutor

3. **Find 1 − (−2).**

$$1 - (-2) = 1 + 2 \qquad \text{To subtract } -2, \text{ add } 2.$$
$$= 3 \qquad \text{Simplify.}$$

4. **Find −10 − (−7).**

$$-10 - (-7) = -10 + 7 \qquad \text{To subtract } -7, \text{ add } 7.$$
$$= -3 \qquad \text{Simplify.}$$

Got It? Do these problems to find out.

d. $4 - (-12)$ **e.** $-15 - (-5)$ **f.** $18 - (-6)$

 STOP **and Reflect**

Circle the integer below that will make this number sentence true.
$$-5 - (?) = -3$$

−8 −2 2

Show your work.

d. _____

e. _____

f. _____

Examples

Tutor

5. **Evaluate $x - y$ if $x = -6$ and $y = -5$.**

$$x - y = -6 - (-5) \qquad \text{Replace } x \text{ with } -6 \text{ and } y \text{ with } -5.$$
$$= -6 + 5 \qquad \text{To subtract } -5, \text{ add } 5.$$
$$= -1 \qquad \text{Simplify.}$$

6. **Evaluate $m - n$ if $m = -15$ and $n = 8$.**

$$m - n = -15 - 8 \qquad \text{Replace } m \text{ with } -15 \text{ and } n \text{ with } 8.$$
$$= -15 + (-8) \qquad \text{To subtract } 8, \text{ add } -8.$$
$$= -23 \qquad \text{Simplify.}$$

Got It? Do these problems to find out.

Evaluate each expression if $a = 5$, $b = -8$, and $c = -9$.

g. $b - 10$ **h.** $a - b$ **i.** $c - a$

g. _____

h. _____

i. _____

 Example Tutor

7. The temperatures on the Moon vary from −173°C to 127°C. Find the difference between the maximum and minimum temperatures.

Subtract the lower temperature from the higher temperature.

Estimate $100 − (−200) = 300$

$127 − (−173) = 127 + 173$ To subtract −173, add 173.

$\qquad\qquad\quad = 300$ Simplify.

So, the difference between the temperatures is 300°C.

Got It?   Do this problem to find out.

 Show your work.

j. Brenda had a balance of −$52 in her account. The bank charged her a fee of $10 for having a negative balance. What is her new balance?

j. _____

Guided Practice Check ✓

Subtract. (Examples 1–4)

1. $14 − 17 =$ _____

2. $14 − (−10) =$ _____

3. $12 − 26 =$ _____

4. Evaluate $q − r$ if $q = −14$ and $r = −6$. (Examples 5 and 6)

_____

5. **STEM** The sea surface temperatures range from −2°C to 31°C. Find the difference between the maximum and minimum temperatures. (Example 7) _____

6. **Building on the Essential Question** If x and y are positive integers, is $x − y$ always positive? Explain.

_____

_____

Rate Yourself!

How well do you understand subtracting integers? Circle the image that applies.

Clear   Somewhat Clear   Not So Clear

For more help, go online to access a Personal Tutor. Tutor

FOLDABLES Time to update your Foldable!

NASA/Photodisc/Getty Images   Copyright © The McGraw-Hill Companies, Inc.

Independent Practice

Go online for Step-by-Step Solutions

Subtract. (Examples 1–4)

1. $0 - 10 =$ _____

2. $-9 - 5 =$ _____

3 $-4 - 8 =$ _____

4. $31 - 48 =$ _____

5. $-25 - 5 =$ _____

6. $-44 - 41 =$ _____

7. $4 - (-19) =$ _____

8. $-11 - (-42) =$ _____

9. $52 - (-52) =$ _____

Evaluate each expression if $f = -6$, $g = 7$, and $h = 9$. (Examples 5 and 6)

10. $g - 7$ _____

11. $-h - (-9)$ _____

12. $f - g$ _____

13 CCGPS **Use Math Tools** Use the information below. (Example 7)

State	Alabama	California	Florida	Louisiana	New Mexico
Lowest Elevation (ft)	0	−282	0	−8	2,842
Highest Elevation (ft)	2,407	14,494	345	535	13,161

a. What is the difference between the highest elevation in Alabama and the lowest elevation in Louisiana? _____

b. Find the difference between the lowest elevation in New Mexico and the lowest elevation in California. _____

c. Find the difference between the highest elevation in Florida and the lowest elevation in California. _____

d. What is the difference between the lowest elevation in Alabama and the lowest elevation in Louisiana? _____

Evaluate each expression if $h = -12$, $j = 4$, and $k = 15$.

14. $-j + h - k$ _____

15. $|h - j|$ _____

16. $k - j - h$ _____

H.O.T. Problems Higher Order Thinking

17. **CCGPS Identify Structure** Write a subtraction sentence using integers. Then, write the equivalent addition sentence and explain how to find the sum.

_____

_____

18. **CCGPS Identify Structure** Use the properties of operations.

   a. The Commutative Property is true for addition. For example, $7 + 2 = 2 + 7$. Does the Commutative Property apply to subtraction. Is $2 - 7$ equal to $7 - 2$? Explain. _____

   _____

   b. Using the Associative Property, $9 + (6 + 3) = (9 + 6) + 3$.
   Is $9 - (6 - 3)$ equal to $(9 - 6) - 3$? Explain. _____

   _____

19. **CCGPS Find the Error** Hiroshi is finding $-15 - (-18)$. Find his mistake and correct it.

_____

_____

_____

$$-15 - (-18) = -15 + (-18)$$
$$= -33$$

20. **CCGPS Reason Abstractly** *True* or *False*? When n is a negative integer, $n - n = 0$.

_____

Georgia Test Practice

21. Which of the following expressions is equal to -8?

   Ⓐ $15 - 7$ Ⓑ $-15 - 7$ Ⓒ $15 - (-7)$ Ⓓ $-15 - (-7)$

Extra Practice

Subtract.

22. $13 - 17 = \underline{-4}$

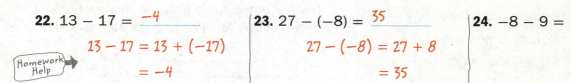
Homework Help →

$13 - 17 = 13 + (-17)$
$= -4$

23. $27 - (-8) = \underline{35}$

$27 - (-8) = 27 + 8$
$= 35$

24. $-8 - 9 = \underline{\hspace{2cm}}$

25. $-34 - (-20) = \underline{\hspace{2cm}}$

26. $15 - (-14) = \underline{\hspace{2cm}}$

27. $-27 - (-33) = \underline{\hspace{2cm}}$

Evaluate each expression if $f = -6$, $g = 7$, and $h = 9$.

28. $f - 6$ _____

29. $h - f$ _____

30. $g - h$ _____

31. $5 - f$ _____

32. $4 - (-g)$ _____

33. $-8 - (-h)$ _____

34. CCGPS **Be Precise** To find the percent error, you can use this equation.

$$\text{percent error} = \frac{\text{amount of error}}{\text{actual amount}} \times 100$$

Bryan estimates the cost of a vacation to be $730. The actual cost of the vacation is $850. Find the percent error. Round to the nearest whole percent if necessary. Is the percent positive or negative? Explain.

_____

_____

35. Which sentence about integers is *not* always true?

   Ⓐ positive − positive = positive

   Ⓑ positive + positive = positive

   Ⓒ negative + negative = negative

   Ⓓ positive − negative = positive

36. Morgan drove from Los Angeles (elevation 330 feet) to Death Valley (elevation −282 feet). What is the difference in elevation between Los Angeles and Death Valley?

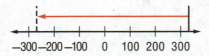

   Ⓕ 48 feet   Ⓗ 582 feet

   Ⓖ 148 feet   Ⓘ 612 feet

37. Short Response In a football game, Landon gained 10 yards on his first carry. He was tackled for a loss of 12 yards on his second carry. Write a subtraction expression to represent Landon's net yardage after the first two plays.

_____

Common Core Review

Multiply. MCC5.NBT.5

38. 18(10) = _____

39. 15(13) = _____

40. 12(30) = _____

Evaluate each expression. MCC6.NS.7

41. $|-12|$ = _____

42. $|-3| + |-5|$ = _____

43. $|-25| \div 5 - |-3|$ = _____

44. State the quadrant in which the graphed point is located. MCC6.NS.6

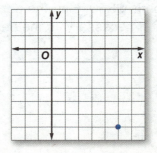

_____

Inquiry **HOW is the distance between two rational numbers related to their difference?**

CCGPS Content Standards
MCC7.NS.1,
MCC7.NS.1c

Mathematical Practices
1, 2, 3, 8

Weather For a science project, Carmelo recorded the daily low and high temperatures for four days in January. His results are shown in the table below. Find the day that had the greatest difference in temperature readings.

	M	T	W	Th
Low Temperature (°F)	1	−3	−4	−3
High Temperature (°F)	5	0	2	−1

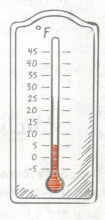

Investigation

Step 1 In the table below, a represents each daily low temperature, and b represents each daily high temperature. Find $a + b$ and $a - b$. Record your results in the table.

Day	a	b	$a + b$	$a - b$	Distance
M	1	5	6	−4	4 units
T	−3	0			
W	−4	2			
Th	−3	−1			

Step 2 Use a number line to find the distance between each rational number a and b. For example, the distance between 1 and 5 on the number line below is ☐ units.

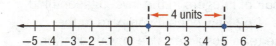

Complete the last column in the table.

Step 3 Compare the distances.

So, the day with the greatest difference in temperature readings was _____.

Collaborate

Work with a partner to find the distance between each pair of numbers without using a number line. Then use a number line to check your answer.

1. The distance between −9 and −3 is _____.

2. The distance between −2 and 5 _____.

Analyze

CCGPS **Identify Repeated Reasoning** Work with a partner to answer the following questions. Refer back to the table in Step 1 of the Investigation.

3. Is there a relationship between the sum of each pair of integers and the distance between them? If so, explain.

_____

_____

4. Is there a relationship between the difference of the integers and the

distance between them? If so, explain. _____

_____

Reflect

5. **CCGPS** **Reason Inductively** For each pair of integers in the Investigation, find $b - a$. How does $b - a$ compare to $a - b$? How does it compare to the distance between the points? Use the term *absolute value* in your answer.

_____

_____

6. **Inquiry** HOW is the distance between two rational numbers related to their

difference? _____

_____

_____

Content Standards
MCC7.NS.3, MCC7.EE.3
Mathematical Practices
1, 4, 8

Case #1 Shooting Star

Laura wants to make the girls basketball team and knows that making free throws is a skill that impresses the coach. In practice, she makes about 3 out of every 5 free throws she attempts. In tryouts, she has to shoot the ball 30 times from the free throw line.

How many of these can she expect to make?

1 Understand *What are the facts?*

- Laura can make 3 out of 5 free throw attempts.
- In tryouts, she will have to shoot the ball 30 times from the free throw line.

2 Plan *What is your strategy to solve this problem?*

Make a table. How can you extend the pattern to solve the problem?

3 Solve *How can you apply the strategy?*

Make a table to extend the pattern. Complete the table below.

$+3$ $+3$ $+3$ $+3$ $+3$

Free Throws	3	6	9	12	
Shots Attempted	5	10	15	20	

$+5$ $+5$ $+5$ $+5$ $+5$

If Laura attempts 30 shots, how many should she make? ☐

4 Check *Does the answer make sense?*

She makes free throws a little more than half the time. Since 18 is a little more than 15, the answer is reasonable.

Analyze the Strategy
Watch ▶ **Tutor** 💬

Identify Repeated Reasoning How would the results have changed if

Laura could make 4 out of 5 free throw attempts? _____

_____

Case #2 Display Dilemma

Tomás looks through a window and sees the top 3 rows of a 7-row display of digital cameras. He sees 4, 6, and 8 cameras in these 3 rows.

How many cameras are there in the whole display?

 Understand

Read the problem. What are you being asked to find?

I need to find _____.

Underline key words and values. What information do you know?

The display contains ☐ rows of digital cameras. The problem states that the top three rows have ☐ cameras, ☐ cameras, and ☐ cameras.

Is there any information that you do *not* need to know?

I do not need to know _____.

2 Plan

Choose a problem-solving strategy.

I will use the _____ strategy.

3 Solve

Describe the pattern in the table. Then extend it using your problem-solving strategy. _____

_____

Row	7	6	5			
Number of Cameras	4	6	8			

The total number of cameras is ☐.

So, _____.

 Check

Use information from the problem to check your answer.

_____

Digital Vision/Getty Images

Collaborate Work with a small group to solve the following cases. Show your work on a separate piece of paper.

Case #3 Nature

A sunflower usually has two different spirals of seeds, one with 34 seeds and the other with 55 seeds. The numbers 34 and 55 are part of the Fibonacci sequence.

1, 1, 2, 3, 5, 8, 13, 21, 34, 55, ...

Find the pattern in the Fibonacci sequence and identify the next two terms.

Case #4 Financial Literacy

Peter is saving money to buy an MP3 player. After one month, he has $50. After 2 months, he has $85. After 3 months, he has $120. After 4 months, he has $155.

At this rate, how long will it take Peter to save enough money to buy an MP3 player that costs $295?

Case #5 Geometry

The pattern at the right is made from toothpicks.

How many toothpicks would be needed for the sixth term in the pattern?

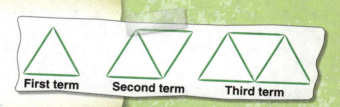

First term **Second term** **Third term**

Circle a strategy below to solve the problem.

- Draw a diagram.
- Act it out.
- Make a model.
- Make a table.

Case #6 Diving

A diver descends to −15 feet after 1 minute, −30 feet after 2 minutes, and −45 feet after 3 minutes.

If she keeps descending at this rate, find the diver's position after ten minutes.

Mid-Chapter Check

Vocabulary Check

1. Define *integer*. Give an example of a number that is an integer and a number that is not an integer. (Lesson 1)

_____

_____

2. Fill in the blank in the sentence below with the correct term. (Lesson 1)

   The _____ of a number is the distance between the number and zero on a number line.

Skills Check and Problem Solving

Evaluate each expression. (Lessons 1, 2, and 3)

3. $|-6| =$ _____

4. $-4 + (-8) =$ _____

5. $3 + 4 + (-5) =$ _____

6. $-3 - 10 =$ _____

7. $8 - (-12) =$ _____

8. $|-5| - |-9| =$ _____

9. The melting point of mercury is $-36°F$ and its boiling point is $672°F$. What is the difference between the boiling point and the melting point? (Lesson 3)

   _____

10. **Georgia Test Practice** Which of the following numerical expressions results in a positive number? (Lessons 1 and 2)

    Ⓐ $-4 + (-7)$

    Ⓒ $-4 + 7$

    Ⓑ $4 + (-7)$

    Ⓓ $|-2| + 7 + (-11)$

Inquiry WHEN is the product of two integers a positive number? WHEN is the product a negative number?

CCGPS **Content Standards**
MCC7.NS.2,
MCC7.NS.3

Mathematical Practices
1, 3, 4

School The number of students who bring their lunch to Phoenix Middle School had been decreasing at a rate of 4 students each month. What integer represents the total change in the number of students bringing their lunch after three months?

What do you know? _____

_____

What do you need to find? _____

_____

Investigation 1

The integer ☐ represents a decrease of 4 students each month. After three months, the total change will be $3 \times (-4)$.

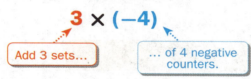

3 × (−4)

Add 3 sets... ... of 4 negative counters.

Step 1 Add 3 sets of 4 negative counters to the mat.

Step 2 Count the number of negative counters.

There are ☐ negative counters.

So, $3 \times (-4) =$ ☐. After three months, the total change in the

number of students bringing their lunch will be ☐.

Investigation 2

Use counters to find −2 × 3.

If the first factor is negative, you need to *remove* counters from the mat.

Step 1	Start with 2 sets of 3 zero pairs on the mat. The value on the mat is zero.

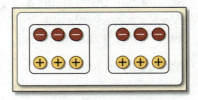

Step 2	Remove 2 sets of 3 positive counters from the mat.

There are ☐ negative counters remaining.

So, −2 × 3 = ☐.

Investigation 3

Use counters to find −2 × (−4).

Remove ☐ sets of ☐ negative counters from the mat.

Step 1	Draw 2 sets of 4 zero pairs on the mat.
Step 2	Cross out 2 sets of 4 negative counters from the mat.

There are ☐ positive counters remaining.

So, −2 × (−4) = ☐.

Collaborate

Work with a partner. Find each product. Show your work using drawings.

1. $2 \times (-3) =$ _____

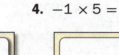

2. $6 \times (-1) =$ _____

3. $-2 \times 4 =$ _____

4. $-1 \times 5 =$ _____

5. $-4 \times 2 =$ _____

6. $-2 \times (-4) =$ _____

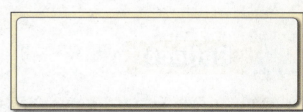

7. $-3 \times (-1) =$ _____

8. $-6 \times (-2) =$ _____

Analyze

Work with a partner to complete the table. Use counters if needed. The first one is already done for you.

	Multiplication Expression	Same Signs or Different Signs?	Product	Positive or Negative?
	2×6	Same signs	12	Positive
9.	$7 \times (-2)$			
10.	$-3 \times (-4)$			
11.	$5 \times (-3)$			
12.	2×8			
13.	$-4 \times (-1)$			
14.	-3×6			
15.	-2×5			

16. **CCGPS** **Reason Inductively** Can you find any patterns in the table? If so, describe them.

_____

_____

Reflect

17. **CCGPS** **Model with Mathematics** Write a real-world problem that could be represented by the expression -5×4.

_____

_____

_____

18. **inquiry** WHEN is the product of two integers a positive number? WHEN is the product a negative number?

_____

_____

_____

Multiply Integers

What You'll Learn

Scan the rest of the lesson. List two headings you would use to make an outline of the lesson.

- _____
- _____

Essential Question

WHAT happens when you add, subtract, multiply, and divide integers?

Common Core GPS

Content Standards
MCC7.NS.2, MCC7.NS.2a, MCC7.NS.2c, MCC7.NS.3, MCC7.EE.3

Mathematical Practices
1, 3, 4, 8

Real-World Link

Skydiving Once a parachute is deployed, a skydiver descends at a rate of about 5 meters per second. Where will the skydiver be in relation to where the parachute deployed after 4 seconds?

1. Descending is usually represented by a negative integer. What integer should you use to represent the position of the skydiver in relation to the parachute's deployment after 1 second? [____]

2. Complete the graphic below. What is the skydiver's position after 2, 3, and 4 seconds?

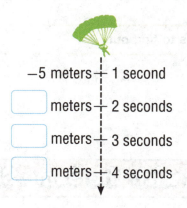

−5 meters ┼ 1 second

[____] meters ┼ 2 seconds

[____] meters ┼ 3 seconds

[____] meters ┼ 4 seconds

Look Mom, no hands!

3. Write a multiplication sentence to represent the skydiver's position after 5 seconds.

_____

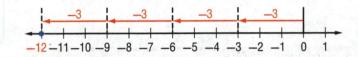

Multiply Integers with Different Signs

Work Zone

Words   The product of two integers with different signs is negative.

Examples $6(-4) = -24$ $-5(7) = -35$

Remember that multiplication is the same as repeated addition.

$4(-3) = (-3) + (-3) + (-3) + (-3)$ −3 is used as an addend four times.

$= -12$

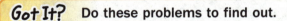

The Commutative Property of Multiplication states that you can multiply in any order. So, $4(-3) = -3(4)$.

Examples

1. **Find 3(−5).**

$3(-5) = -15$ The integers have different signs. The product is negative.

2. **Find −6(8).**

$-6(8) = -48$ The integers have different signs. The product is negative.

Show your work.

Got It?   Do these problems to find out.

a. _____

b. _____

a. $9(-2)$ **b.** $-7(4)$

Key Concept

Multiply Integers with the Same Signs

Words   The product of two integers with the same sign is positive.

Examples $2(6) = 12$ $-10(-6) = 60$

The product of two positive integers is positive. You can use a pattern to find the sign of the product of two negative integers. Start with $(2)(-3) = -6$ and $(1)(-3) = -3$.

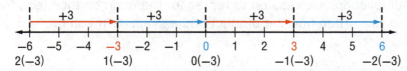

positive × negative = negative ⟶ $(2)(-3) = -6$ ⎤ +3

$(1)(-3) = -3$ ⎤ +3

The Multiplicative Property of Zero ⟶ $(0)(-3) = 0$ ⎤ +3

$(-1)(-3) = 3$ ⎤ +3

negative × negative = positive ⟶ $(-2)(-3) = 6$ ⎤ +3

Each product is 3 more than the previous product. This pattern can also be shown on a number line.

If you extend the pattern, the next two products are $(-3)(-3) = 9$ and $(-4)(-3) = 12$.

Examples

Tutor

3. Find $-11(-9)$.

$-11(-9) = 99$ The integers have the same sign. The product is positive.

4. Find $(-4)^2$.

$(-4)^2 = (-4)(-4)$ There are two factors of -4.

$= 16$ The product is positive.

5. Find $-3(-4)(-2)$.

$-3(-4)(-2) = [-3(-4)](-2)$ Associative Property

$= 12(-2)$ $-3(-4) = 12$

$= -24$ $12(-2) = -24$

Got It?   Do these problems to find out.

c. $-12(-4)$ **d.** $(-5)^2$ **e.** $-7(-5)(-3)$

Copyright © The McGraw-Hill Companies, Inc.

STOP and Reflect

Write three integers with a positive product. At least one of them must be a negative integer. Show your work below.

Show your work.

c. _____

d. _____

e. _____

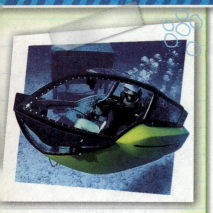

 Watch Tutor

Example

6. **A submersible is diving from the surface of the water at a rate of 90 feet per minute. What is the depth of the submersible after 7 minutes?**

The submersible descends 90 feet per minute. After 7 minutes, the vessel will be at 7(−90) or −630 feet. The submersible will descend to 630 feet below the surface.

Got It? Do this problem to find out.

 Show your work.

f. Financial Literacy Mr. Simon's bank automatically deducts a $4 monthly maintenance fee from his savings account. Write a multiplication expression to represent the maintenance fees for one year. Then find the product and explain its meaning.

f. _____

Guided Practice

 Check ✓

Multiply. (Examples 1–5)

 Show your work.

1. 6(−10) = _____

2. $(−3)^3$ = _____

3. (−1)(−3)(−4) = _____

4. Financial Literacy Tamera owns 100 shares of a certain stock. Suppose the price of the stock drops by $3 per share. Write a multiplication expression to find the change in Tamera's investment. Explain your answer. (Example 6)

_____

_____

_____

5. **Building on the Essential Question** When is the product of two or more integers a positive number?

_____

_____

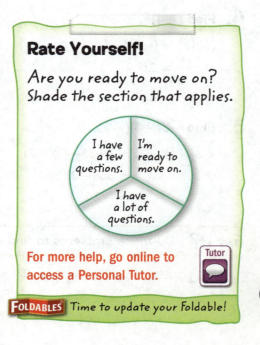

Rate Yourself!

Are you ready to move on? Shade the section that applies.

- I have a few questions.
- I'm ready to move on.
- I have a lot of questions.

For more help, go online to access a Personal Tutor. Tutor

FOLDABLES Time to update your Foldable!

Independent Practice

Go online for Step-by-Step Solutions

Multiply. (Examples 1–5)

1. $8(-12) =$ _____ -96

2. $-15(-4) =$ _____ 60

3. $(-6)^2 =$ _____ 36

Show your work.

4. $(-5)^3 =$ _____ -125

5. $-4(-2)(-8) =$ _____ -64

6. $-3(-2)(1) =$ _____ 6

Write a multiplication expression to represent each situation. Then find each product and explain its meaning. (Example 6)

7. Ethan burns 650 Calories when he runs for 1 hour. Suppose he runs 5 hours in one week.

_____

_____

8. Wave erosion causes a certain coastline to recede at a rate of 3 centimeters each year. This occurs uninterrupted for a period of 8 years.

_____

_____

_____

9. CCGPS **Model with Mathematics** Refer to the graphic novel frame below. How many black T-shirts would Hannah and Dario need to sell to make up the loss in profit?

_____

Watch ▶ Replay it online!

10. 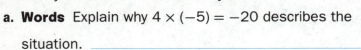 **Multiple Representations** When a movie is rented it has a due date. If the movie is not returned on time, a late fee is assessed. Kaitlyn is charged $5 each day for a movie that is 4 days late.

   a. **Words** Explain why $4 \times (-5) = -20$ describes the situation. _____

   _____

   b. **Algebra** Write an expression to represent the fee when the movie is x days late. _____

11. **CCGPS** **Identify Repeated Reasoning** When you multiply two positive integers, the product is a positive integer. Complete the graphic organizer to help you remember the other rules for multiplying integers. Describe any patterns in the products.

×	+	−
+		
−		

_____

_____

_____

 ## H.O.T. Problems *Higher Order Thinking*

12. **CCGPS** **Model with Mathematics** Write a multiplication sentence with a product of −18.

_____

13. **CCGPS** **Justify Conclusions** Explain how to evaluate $(-9)(-6)(15)(-7 + 7)$ as simply as possible.

_____

_____

14. **CCGPS** **Reason Inductively** Evaluate $(-1)^{50}$. Explain your reasoning.

_____

_____

Georgia Test Practice

15. The temperature drops 2 degrees per hour for 3 hours. Which expression does *not* describe the change in temperature?

   Ⓐ $-2(3)$ Ⓒ $-2 - 2 - 2$

   Ⓑ $-2 + (-2) + (-2)$ Ⓓ $2(3)$

Extra Practice

Multiply.

16. $-7(11) =$ ___-77___

$-7(11) = -77$

The integers have different signs. The product is negative.

17. $-20(-8) =$ _____

18. $25(-2) =$ _____

19. $(-4)^3 =$ _____

20. $(-9)^2 =$ _____

21. $-9(-1)(-5) =$ _____

Write a multiplication expression to represent each situation. Then find each product and explain its meaning.

22. The average person loses 50 to 80 hairs per day to make way for new growth. Suppose you lose 65 hairs per day for 15 days without growing any.

_____
_____
_____

23. **CCGPS** **Financial Literacy** Lily has a $100 gift card to her favorite pastry shop. She spends $4 a day at the shop for the next 12 days.

_____
_____
_____

Copy and Solve Evaluate each expression if $a = -6$, $b = -4$, $c = 3$, and $d = 9$. Show your work on a separate sheet of paper.

24. $-5c =$

25. $b^2 =$

26. $2a =$

27. $bc =$

28. $abc =$

29. $abc^3 =$

30. $-3a^2 =$

31. $-cd^2 =$

32. $-2a + b =$

33. **CCGPS** **Find the Error** Jamar is finding $(-2)(-3)(-4)$. Find his mistake and correct it. Explain your answer.

_____
_____
_____
_____

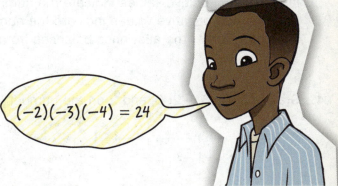

$(-2)(-3)(-4) = 24$

34. Which number is the seventh number in the sequence shown?

Position	1	2	3	4	5	6	7
Number	1	−2	4	−8	16	?	?

Ⓐ −64

Ⓑ −32

Ⓒ 32

Ⓓ 64

35. Short Response J.J. withdraws $15 from his bank account every week for lunch. Suppose he does not make any additional deposits or withdrawals. What integer represents the change in value of J.J.'s bank account after 8 weeks? Write and evaluate an expression.

36. A camera dropped from a boat descends 9 meters every minute. What will be the change in location of the camera after 5 minutes?

Ⓕ 45 m

Ⓖ 14 m

Ⓗ −14 m

Ⓘ −45 m

37. The table shows the temperatures on Wednesday night.

Time	Temperature (°F)
3 P.M.	14
5 P.M.	11

At 5 P.M., the temperature began dropping 3°F every hour for 6 hours. What was the temperature after 6 hours?

Ⓐ −7°F

Ⓑ −29°F

Ⓒ 7°F

Ⓓ 29°F

Fill in each ◯ with < or > to make a true sentence. MCC6.NS.7b

38. 0 ◯ −1

39. −9 ◯ 9

40. −84 ◯ 48

41. 32 ◯ −27

42. Laura's allowance balances over the last three months are shown in the table. Positive values indicate the number of dollars she had left over, and negative values indicate the number of dollars she overspent. Order the allowance balances from least to greatest. MCC6.NS.7

Month	Allowance Balances ($)
May	−10
June	5
July	−2

43. Graph 1, −4, 3, −2, 0, and 2 on the number line below. MCC6.NS.6

Inquiry HOW can properties be used to prove rules for multiplying integers?

CCGPS Content Standards
MCC7.NS.2,
MCC7.NS.2a,
MCC7.NS.2c

Mathematical Practices
1, 3

Scientific Properties Properties are used by scientists to classify elements into categories, such as metals. One property of a metal is that it is shiny.

Investigation

You have studied the mathematical properties listed in the table below. In mathematics, properties can be used to justify statements you make while verifying or proving another statement.

Properties of Mathematics	
Additive Inverse	Multiplicative Property of Zero
Distributive Property	Multiplicative Identity

For example, you have used models to show that $2(-1) = -2$.

You can *prove* $2(-1) = -2$ by using properties.

Write the correct property from the table above to provide the missing justifications. Use each property name once.

Statements	Properties
$0 = 2(0)$	_____
$0 = 2[1 + (-1)]$	_____
$0 = 2(1) + 2(-1)$	_____
$0 = 2 + 2(-1)$	_____

Conclusion In the last statement, $0 = 2 + 2(-1)$. In order for this to be true, $2(-1)$ must equal -2. Therefore, $2(-1) = \boxed{}$.

Collaborate

The sentence $(-2)(-1) = 2$ is an example of the rule that states the product of a negative integer and a negative integer is a positive integer.

Work with a partner to provide the missing information for the statements below.

1. Show that $(-2)(-1) = 2$.

Statements	Properties
$0 = -2(0)$	_____
$0 = -2[1 + (-1)]$	_____
$0 = -2(1) + (-2)(-1)$	_____
$0 = -2 + (-2)(-1)$	_____

Analyze

Work with a partner.

2. **CCGPS Justify Conclusions** Write a conclusion for Exercise 1.

_____

_____

Reflect

3. **CCGPS Construct an Argument** When you prove a statement mathematically, you must show that the statement is true for all possible values. How could you prove the product of any two negative numbers is a positive number? Explain your reasoning to a classmate.

_____

_____

_____

4. **Inquiry** HOW can properties be used to prove rules for multiplying integers?

_____

_____

Divide Integers

What You'll Learn

Scan the lesson. List two headings you would use to make an outline of the lesson.

- _____
_____

- _____
_____

Essential Question

WHAT happens when you add, subtract, multiply, and divide integers?

CCGPS Common Core GPS

Content Standards
MCC7.NS.2, MCC7.NS.2b, MCC7.NS.2c, MCC7.NS.3

Mathematical Practices
1, 3, 4, 5, 7

 ## Real-World Link

Sharks A Great White Shark has 3,000 teeth! It gains and loses teeth often in its lifetime. Suppose a Great White loses 3 teeth each day for 5 days without gaining any. The shark has lost 15 teeth in all.

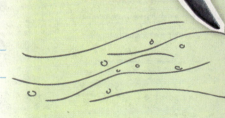

1. Write a multiplication sentence for this situation.

   _____

2. Division is related to multiplication. Write two division sentences related to the multiplication sentence you wrote for Exercise 1.

   _____

   _____

 Collaborate Work with a partner to complete the table. The first one is done for you.

Multiplication Sentence	Division Sentences	Same Signs or Different Signs?	Quotient	Positive or Negative?
$2 \times 6 = 12$	$12 \div 6 = 2$	Same signs	2	Positive
	$12 \div 2 = 6$	Same signs	6	Positive
3. $2 \times (-4) = -8$				
4. $-3 \times 5 = -15$				
5. $-2 \times (-5) = 10$				

Divide Integers with Different Signs

Words The quotient of two integers with different signs is negative.

Examples $33 \div (-11) = -3$ $-64 \div 8 = -8$

You can divide integers provided that the divisor is not zero. Since multiplication and division sentences are related, you can use them to find the quotient of integers with different signs.

different signs	$2(-6) = -12$ →	$-12 \div 2 = -6$	negative quotient
	$-2(-6) = 12$ →	$12 \div (-2) = -6$	

Work Zone

Examples

 Tutor

1. **Find $80 \div (-10)$.**   The integers have different signs.

$80 \div (-10) = -8$ The quotient is negative.

2. **Find $\dfrac{-55}{11}$.**   The integers have different signs.

$\dfrac{-55}{11} = -5$ The quotient is negative.

Dividing Integers

If p and q are integers and q does not equal 0,

then $-\dfrac{p}{q} = \dfrac{-p}{q} = \dfrac{p}{-q}$.

In Example 2, $-\dfrac{55}{11} = \dfrac{-55}{11}$ $= \dfrac{55}{-11}$.

3. **Use the table to find the constant rate of change in centimeters per hour.**

The height of the candle decreases by 2 centimeters each hour.

Time (h)	Height (cm)
1	10
2	8
3	6
4	4

+1↘ +1↘ +1↘   ↘−2 ↘−2 ↘−2

$\dfrac{\text{change in height}}{\text{change in hours}} = \dfrac{-2}{1}$

So, the constant rate of change is −2 centimeters per hour.

Show your work.

a. _____

b. _____

c. _____

Got It? Do these problems to find out.

a. $20 \div (-4)$ **b.** $\dfrac{-81}{9}$ **c.** $-45 \div 9$

Divide Integers with the Same Signs

Words   The quotient of two integers with the same sign is positive.

Examples $15 \div 5 = 3$ $-64 \div (-8) = 8$

You can also use multiplication and division sentences to find the quotient of integers with the same sign.

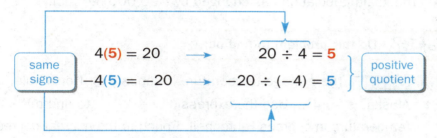

| same signs | $4(5) = 20$ $\longrightarrow$ | $20 \div 4 = 5$ | positive quotient |
| | $-4(5) = -20$ $\longrightarrow$ | $-20 \div (-4) = 5$ | |

Examples

 Tutor

4. **Find $-14 \div (-7)$.**   The integers have the same sign.

$-14 \div (-7) = 2$ The quotient is positive.

5. **Find $\dfrac{-27}{-3}$.**   The integers have the same sign.

$\dfrac{-27}{-3} = 9$ The quotient is positive.

6. **Evaluate $-16 \div x$ if $x = -4$.**

$-16 \div x = -16 \div (-4)$ Replace x with -4.

$= 4$ Divide. The quotient is positive.

Got It?   Do these problems to find out.

d. $-24 \div (-4)$ **e.** $-9 \div (-3)$ **f.** $\dfrac{-28}{-7}$

g. Evaluate $a \div b$ if $a = -33$ and $b = -3$.

Show your work.

d. _____

e. _____

f. _____

g. _____

7. **STEM** One year, the estimated Australian koala population was 1,000,000. After 10 years, there were about 100,000 koalas. Find the average change in the koala population per year. Then explain its meaning.

$$\frac{N - P}{10} = \frac{100,000 - 1,000,000}{10}$$ *N* is the new population, 100,000. *P* is the previous population, 1,000,000.

$$= \frac{-900,000}{10} \text{ or } -90,000$$ Divide.

The koala population has changed by −90,000 per year.

Got It? Do this problem to find out.

Show your work.

h. **STEM** The average temperature in January for North Pole, Alaska, is −24°C. Use the expression $\frac{9C + 160}{5}$ to find this temperature in degrees Fahrenheit. Round to the nearest degree. Then explain its meaning.

h. _____

Guided Practice

 Check ✓

Divide. (Examples 1, 2, 4, and 5)

Show your work.

1. −16 ÷ 2 = _____

2. $\frac{42}{-7}$ = _____

3. −30 ÷ (−5) = _____

Evaluate each expression if *x* = 8 **and** *y* = −5. (Example 6)

4. 15 ÷ *y* _____

5. *xy* ÷ (−10) _____

6. (*x* + *y*) ÷ (−3) _____

7. The lowest recorded temperature in Wisconsin is −55°F on February 4, 1996. Use the expression $\frac{5(F - 32)}{9}$ to find this temperature in degrees Celsius. Round to the nearest tenth. Explain its meaning. (Example 7)

_____

_____

8. **Building on the Essential Question** How is dividing integers similar to multiplying integers?

_____

_____

Rate Yourself!

How confident are you about dividing integers? Check the box that applies.

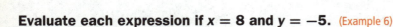

☐ ☐ ☐ ☐ ☐

For more help, go online to access a Personal Tutor.

 Tutor

 FOLDABLES *Time to update your Foldable!*

Independent Practice

Go online for Step-by-Step Solutions

Divide. (Examples 1, 2, 4, and 5)

1. $50 \div (-5) =$
_−10_

2. $-18 \div 9 =$
_−2_

3 $-15 \div (-3) =$
_5_

4. $-100 \div (-10) =$
_10_

Show your work.

5. $\frac{22}{-2} =$ _−11_

6. $\frac{84}{-12} =$ _−7_

7. $\frac{-26}{13} =$ _−2_

8. $\frac{-21}{-7} =$ _3_

Evaluate each expression if $r = 12$, $s = -4$, and $t = -6$. (Example 6)

9. $r \div s$ _−3_

10. $rs \div 16$ _−3_

11. $\frac{t - r}{3}$ _−6_

12. $\frac{8 - r}{-2}$ _2_

13 The distance remaining for a road trip over several hours is shown in the table. Use the information to find the constant rate of change in miles per hour. (Example 3)

_____

Time (h)	Distance Remaining (mi)
2	480
4	360
6	240
8	120

14. **CCGPS** **Justify Conclusions** Last year, Mr. Engle's total income was $52,000, while his total expenses were $53,800. Use the expression $\frac{I - E}{12}$, where I represents total income and E represents total expenses, to find the average difference between his income and expenses each month. Then explain its meaning. (Example 7) _____

_____

Evaluate each expression if $d = -9$, $f = 36$, and $g = -6$.

15. $\dfrac{-f}{d}$ _____

16. $\dfrac{12 - (-f)}{-g}$ _____

17. $\dfrac{f^2}{d^2}$ _____

18. **STEM** The temperature on Mars ranges widely from $-207°F$ to $80°F$.

Find the average of the temperature extremes on Mars. _____

H.O.T. Problems   Higher Order Thinking

19. **CCGPS** **Construct an Argument** You know that multiplication is commutative because $9 \times 3 = 3 \times 9$. Is division commutative? Explain.

_____

_____

CCGPS **Identify Structure** Use the graphs shown below to find the slope of each line.

20. _____

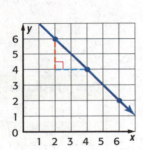

21. _____

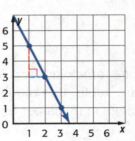

22. **CCGPS** **Identify Structure** Find values for x, y, and z so that all of the following statements are true.
- $y > x$, $z < y$, and $x < 0$
- $x \div z = -z$
- $z \div 2$ and $z \div 3$ are integers
- $x \div y = z$

$x =$ _____ $y =$ _____ $z =$ _____

Georgia Test Practice

23. On December 24, 1924, the temperature in Fairfield, Montana, fell from $63°F$ at noon to $-21°F$ at midnight. What was the average temperature change per hour?

Ⓐ $-3.5°F$ Ⓒ $-42°F$

Ⓑ $-7°F$ Ⓓ $-84°F$

Extra Practice

Divide.

24. $56 \div (-8) = \underline{\ -7\ }$

Homework Help →

$56 \div (-8) = -7$
The integers have different
signs. The quotient is negative.

25. $-36 \div (-4) = 9$

$-36 \div (-4) = 9$
The integers have the same
signs. The quotient is positive.

26. $32 \div (-8) = \underline{\hspace{2cm}}$

27. $\dfrac{-16}{-4} = \underline{\hspace{2cm}}$

28. $\dfrac{-27}{3} = \underline{\hspace{2cm}}$

29. $\dfrac{-54}{-6} = \underline{\hspace{2cm}}$

Evaluate each expression if $r = 12$, $s = -4$, and $t = -6$.

30. $-12 \div r$ _____

31. $72 \div t$ _____

32. $\dfrac{s+t}{5}$ _____

33. Divide -200 by -100. _____

34. Find the quotient of -65 and -13. _____

35. **STEM** The boiling point of water is affected by changes in elevation. Use the expression $\dfrac{-2A}{1,000}$, where A represents the altitude in feet, to find the number of degrees Fahrenheit at which the boiling point of water changes at an altitude of 5,000 feet. Then explain its meaning.

_____

36. **CCGPS** **Use Math Tools** The change in altitude over time for several hot air balloons is shown. Find the rate of change in feet per minute for each balloon.

Balloon	Change in Altitude (ft)	Time (min)	Rate of Change (ft/min)
Midnight Express	−2,700	135	
Neon Lights	480	30	
Star Wonder	−1,500	60	

37. A hang glider flew to an altitude of 10,000 feet. Fifteen minutes later, its altitude was 7,000 feet. What was the average change in elevation per minute?

Ⓐ −300 ft/min   Ⓒ 200 ft/min

Ⓑ −200 ft/min   Ⓓ 300 ft/min

38. Short Response During the past week, Mrs. Thorne recorded the following amounts in her checkbook: $150, −$75, −$15, and −$32. Write and evaluate an expression to find the average of these amounts.

_____

39. Short Response The table shows the points that each student lost on the first math test. Each question on the test was worth an equal number of points. If Christoper answered 6 questions incorrectly, how many questions did Nythia answer incorrectly? Explain.

Student	Points
Christopher	−24
Nythia	−16
Raul	−4

_____

_____

_____

Write the opposite of each integer. MCC6.NS.6a

40. 8 _____

41. 9 _____

42. −7 _____

43. −5 _____

44. A display of cereal boxes has one box in the top row, two boxes in the second row, three boxes in the third row, and so on, as shown. How many rows of boxes will there be in a display of 45 boxes? MCC5.OA.3

_____

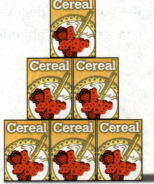

45. Name the quadrant in which the point (−4, −3) could be found on the coordinate plane. MCC6.NS.6b _____

21ST CENTURY CAREER
in Astronomy

Space Weather Forecaster

Did you know that space weather, or the conditions on the Sun and in space, can directly affect communication systems and power grids here on Earth? If you enjoy learning about the mysteries of space, then you should consider a career involving space weather. A space weather forecaster uses spacecraft, telescopes, radar, and supercomputers to monitor the sun, solar winds, and the space environment in order to forecast the weather in space.

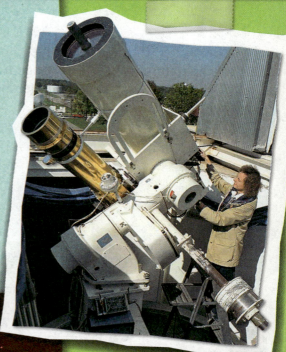

Explore college and careers at ccr.mcgraw-hill.com

Is This the Career for You?

Are you interested in a career as a space weather forecaster? Take some of the following courses in high school.

◆ Astronomy
◆ Calculus
◆ Chemistry
◆ Earth Science
◆ Physics

Find out how math relates to a career in Astronomy.

Predicting Space Storms!

Use the information in the table to solve each problem.

1. Graph the average temperatures for Earth, Jupiter, Mars, Mercury, Neptune, and Saturn on a number line. Label the points.

2. The temperatures on Mercury range from −279°F to 800°F. What is the difference between the highest and lowest temperatures? _____

3. How much greater is the average temperature on Earth than the average temperature on Jupiter? _____

4. One of Neptune's moons, Triton, has a surface temperature that is 61°F less than Neptune's average temperature. What is Triton's surface temperature? _____

5. The temperature on Mars can reach a low of −187°C. Find the value of the expression $\dfrac{9(-187) + 160}{5}$ to determine this temperature in degrees Fahrenheit. _____

Average Temperature of Planets			
Planet	**Average Temperature (°F)**	**Planet**	**Average Temperature (°F)**
Earth	59	Neptune	−330
Jupiter	−166	Saturn	−220
Mars	−85	Uranus	−320
Mercury	333	Venus	867

Career Project

It's time to update your career portfolio! Investigate the education and training requirements for a career as a space weather forecaster.

_____

_____

_____

_____

_____

List other careers that someone with an interest in astronomy could pursue.

- _____
- _____
- _____
- _____
- _____

Vocabulary Check

Complete each sentence using the vocabulary list at the beginning of the chapter.

1. The sum of an integer and its _____ inverse is 0.

2. A(n) _____ integer is greater than 0.

3. The set of _____ contains all the whole numbers and their opposites.

4. The _____ value of a number is the distance it is from 0 on a number line.

5. 5 and −5 are _____.

6. The result when one positive counter is paired with one negative counter is

   a _____ pair.

Reconstruct the vocabulary word and definition from the letters under the grid. The letters for each column are scrambled directly under that column.

| N | E | G | A | T | I | V | E | | I | N | T | E | G | E | R | : | | | |

Column letters below the grid:

		E		E	R							W	G				
I	E	A	N	T	V				E		I	R	N				E
N	N	T	E	G	E	E	S	A	H	N	N	E	G	E	I	I	E	A	N
T	N	T	A	G	Z	R	R	T	A	A	T	E	I	A	T	L	T	E	N
I	H	G	W	I	T	H	E	O	R	R	T	S	G	S	R	T	V	S	S

Use Your FOLDABLES

Use your Foldable to help review the chapter.

Tape here →

Operations with Integers

How do I add integers with different signs?

How do I subtract integers with different signs?

How do I multiply integers with different signs?

How do I divide integers with different signs?

Got it?

Find the Error The problems below may or may not contain an error. If the problem is correct, write a "✓" by the answer. If the problem is not correct, write an "X" over the answer and correct the problem.

1. $|-5| + |2| = -3$ ✗

   $|-5| + |2| = 5 + 2$ or 7

   The first one is done for you. →

2. $3|-6| = 18$

3. $-24 \div |-2| = 12$

For Exercises 1–3, use the table that shows the freezing point of various elements.

Element	Freezing Point (°C)
Chlorine	−101
Helium	−272
Krypton	−157
Neon	−249
Nitrogen	−201

1. Graph the temperatures on the number line. (Lesson 1)

2. CCGPS **Justify Conclusions** Is the absolute value of the freezing point of chlorine greater than the absolute value of the freezing point of nitrogen? Explain. (Lesson 1)

_____

_____

_____

3. Find the difference between the freezing point of chlorine and the freezing point of nitrogen. (Lesson 3) _____

_____

4. Alicia was rock climbing. She climbed to a height of 22 feet. Next, she descended 8 feet. Then, she climbed up another 34 feet. What was Alicia's elevation? (Lesson 2) _____

_____

5. **Financial Literacy** The price of a certain stock fell $2 each day for 4 consecutive days. Write an expression that you could use to find the change in the stock's price after 4 days. Suppose the original price of the stock was $41. What was the price of the stock after 4 days? (Lesson 4)

Expression: _____   Price: _____

6. The daily high temperature readings for four days in January are shown in the table. Find the average daily temperature for the four days. (Lessons 1 and 5) _____

_____

Day	Temperature (°F)
1	−19
2	−21
3	−22
4	−22

Reflect

 Answering the Essential Question

Use what you learned about integers to complete the graphic organizer.
Explain how to determine the sign of the result when performing each
operation.

Addition and Subtraction

Essential Question

**WHAT happens when you
add, subtract, multiply,
and divide integers?**

Multiply and Divide

Answer the Essential Question. WHAT happens when you add, subtract,
multiply, and divide integers?

Chapter 2

Rational Numbers

Essential Question

WHAT happens when you add, subtract, multiply, and divide fractions?

Common Core GPS

Content Standards
MCC7.NS.1, MCC7.NS.1b, MCC7.NS.1c, MCC7.NS.1d, MCC7.NS.2, MCC7.NS.2a, MCC7.NS.2b, MCC7.NS.2c, MCC7.NS.2d, MCC7.NS.3, MCC7.RP.3, MCC7.EE.3

Mathematical Practices
1, 3, 4, 5, 6, 7, 8

Math in the Real World

Tennis About 70,000 tennis balls are used at the U.S. Open tennis tournament each year. This is only a small fraction of the 300,000,000 tennis balls produced each year. Write a fraction in simplest form that compares the number of tennis balls used at the U.S. Open to the number produced per year.

FOLDABLES
Study Organizer

1 Cut out the correct Foldable from the FL pages in the back of this book.

2 Place your Foldable on the Key Concept page toward the end of this chapter.

3 Use the Foldable throughout this chapter to help you learn about rational numbers.

What Tools Do You Need?

Vocabulary

bar notation

common denominator

least common denominator

like fractions

rational numbers

repeating decimal

terminating decimal

unlike fractions

Review Vocabulary

An *improper fraction* is a fraction in which the numerator is greater than or equal to the denominator, such as $\frac{21}{4}$. A *mixed number* is a number composed of a whole number and a fraction, such as $5\frac{1}{4}$.

In the organizer below, write each mixed number as an improper fraction and each improper fraction as a mixed number. The first one in each column is done for you.

Mixed Numbers and Improper Fractions

Change Mixed Numbers	Change Improper Fractions
$3\frac{1}{2} = \frac{7}{2}$	$\frac{41}{4} = 10\frac{1}{4}$
$5\frac{1}{3} =$	$\frac{16}{3} =$
$8\frac{2}{5} =$	$\frac{23}{5} =$
$6\frac{4}{9} =$	$\frac{90}{11} =$
$10\frac{3}{8} =$	$\frac{66}{7} =$
$7\frac{3}{4} =$	$\frac{101}{2} =$
$15\frac{5}{6} =$	$\frac{87}{20} =$

Copyright © The McGraw-Hill Companies, Inc.

**Try the Quick Check below.
Or, take the Online Readiness Quiz.** Check ✓

Example 1

Write $\frac{25}{100}$ in simplest form.

$$\frac{25}{100} = \frac{1}{4}$$
÷25 (over) ÷25

Divide the numerator and denominator by the GCF, 25.

Since the GCF of 1 and 4 is 1, the fraction $\frac{1}{4}$ is in simplest form.

Example 2

Graph $3\frac{2}{3}$ on a number line.

Find the two whole numbers between which $3\frac{2}{3}$ lies.

$3 < 3\frac{2}{3} < 4$

Since the denominator is 3, divide each space into 3 sections.

Draw a dot at $3\frac{2}{3}$.

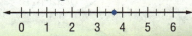

Quick Check

Fractions Write each fraction in simplest form.

1. $\frac{24}{36} =$ _____

 Show your work.

2. $\frac{45}{50} =$ _____

3. $\frac{88}{121} =$ _____

Graphing Graph each fraction or mixed number on the number line below.

4. $\frac{1}{2}$

5. $\frac{3}{4}$

6. $1\frac{1}{4}$

7. $2\frac{1}{2}$

 **How Did You Do?**

**Which problems did you answer correctly in the Quick Check?
Shade those exercise numbers below.**

① ② ③ ④ ⑤ ⑥ ⑦

Inquiry HOW can you graph negative fractions on the number line?

Content Standards
Preparation for MCC7.NS.1

Mathematical Practices
1, 3, 8

Evaporation Water evaporates from Earth at an average of about $-\frac{3}{4}$ inch per week.

Investigation

Graph $-\frac{3}{4}$ on a number line.

Step 1 Use the fraction strip below that is divided in fourths above a number line.

Mark a 0 on the right side and a −1 on the left side.

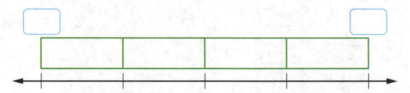

Step 2 Starting from the right, shade three fourths. Label the number line with $-\frac{1}{4}$, $-\frac{2}{4}$, and $-\frac{3}{4}$.

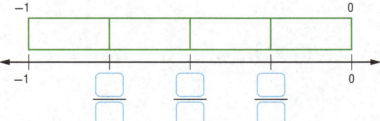

Step 3 Draw the number line portion of the model in Step 2.

Place a dot on the number line to represent $-\frac{3}{4}$.

So, on a number line, $-\frac{3}{4}$ is between $\boxed{}$ and $\frac{\boxed{}}{\boxed{}}$ or $\frac{\boxed{}}{\boxed{}}$.

Model with Mathematics Work with a partner. Graph each fraction on a number line. Use a fraction strip if needed.

1. $-\dfrac{3}{8}$

Show your work.

2. $-1\dfrac{2}{5}$

Analyze

Work with a partner to complete each table. Use a number line if needed.

	< or >	
$\dfrac{7}{8}$	>	$\dfrac{3}{8}$
3. $\dfrac{9}{8}$		$\dfrac{5}{8}$
4. $\dfrac{13}{8}$		$\dfrac{3}{8}$
5. $\dfrac{15}{8}$		$\dfrac{13}{8}$

	< or >	
$-\dfrac{7}{8}$	<	$-\dfrac{3}{8}$
6. $-\dfrac{9}{8}$		$-\dfrac{5}{8}$
7. $-\dfrac{13}{8}$		$-\dfrac{3}{8}$
8. $-\dfrac{15}{8}$		$-\dfrac{13}{8}$

9. **Identify Repeated Reasoning** Compare and contrast the information in the tables.

_____

_____

Reflect

10. **Reason Inductively** How does graphing $-\dfrac{3}{4}$ differ from graphing $\dfrac{3}{4}$?

_____

_____

11. **Inquiry** HOW can you graph negative fractions on the number line?

_____

_____

Terminating and Repeating Decimals

What You'll Learn

Scan the lesson. List two headings you would use to make an outline of the lesson.

- _____
  _____

- _____

Essential Question

WHAT happens when you add, subtract, multiply, and divide fractions?

Vocabulary

repeating decimal
bar notation
terminating decimal

Common Core GPS

Content Standards
MCC7.NS.2, MCC7.NS.2d, MCC7.EE.3

Mathematical Practices
1, 3, 4, 6, 7

Vocabulary Start-Up

Any fraction can be expressed as a decimal by dividing the numerator by the denominator.

The decimal form of a fraction is called a **repeating decimal**. Repeating decimals can be represented using **bar notation**. In bar notation, a bar is drawn only over the digit(s) that repeat.

$$0.3333... = 0.\overline{3} \qquad 0.1212... = 0.\overline{12} \qquad 11.38585... = 11.3\overline{85}$$

If the repeating digit is zero, the decimal is a **terminating decimal**. The terminating decimal $0.25\overline{0}$ is typically written as 0.25.

Match each repeating decimal to the correct bar notation.

0.1111...	$0.6\overline{1}$
0.61111...	$0.\overline{1}$
0.616161...	$0.\overline{61}$

🌎 Real-World Link

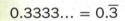

Jamie had two hits on her first nine times at bat. To find her batting "average," she divided 2 by 9.

$$2 \div 9 = 0.2222...$$

Write 0.2222... using bar notation. [   ]

Round 0.2222... to the nearest thousandth. [   ]

Write Fractions as Decimals

Our decimal system is based on powers of 10 such as 10, 100, and 1,000. If the denominator of a fraction is a power of 10, you can use place value to write the fraction as a decimal.

Complete the table below. Write fractions in simplest form.

Words	Fraction	Decimal
seven tenths	$\frac{7}{10}$	0.7
nineteen hundredths		
one-hundred five thousandths		

If the denominator of a fraction is a *factor* of 10, 100, 1,000, or any greater power of ten, you can use mental math and place value.

Examples

Tutor

Write each fraction or mixed number as a decimal.

1. $\frac{74}{100}$

Use place value to write the equivalent decimal.

$\frac{74}{100} = 0.74$ Read $\frac{74}{100}$ as *seventy-four hundredths*.

So, $\frac{74}{100} = 0.74$.

2. $\frac{7}{20}$

Think $\frac{7}{20} = \frac{35}{100}$

So, $\frac{7}{20} = 0.35$.

3. $5\frac{3}{4}$

$5\frac{3}{4} = 5 + \frac{3}{4}$ Think of it as a sum.

$= 5 + 0.75$ You know that $\frac{3}{4} = 0.75$.

$= 5.75$ Add mentally.

So, $5\frac{3}{4} = 5.75$.

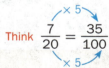 Show your work.

Got It? Do these problems to find out.

a. $\frac{3}{10}$

b. $\frac{3}{25}$

c. $-6\frac{1}{2}$

a. _____

b. _____

c. _____

4. Write $\frac{3}{8}$ as a decimal.

$$
\begin{array}{r}
0.375 \\
8\overline{)3.000} \\
\underline{-24} \\
60 \\
\underline{-56} \\
40 \\
\underline{-40} \\
0
\end{array}
$$

Divide 3 by 8.

Division ends when the remainder is 0.

So, $\frac{3}{8} = 0.375$.

5. Write $-\frac{1}{40}$ as a decimal.

$$
\begin{array}{r}
0.025 \\
40\overline{)1.000} \\
\underline{-80} \\
200 \\
\underline{-200} \\
0
\end{array}
$$

Divide 1 by 40.

So, $-\frac{1}{40} = -0.025$.

6. Write $\frac{7}{9}$ as a decimal.

$$
\begin{array}{r}
0.777... \\
9\overline{)7.000} \\
\underline{-63} \\
70 \\
\underline{-63} \\
70 \\
\underline{-63} \\
7
\end{array}
$$

Divide 7 by 9.

Notice that the division will never terminate in zero.

So, $\frac{7}{9} = 0.777...$ or $0.\overline{7}$.

Got It? Do these problems to find out.

Write each fraction or mixed number as a decimal. Use bar notation if needed.

d. $-\frac{7}{8}$

e. $2\frac{1}{8}$

f. $-\frac{3}{11}$

g. $8\frac{1}{3}$

Bar Notation

Remember that you can use bar notation to indicate a number pattern that repeats indefinitely. $0.333... = 0.\overline{3}$.

Show your work.

d. _____

e. _____

f. _____

g. _____

Write Decimals as Fractions

Every terminating decimal can be written as a fraction with a denominator of 10, 100, 1,000, or a greater power of ten. Use the place value of the final digit as the denominator.

Show your work.

h. _____

i. _____

j. _____

Real World Example

7. Find the fraction of the fish in the aquarium that are goldfish. Write in simplest form.

$0.15 = \dfrac{15}{100}$ The digit 5 is in the hundredths place.

$= \dfrac{3}{20}$ Simplify.

So, $\dfrac{3}{20}$ of the fish are goldfish.

Fish	Amount
Guppy	0.25
Angelfish	0.4
Goldfish	0.15
Molly	0.2

Got It? Do these problems to find out.

Determine the fraction of the aquarium made up by each fish. Write the answer in simplest form.

h. molly   **i.** guppy   **j.** angelfish

Guided Practice

Write each fraction or mixed number as a decimal. Use bar notation if needed. (Examples 1–6)

1. $\dfrac{2}{5} =$ _____

2. $-\dfrac{9}{10} =$ _____

3. $\dfrac{5}{9} =$ _____

Show your work.

4. During a hockey game, an ice resurfacer travels 0.75 mile. What fraction represents this distance? (Example 7)

_____

5. **Building on the Essential Question** How can you write a fraction as a decimal?

_____

_____

_____

Independent Practice

Go online for Step-by-Step Solutions

Write each fraction or mixed number as a decimal. Use bar notation if needed. (Examples 1–6)

1. $\frac{1}{2} =$ 0.50

2. $-4\frac{4}{25} =$ -4.16

3. $\frac{1}{8} =$ 0.125

4. $\frac{3}{16} =$ 0.1875

 Show your work.

5. $-\frac{33}{50} =$ -0.66

6. $-\frac{17}{40} =$ -0.1740

7. $5\frac{7}{8} =$ 5.875

8. $9\frac{3}{8} =$ 9.375

9. $-\frac{8}{9} =$ -0.$\overline{8}$

10. $-\frac{1}{6} =$ -0.1$\overline{6}$

11. $-\frac{8}{11} =$ -0.$\overline{72}$

12. $2\frac{6}{11} =$ 2.5$\overline{4}$

Write each decimal as a fraction or mixed number in simplest form. (Example 7)

13. $-0.2 =$ 1/5

14. $0.55 =$ 11/20

15. $5.96 =$ 5 24/25

16. The screen on Brianna's new phone is 2.85 centimeters long. What mixed number represents the length of the phone screen? (Example 7)

57/20 = 2 17/20

17. **STEM** A praying mantis is an interesting insect that can rotate its head 180 degrees. Suppose the praying mantis at the right is 10.5 centimeters long. What mixed number represents this length? (Example 7)

21/2 = 10 1/2

18. **Persevere with Problems** Suppose you buy a 1.25-pound package of ham at $5.20 per pound.

   a. What fraction of a pound did you buy?

   _____

   b. How much money did you spend?

   _____

 ## H.O.T. Problems Higher Order Thinking

19. CCGPS **Identify Structure** Write a fraction that is equivalent to a terminating decimal between 0.5 and 0.75.

_____

20. CCGPS **Persevere with Problems** Fractions in simplest form that have denominators of 2, 4, 8, 16, and 32 produce terminating decimals. Fractions with denominators of 6, 12, 18, and 24 produce repeating decimals. What causes the difference? Explain.

_____

_____

_____

21. CCGPS **Persevere with Problems** The value of pi (π) is 3.1415926... . The mathematician Archimedes believed that π was between $3\frac{1}{7}$ and $3\frac{10}{71}$. Was Archimedes correct? Explain your reasoning.

_____

_____

_____

Georgia Test Practice

22. Tanya drew a model for the fraction $\frac{4}{6}$.

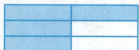

Which of the following decimals is equal to $\frac{4}{6}$?

Ⓐ 0.666

Ⓑ 0.$\overline{6}$

Ⓒ 0.667

Ⓓ 0.66$\overline{7}$

Extra Practice

Write each fraction or mixed number as a decimal. Use bar notation if needed.

23. $\frac{4}{5} =$ <u>*0.8*</u>

Homework Help →

$$\overset{\times 2}{\overbrace{\frac{4}{5}}} = \frac{8}{10}$$
$$\underset{\times 2}{}$$

So, $\frac{4}{5} = 0.8$.

24. $-7\frac{1}{20} =$ _____

25. $-\frac{4}{9} =$ _____

26. $5\frac{1}{3} =$ _____

27. The fraction of a dime that is made up of copper is $\frac{12}{16}$. Write this fraction as a decimal.

_____

Write each decimal as a fraction or mixed number in simplest form.

28. $-0.9 =$ _____

29. $0.34 =$ _____

30. $2.66 =$ _____

Write each of the following as an improper fraction.

31. $-13 =$ _____

32. $7\frac{1}{3} =$ _____

33. $-3.2 =$ _____

34. **CCGPS** **Be Precise** Nicolás practiced playing the cello for 2 hours and 18 minutes. Write the time Nicolás spent practicing as a decimal.

_____

35. Use the table that shows decimal and fraction equivalents.

Decimal	Fraction
$0.\overline{3}$	$\frac{3}{9}$
$0.\overline{4}$	$\frac{4}{9}$
$0.\overline{5}$	$\frac{5}{9}$
$0.\overline{6}$	$\frac{6}{9}$

Which fraction represents $0.\overline{8}$?

Ⓐ $\frac{4}{5}$ Ⓒ $\frac{5}{6}$

Ⓑ $\frac{80}{99}$ Ⓓ $\frac{8}{9}$

36. The sign shows the lengths of four hiking trails.

HIKING TRAILS
Lakeview .... $1\frac{1}{4}$ mi
Forest Lane .... $1\frac{1}{3}$ mi
Sparrow Stroll........ $1\frac{3}{10}$ mi
Mountain Climb .... $1\frac{2}{3}$ mi

Which trail length is equivalent to $1.\overline{3}$?

Ⓕ Forest Lane Ⓗ Mountain Climb

Ⓖ Lakeview Ⓘ Sparrow Stroll

37. Zoe went to lunch with a friend. After tax, her bill was $12.05. Which mixed number represents this amount in simplest form?

Ⓐ $12\frac{1}{2}$ Ⓒ $12\frac{5}{10}$

Ⓑ $12\frac{1}{20}$ Ⓓ $12\frac{5}{100}$

Common Core Review

Round each decimal to the tenths place. MCC5.NBT.4

38. $5.69 \approx$ _____

39. $0.05 \approx$ _____

40. $98.99 \approx$ _____

Graph and label each fraction on the number line below. MCC6.NS.6

41. $\frac{1}{2}$

42. $\frac{3}{4}$

43. $\frac{2}{3}$

```
|---+---+---+---+---+---+---+---+---+---+---|
0                                           1
```

44. The table shows the discount on athletic shoes at two stores selling sporting equipment. Which store is offering the greater discount? Explain. MCC6.NS.7

Store	Discount
Good Sports	$\frac{1}{5}$
Go Time	25%

_____

_____

Compare and Order Rational Numbers

What You'll Learn

Scan the lesson. Write the definitions of common denominator and least common denominator (LCD).

• Common Denominator _____

_____

• Least Common Denominator _____

_____

  Essential Question

WHAT happens when you add, subtract, multiply, and divide fractions?

 Vocabulary

rational number
common denominator
least common denominator

 Common Core GPS

Content Standards
MCC7.NS.2, MCC7.NS.2b, MCC7.EE.3

Mathematical Practices
1, 3, 4

Vocabulary Start-Up

A **rational number** is a number that can be expressed as a ratio of two integers written as a fraction, in which the denominator is not zero. The Venn diagram below shows that the number 2 can be called many things. It is a whole number, integer, and rational number. The number −1.4444... is only a rational number.

Common fractions, terminating and repeating decimals, percents, and integers are all rational numbers.

Write the numbers from the number bank on the diagram.

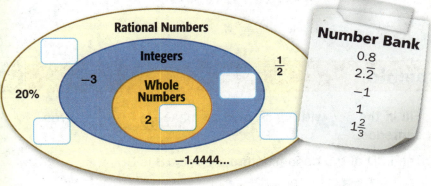

Number Bank
0.8
$2.\overline{2}$
−1
1
$1\frac{2}{3}$

Real-World Link

Not all numbers are rational numbers. The Greek letter π (pi) represents the nonterminating and nonrepeating number whose first few digits are 3.14... . This number is an *irrational number*.

Use the Internet to search for the digits of pi. Describe what you find. _____

_____

Compare Rational Numbers

A **common denominator** is a common multiple of the denominators of two or more fractions. The **least common denominator** or **LCD** is the LCM or least common multiple of the denominators. You can use the LCD to compare fractions. You can also use a number line.

Example

1. Fill in the $\bigcirc$ with <, >, or = to make $-1\frac{5}{6}$ $\bigcirc$ $-1\frac{1}{6}$ a true sentence.

Graph each rational number on a number line.
Mark off equal-size increments of $\frac{1}{6}$ between -2 and -1.

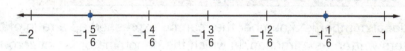

The number line shows that $-1\frac{5}{6} < -1\frac{1}{6}$.

Got It? Do this problem to find out.

a. Use the number line to compare $-5\frac{5}{9}$ and $-5\frac{1}{9}$.

$\leftarrow \quad\quad\quad\quad\quad\quad\quad\quad\quad\quad\quad\quad\quad\quad \rightarrow$
$\quad\quad -6 \quad\quad\quad\quad\quad\quad\quad\quad\quad\quad\quad\quad -5$

Show your work.

a. _____

LCD
To find the least common denominator for $\frac{7}{12}$ and $\frac{8}{18}$, find the LCM of 12 and 18.
$12 = 2 \times 2 \times 3$
$18 = 2 \times 3 \times 3$
$LCM = 2 \times 2 \times 3 \times 3$
$\quad\quad = 36$

Example

2. Fill in the $\bigcirc$ with <, >, or = to make $\frac{7}{12}$ $\bigcirc$ $\frac{8}{18}$ a true sentence.

The LCD of the denominators 12 and 18 is 36.

$$\frac{7}{12} = \frac{7 \times 3}{12 \times 3} \quad\quad\quad \frac{8}{18} = \frac{8 \times 2}{18 \times 2}$$

$$= \frac{21}{36} \quad\quad\quad\quad\quad = \frac{16}{36}$$

Since $\frac{21}{36} > \frac{16}{36}$, $\frac{7}{12} > \frac{8}{18}$.

Got It? Do these problems to find out.

b. $\frac{5}{6}$ $\bigcirc$ $\frac{7}{9}$ **c.** $\frac{1}{5}$ $\bigcirc$ $\frac{7}{50}$ **d.** $-\frac{9}{16}$ $\bigcirc$ $-\frac{7}{10}$

Example

3. In Mr. Huang's class, 20% of students own roller shoes. In Mrs. Trevino's class, 5 out of 29 students own roller shoes. In which class does a greater fraction of students own roller shoes?

Express each number as a decimal and then compare.

$20\% = 0.2$ $\dfrac{5}{29} = 5 \div 29 \approx 0.1724$

Since $0.2 > 0.1724$, $20\% > \dfrac{5}{29}$.

More students in Mr. Huang's class own roller shoes.

Got It?   Do this problem to find out.

e. In a second period class, 37.5% of students like to bowl. In a fifth period class, 12 out of 29 students like to bowl. In which class does a greater fraction of the students like to bowl?

Order Rational Numbers

You can order rational numbers using place value.

Example

Tutor

4. Order the set $\{3.44, \pi, 3.14, 3.\overline{4}\}$ from least to greatest.

Line up the decimal points and compare using place value.

3.14**0** Annex a zero.	3.44**0** Annex a zero.
3.14**1**5926... $\pi \approx 3.1415926...$	3.44**4**... $3.\overline{4} = 3.444...$
Since $0 < 1$, $3.14 < \pi$.	Since $0 < 4$, $3.44 < 3.\overline{4}$.

So, the order of the numbers from least to greatest is 3.14, π, 3.44, and $3.\overline{4}$.

Got It?   Do this problem to find out.

f. Order the set $\{23\%, 0.21, \frac{1}{4}, \frac{1}{5}\}$ from least to greatest.

Percents as Decimals

To write a percent as a decimal, remove the percent sign and then move the decimal point two places to the left. Add zeros if necessary.

$20\% = 20\%$

$= 0.20$

Show your work.

e. _____

Show your work.

f. _____

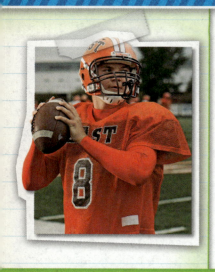

Example

5. Nolan is the quarterback on the football team. He completed 67% of his passes in the first game. He completed 0.64, $\frac{3}{5}$, and 69% of his passes in the next three games. List Nolan's completed passing numbers from least to greatest.

Express each number as a decimal and then compare.

$67\% = 0.67$ $0.64 = 64\%$ $\frac{3}{5} = 0.6$ $69\% = 0.69$

Nolan's completed passing numbers from least to greatest are $\frac{3}{5}$, 0.64, 67%, and 69%.

Guided Practice

Fill in each ◯ with <, >, or = to make a true sentence. Use a number line if necessary. (Examples 1 and 2)

1. $-\frac{4}{5}$ ◯ $-\frac{1}{5}$

2. $1\frac{3}{4}$ ◯ $1\frac{5}{8}$

3. Elliot and Shanna are both soccer goalies. Elliot saves 3 goals out of 4. Shanna saves 7 goals out of 11. Who has the better average, Elliot or Shanna? Explain. (Example 3)

_____

_____

4. The lengths of four insects are 0.02 inch, $\frac{1}{8}$ inch, 0.1 inch, and $\frac{2}{3}$ inch. List the lengths in inches from least to greatest. (Examples 4 and 5)

_____

5. **Building on the Essential Question** How can you compare two fractions? _____

_____

_____

_____

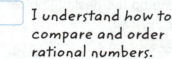

Rate Yourself!

☐ I understand how to compare and order rational numbers.

▶▶ Great! You're ready to move on!

☐ I still have some questions about comparing and ordering rational numbers.

 Go online to access a Personal Tutor.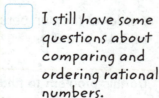

Independent Practice

Go online for Step-by-Step Solutions

Fill in each ◯ with <, >, or = to make a true sentence. Use a number line if necessary. (Examples 1 and 2)

1. $-\dfrac{3}{5}$ ⊝ $-\dfrac{4}{5}$ (>)

2. $-7\dfrac{5}{8}$ ⊝ $-7\dfrac{1}{8}$ (<)

3. $6\dfrac{2}{3}$ ⊝ $6\dfrac{1}{2}$ (>)

4. $-\dfrac{17}{24}$ ⊝ $-\dfrac{11}{12}$ (>)

5 On her first quiz in social studies, Meg answered 92% of the questions correctly. On her second quiz, she answered 27 out of 30 questions correctly. On which quiz did Meg have the better score? (Example 3)

The first one because 92% > 90%

Order each set of numbers from least to greatest. (Example 4)

6. $\{0.23, 19\%, \dfrac{1}{5}\}$

19%, 1/5, 0.23

23% 19% 20

7. $\{-0.615, -\dfrac{5}{8}, -0.62\}$

-5/8, -0.62, -0.615

-0.615, -0.625, -0.62

8. Liberty Middle School is holding a fundraiser. The sixth-graders have raised 52% of their goal amount. The seventh- and eighth-graders have raised 0.57 and $\dfrac{2}{5}$ of their goal amounts, respectively. List the classes in order from least to greatest of their goal amounts. (Example 5)

8, 6, 7

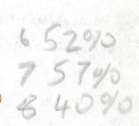
6   52%
7   57%
8   40%

Fill in each ◯ with <, >, or = to make a true sentence.

9 $1\dfrac{7}{12}$ gallons ⊝ $1\dfrac{5}{8}$ gallons   (<)

10. $2\dfrac{5}{6}$ hours ⊝ 2.8 hours   (>)

11. **CCGPS** **Model with Mathematics** Refer to the graphic novel frame below. If the closet organizer has a total width of $69\frac{1}{8}$ inches and the closet is $69\frac{3}{4}$ inches wide, will the organizer fit? Explain.

Yes, because 69 1/8 < 69 3/4

Watch ▶ **Replay it online!**

We can do this! All we need to do is find a common denominator for all of the measurements before we add.

Caitlyn and Theresa are helping me install a new closet organizer.

🔥 H.O.T. Problems Higher Order Thinking

12. **CCGPS** **Justify Conclusions** Identify the ratio that does not have the same value as the other three. Explain your reasoning.

| 12 out of 15 | 0.08 | 80% | $\frac{4}{5}$ |

0.8   0.08   0.8   0.8

0.08, because all the other answers are 0.8

13. **CCGPS** **Persevere with Problems** Explain how you know which number, $1\frac{15}{16}$, $\frac{17}{8}$, or $\frac{63}{32}$, is closest to 2.

I know 63/32 is the closest because if you convert it to a decimal it is 0.04 away from 0 while the others are 0.07 and 0.12

✏️ Georgia Test Practice

14. Which of the following fractions is the least?

Ⓐ $-\frac{7}{8}$　　　　　Ⓒ $-\frac{7}{10}$

Ⓑ $-\frac{7}{9}$　　　　　Ⓓ $-\frac{7}{11}$

Extra Practice

Fill in each ◯ with <, >, or = to make a true sentence. Use a number line if necessary.

15. $-\dfrac{5}{7}$ ⬤(<) $-\dfrac{2}{7}$

Mark off equal-size increments of $\frac{1}{7}$ between -1 and 0.

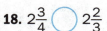

$-1 \quad -\dfrac{6}{7} \quad -\dfrac{5}{7} \quad -\dfrac{4}{7} \quad -\dfrac{3}{7} \quad -\dfrac{2}{7} \quad -\dfrac{1}{7} \quad 0$

16. $-3\dfrac{2}{3}$ ◯ $-3\dfrac{4}{6}$

17. $\dfrac{4}{7}$ ⬤(<) $\dfrac{5}{8}$

The LCD of the denominators 7 and 8 is 56.

$\dfrac{4}{7} = \dfrac{4 \times 8}{7 \times 8} = \dfrac{32}{56}$ and $\dfrac{5}{8} = \dfrac{5 \times 7}{8 \times 7} = \dfrac{35}{56}$

Since $\dfrac{32}{56} < \dfrac{35}{56}$, $\dfrac{4}{7} < \dfrac{5}{8}$.

18. $2\dfrac{3}{4}$ ◯ $2\dfrac{2}{3}$

19. Gracia and Jim were shooting free throws. Gracia made 4 out of 15 free throws. Jim *missed* 6 out of 16 free throws. Who made the free throw a greater fraction of the time? _____

Order each set of numbers from least to greatest.

20. $\{7.49, 7\dfrac{49}{50}, 7.5\%\}$

_____

21. $\{-1.4, -1\dfrac{1}{25}, -1.25\}$

_____

22. **STEM** Use the table that shows the lengths of small mammals.
a. Which animal is the smallest mammal?

_____

b. Which animal is smaller than the European Mole but larger than the Spiny Pocket Mouse?

_____

c. Order the animals from greatest to least size.

_____

_____

Animal	Length (ft)
Eastern Chipmunk	$\dfrac{1}{3}$
European Mole	$\dfrac{5}{12}$
Masked Shrew	$\dfrac{1}{6}$
Spiny Pocket Mouse	0.25

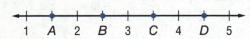

23. Which point shows the location of $\frac{7}{2}$ on the number line?

```
 1   A   2   B   3   C   4   D   5
```

- Ⓐ point *A*
- Ⓑ point *B*
- Ⓒ point *C*
- Ⓓ point *D*

24. Which list of numbers is ordered from least to greatest?

- Ⓕ $\frac{1}{4}$, $4\frac{1}{4}$, 0.4, 4%
- Ⓖ 4%, 0.4, $4\frac{1}{4}$, $\frac{1}{4}$
- Ⓗ 4%, $\frac{1}{4}$, 0.4, $4\frac{1}{4}$
- Ⓘ 0.4, $\frac{1}{4}$, 4%, $4\frac{1}{4}$

25. The daily price changes for a stock are shown in the table.

Day	Price Change
Monday	−0.21
Tuesday	−1.05
Wednesday	−0.23
Thursday	+0.42
Friday	−1.15

On which day did the price decrease by the greatest amount?

- Ⓐ Monday
- Ⓑ Tuesday
- Ⓒ Wednesday
- Ⓓ Friday

Fill in each ◯ with < or > to make a true sentence. **MCC6.NS.7**

26. −2 ◯ 2

Show your work.

27. −4 ◯ −5

28. −20 ◯ 20

29. −7 ◯ −8

30. −10 ◯ −1

31. 50 ◯ −100

32. Victoria, Cooper, and Diego are reading the same book for their language arts class. The table shows the fraction of the book each student has read. Which student has read the least amount? Explain your reasoning. **MCC6.NS.7**

Student	Amount Read
Victoria	$\frac{2}{5}$
Cooper	$\frac{1}{5}$
Diego	$\frac{3}{5}$

_____

_____

_____

Inquiry HOW can you use a number line to add and subtract like fractions?

 Content Standards
MCC7.NS.1,
MCC7.NS.1b,
MCC7.NS.3

Mathematical Practices
1, 3, 5

Baseball In eight times at bat, Max hit 2 doubles, 5 singles, and struck out 1 time. Find the fraction of the times that Max hit either a single or a double.

Investigation 1

Step 1 Since there were 8 times at bat, create a vertical number line that is divided into eighths.

Step 2 Graph the fraction of doubles, $\frac{2}{8}$, on the number line.

Step 3 From the $\frac{2}{8}$ point, count $\frac{5}{8}$ more on the number line.

So, $\frac{2}{8} + \frac{5}{8} = \dfrac{\boxed{}}{\boxed{}}$.

Max got a hit $\dfrac{\boxed{}}{\boxed{}}$ of the times he was at bat.

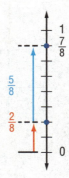

Investigation 2

Find $\frac{3}{6} - \frac{4}{6}$.

Step 1 Divide a number line into sixths. Since we do not know if our answer is negative or positive, include fractions to the left and to the right of zero.

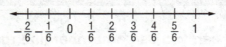

Step 2 Graph $\frac{3}{6}$ on the number line.

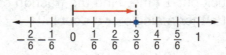

Step 3 Move 4 units to the _____ to show taking away $\frac{4}{6}$.

So, $\frac{3}{6} - \frac{4}{6} = \dfrac{\boxed{}}{\boxed{}}$.

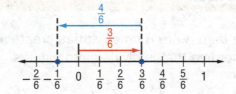

Investigation 3

Find $-\frac{4}{7} - \frac{2}{7}$. Fill in the missing numbers in the diagram below.

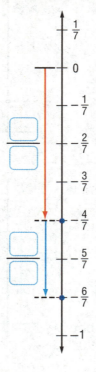

So, $-\frac{4}{7} - \frac{2}{7} = \dfrac{\boxed{}}{\boxed{}}$.

Work with a partner. Use a number line to add or subtract. Write in simplest form.

1. $\frac{1}{5} + \frac{2}{5} =$ _____

2. $-\frac{3}{7} + \left(-\frac{1}{7}\right) =$ _____

3. $-\frac{3}{8} + \frac{5}{8} =$ _____

4. $\frac{8}{12} - \frac{4}{12} =$ _____

5. $-\frac{4}{9} + \frac{5}{9} =$ _____

6. $\frac{4}{7} - \frac{6}{7} =$ _____

CCGPS **Use Math Tools** Work with a partner to complete the table. The first one is done for you.

Expression	Use only the Numerators	Use a number line to add or subtract the fractions.
$-\dfrac{5}{6} - \left(-\dfrac{1}{6}\right)$	$-5 - (-1) = -4$	(number line from $-\frac{5}{6}$ to $\frac{2}{6}$, with $\frac{1}{6}$ and $-\frac{5}{6}$ marked)
7. $-\dfrac{5}{6} - \dfrac{1}{6}$	$-5 - 1 = -6$	(number line, 0 marked at right)
8. $\dfrac{5}{6} - \dfrac{1}{6}$	$5 - 1 = 4$	(number line, 0 marked at left)
9. $-\dfrac{5}{6} + \dfrac{1}{6}$	$-5 + 1 = -4$	(number line, 0 marked at right)

Reflect

10. **CCGPS** **Reason Inductively** Refer back to the Analyze section. Compare your results for using only the numerators with your results for using a number line. Write a rule for adding and subtracting like fractions.

_____

_____

11. **Inquiry** HOW can you use a number line to add and subtract like fractions?

_____

_____

_____

Add and Subtract Like Fractions

What You'll Learn

Scan the lesson. List two real-world scenarios in which you would add or subtract like fractions.

- _____
  _____

- _____
  _____

 Essential Question

WHAT happens when you add, subtract, multiply, and divide fractions?

 Vocabulary

like fractions

Common Core GPS

Content Standards
MCC7.NS.1, MCC7.NS.1c, MCC7.NS.1d, MCC7.NS.3, MCC7.EE.3

Mathematical Practices
1, 3, 4, 7

 Real-World Link

Shoes Sean surveyed ten classmates to find which type of tennis shoe they like to wear.

Shoe Type	Number
Cross Trainer	5
Running	3
High Top	2

1. What fraction of students liked to wear cross trainers?

   Number of students that wear cross trainers. → ☐

   Total number of students surveyed. → ☐

2. What fraction of students liked to wear high tops?

   Number of students that wear high tops. → ☐

   Total number of students surveyed. → ☐

3. What fraction of students liked to wear either cross trainers or high tops?

   Fraction of students that wear cross trainers.   Fraction of students that wear high tops.

   $\dfrac{\boxed{}}{\boxed{}}$ + $\dfrac{\boxed{}}{\boxed{}}$ = $\dfrac{\boxed{}}{\boxed{}}$

   So, _____ of the students liked to wear either cross trainers or high tops.

4. Explain how to find $\dfrac{3}{10} + \dfrac{2}{10}$. Then find the sum.

   _____

   _____

Add and Subtract Like Fractions

Words   To add or subtract like fractions, add or subtract the numerators and write the result over the denominator.

Examples

Numbers	Algebra

$$\frac{5}{10} + \frac{2}{10} = \frac{5+2}{10} \text{ or } \frac{7}{10} \qquad \frac{a}{c} + \frac{b}{c} = \frac{a+b}{c}, \text{ where } c \neq 0$$

$$\frac{11}{12} - \frac{4}{12} = \frac{11-4}{12} \text{ or } \frac{7}{12} \qquad \frac{a}{c} - \frac{b}{c} = \frac{a-b}{c}, \text{ where } c \neq 0$$

Fractions that have the same denominators are called **like fractions**.

Examples

  Tutor

Add. Write in simplest form.

1. $\dfrac{5}{9} + \dfrac{2}{9}$

$$\frac{5}{9} + \frac{2}{9} = \frac{5+2}{9} \qquad \text{Add the numerators.}$$

$$= \frac{7}{9} \qquad \text{Simplify.}$$

Negative Fractions

Remember $-\dfrac{1}{2} = \dfrac{-1}{2} = \dfrac{1}{-2}$.

Typically, the form $\dfrac{-1}{2}$ is used when performing computations.

 Show your work.

2. $-\dfrac{3}{5} + \left(-\dfrac{1}{5}\right)$

$$-\frac{3}{5} + \left(-\frac{1}{5}\right) = \frac{-3}{5} + \left(\frac{-1}{5}\right)$$

$$= \frac{-3 + (-1)}{5} \qquad \text{Add the numerators.}$$

$$= \frac{-4}{5} \text{ or } -\frac{4}{5} \qquad \text{Use the rules for adding integers.}$$

a. _____

b. _____

c. _____

d. _____

Got It? Do these problems to find out.

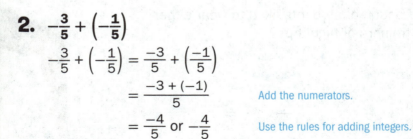

a. $\dfrac{1}{3} + \dfrac{2}{3}$

b. $-\dfrac{3}{7} + \dfrac{1}{7}$

c. $-\dfrac{2}{5} + \left(-\dfrac{2}{5}\right)$

d. $-\dfrac{1}{4} + \dfrac{1}{4}$

Example

3. Sofia ate $\frac{3}{5}$ of a cheese pizza. Jack ate $\frac{1}{5}$ of a cheese pizza and $\frac{2}{5}$ of a pepperoni pizza. How much pizza did Sofia and Jack eat altogether?

$$\frac{3}{5} + \left(\frac{1}{5} + \frac{2}{5}\right) = \frac{3}{5} + \left(\frac{2}{5} + \frac{1}{5}\right) \quad \text{Commutative Property of Addition}$$

$$= \left(\frac{3}{5} + \frac{2}{5}\right) + \frac{1}{5} \quad \text{Associative Property of Addition}$$

$$= 1 + \frac{1}{5} \text{ or } 1\frac{1}{5} \quad \text{Simplify.}$$

So, Sofia and Jack ate $1\frac{1}{5}$ pizzas altogether.

Got It? Do this problem to find out.

e. Eduardo used fabric to make three costumes. He used $\frac{1}{4}$ yard for the first, $\frac{2}{4}$ yard for the second, and $\frac{3}{4}$ yard for the third costume. How much fabric did Eduardo use altogether?

Show your work.

e. _____

 Examples

4. Find $-\frac{5}{8} - \frac{3}{8}$.

$$-\frac{5}{8} - \frac{3}{8} = -\frac{5}{8} + \left(-\frac{3}{8}\right) \quad \text{Add } -\frac{3}{8}.$$

$$= \frac{-5 + (-3)}{8} \quad \text{Add the numerators.}$$

$$= -\frac{8}{8} \text{ or } -1 \quad \text{Simplify.}$$

Subtracting Integers
To subtract an integer, add its opposite.
$-9 - (-4) = -9 + 4$
$\qquad = -5$

5. Find $\frac{5}{8} - \frac{7}{8}$.

$$\frac{5}{8} - \frac{7}{8} = \frac{5 - 7}{8} \quad \text{Subtract the numerators.}$$

$$= -\frac{2}{8} \text{ or } -\frac{1}{4} \quad \text{Simplify.}$$

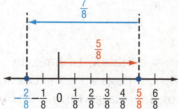
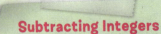

Got It? Do these problems to find out.

f. $\frac{5}{9} - \frac{2}{9}$

g. $-\frac{5}{9} - \frac{2}{9}$

h. $-\frac{11}{12} - \left(-\frac{5}{12}\right)$

f. _____

g. _____

h. _____

Choose an Operation

You can add or subtract like fractions to solve real-world problems.

 Example

6. About $\frac{6}{100}$ of the population of the United States lives in Florida. Another $\frac{4}{100}$ lives in Ohio. About what fraction more of the U.S. population lives in Florida than in Ohio?

$$\frac{6}{100} - \frac{4}{100} = \frac{6-4}{100} \qquad \text{Subtract the numerators.}$$

$$= \frac{2}{100} \text{ or } \frac{1}{50} \qquad \text{Simplify.}$$

About $\frac{1}{50}$ more of the U.S. population lives in Florida than in Ohio.

 Tutor

STOP and Reflect

In Example 6, what word or words indicate that you should subtract to solve the problem? Write your answer below.

Guided Practice

 Check

Add or subtract. Write in simplest form. (Examples 1–5)

1. $\frac{3}{5} + \frac{1}{5} =$ _____

2. $\frac{2}{7} + \frac{1}{7} =$ _____

3. $\left(\frac{5}{8} + \frac{1}{8}\right) + \frac{3}{8} =$ _____

4. $-\frac{4}{5} - \left(-\frac{1}{5}\right) =$ _____

5. $\frac{5}{14} - \left(-\frac{1}{14}\right) =$ _____

6. $\frac{2}{7} - \frac{6}{7} =$ _____

7. Of the 50 states in the United States, 14 have an Atlantic Ocean coastline and 5 have a Pacific Ocean coastline. What fraction of U.S. states have either an Atlantic Ocean or Pacific Ocean coastline? (Example 6)

_____

8. **Building on the Essential Question** What is a simple rule for adding and subtracting like fractions?

_____

_____

Rate Yourself!

How confident are you about adding and subtracting like fractions? Check the box that applies.

For more help, go online to access a Personal Tutor. Tutor

 FOLDABLES Time to update your Foldable!

Independent Practice

Go online for Step-by-Step Solutions   eHelp

Add or subtract. Write in simplest form. (Examples 1, 2, 4, and, 5)

1. $\frac{5}{7} + \frac{6}{7} =$ ___ $\frac{11}{7}$

 Show your work.

2. $\frac{3}{8} + \left(-\frac{7}{8}\right) =$ ___ $\frac{-4}{8}$

3. $-\frac{1}{9} + \left(-\frac{5}{9}\right) =$ ___ $-\frac{12}{3}$

4. $\frac{9}{10} - \frac{3}{10} =$ ___ $\frac{6}{10}$

5. $-\frac{3}{4} + \left(-\frac{3}{4}\right) =$ ___ $\frac{-6}{4}$

6. $-\frac{5}{9} - \frac{2}{9} =$ ___ $\frac{-7}{9}$

7. In Mr. Navarro's first period class, $\frac{17}{28}$ of the students got an A on their math test. In his second period class, $\frac{11}{28}$ of the students got an A. What fraction more of the students got an A in Mr. Navarro's first period class than in his second period class? Write in simplest form. (Example 6)

___ $\frac{6}{28}$

$\frac{17}{28} - \frac{11}{28} = \frac{6}{28}$

8. To make a greeting card, Bryce used $\frac{1}{8}$ sheet of red paper, $\frac{3}{8}$ sheet of green paper, and $\frac{7}{8}$ sheet of white paper. How many sheets of paper did Bryce use? (Example 3)

11/8

$\frac{1}{8} + \frac{3}{8} + \frac{7}{8} = \frac{11}{8}$

9. The table shows the Instant Messenger abbreviations students at Hillside Middle School use the most.

a. What fraction of these students uses LOL or CUL8R when using Instant Messenger? ___ 33/100

b. What fraction of these students uses L8R or BRB when using Instant Messenger? ___ 67/100

c. What fraction more of these students write L8R than CUL8R when using Instant Messenger? ___ 41/100

$\frac{48}{100} - \frac{7}{100} = \frac{41}{100}$

Instant Messenger Abbreviations	
L8R (Later)	$\frac{48}{100}$
LOL (Laughing out loud)	$\frac{26}{100}$
BRB (Be right back)	$\frac{19}{100}$
CUL8R (See you later)	$\frac{7}{100}$

10. **Model with Mathematics** Cross out the expression that does not belong. Explain your reasoning.

10/7+(3/7) doesn't belong beaus the answer is 7/7 and not 5/7

$$\frac{2}{7} + \frac{3}{7} \quad \frac{4}{7} - \left(-\frac{1}{7}\right)$$

$$\frac{8}{7} - \frac{3}{7} \quad \frac{10}{7} + \left(-\frac{3}{7}\right)$$

 H.O.T. Problems Higher Order Thinking

11. **Justify Conclusions** Select two like fractions with a difference of $\frac{1}{3}$ and with denominators that are *not* 3. Justify your selection.

11/18 − 5/18 = 6/18

12. **Persevere with Problems** Simplify the following expression.

$$\frac{14}{15} + \frac{13}{15} - \frac{12}{15} + \frac{11}{15} - \frac{10}{15} + \ldots - \frac{4}{15} + \frac{3}{15} - \frac{2}{15} + \frac{1}{15}$$

93/100

 Georgia Test Practice

13. The body length of a male Jumping Spider is shown below.

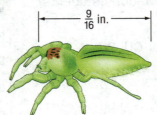

$\frac{9}{16}$ in.

The body length of a female Jumping Spider is about $\frac{5}{16}$ inch.

How much longer is the body length of a male Jumping Spider than the body length of a female Jumping Spider?

Ⓐ $\frac{7}{8}$ inch

Ⓑ $\frac{1}{2}$ inch

Ⓒ $\frac{1}{4}$ inch

Ⓓ $\frac{3}{16}$ inch

Extra Practice

Add or subtract. Write in simplest form.

14. $\frac{4}{5} + \frac{3}{5} = $ _1\frac{2}{5}_

Homework Help ➡

$\frac{4}{5} + \frac{3}{5} = \frac{4+3}{5}$

$= \frac{7}{5} \text{ or } 1\frac{2}{5}$

15. $-\frac{5}{6} + \left(-\frac{5}{6}\right) = $ _____

16. $-\frac{15}{16} + \left(-\frac{7}{16}\right) = $ _____

17. $\frac{5}{8} - \frac{3}{8} = $ _____

18. $\frac{7}{12} - \frac{2}{12} = $ _____

19. $\frac{15}{18} - \frac{13}{18} = $ _____

20. Two nails are $\frac{5}{16}$ inch and $\frac{13}{16}$ inch long. How much shorter is the $\frac{5}{16}$-inch nail? _____

CCGPS **Identify Structure** **Add. Write in simplest form.**

21. $\left(\frac{81}{100} + \frac{47}{100}\right) + \frac{19}{100} = $ _____

22. $\frac{\frac{1}{3}}{6} + \frac{\frac{2}{3}}{6} = $ _____

23. A recipe for Michigan blueberry pancakes calls for $\frac{3}{4}$ cup flour, $\frac{1}{4}$ cup milk, and $\frac{1}{4}$ cup blueberries. How much more flour is needed than milk? Write in simplest form.

_____

24. The graph shows the location of volcanic eruptions.

   a. What fraction represents the volcanic eruptions for both North and South America?

   _____

   b. How much larger is the section for Asia and South Pacific than for Europe? Write in simplest form.

   _____

Worldwide Volcano Eruptions

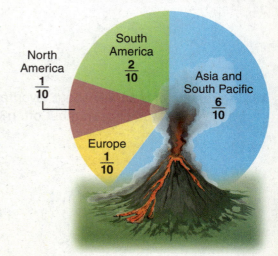

North America $\frac{1}{10}$

South America $\frac{2}{10}$

Asia and South Pacific $\frac{6}{10}$

Europe $\frac{1}{10}$

25. A group of friends bought two large pizzas and ate only part of each pizza. The picture shows how much was left.

First Pizza   Second Pizza

How many pizzas did they eat?

(A) $\frac{3}{8}$ (C) $1\frac{1}{4}$

(B) $\frac{5}{8}$ (D) $1\frac{3}{8}$

26. At a school carnival, homemade pies were cut into 8 equal-size pieces. Eric sold 13 pieces, Elena sold 7 pieces, and Tanya sold 10 pieces. Which expression can be used to find the total number of pies sold by Eric, Elena, and Tanya?

(F) $13 + 7 + 10$ (H) $\frac{13}{8} \times \frac{7}{8} \times \frac{10}{8}$

(G) $8(13 + 7 + 10)$ (I) $\frac{13}{8} + \frac{7}{8} + \frac{10}{8}$

27. Short Response What is the value of x that makes the statement below true? _____

$$\frac{7}{9} - \frac{x}{9} = \frac{1}{3}$$

Common Core Review

Fill in each ⬭ with <, >, or = to make a true sentence. MCC6.NS.7

28. $\frac{7}{8}$ ⬭ $\frac{3}{4}$

29. $\frac{1}{3}$ ⬭ $\frac{7}{9}$

30. $\frac{5}{7}$ ⬭ $\frac{4}{5}$

31. $\frac{6}{11}$ ⬭ $\frac{9}{14}$

Find the least common denominator for each pair of fractions. MCC6.NS.4

32. $\frac{1}{2}$ and $\frac{1}{3}$ _____

33. $\frac{4}{7}$ and $\frac{3}{28}$ _____

34. $\frac{1}{5}$ and $\frac{7}{6}$ _____

35. $\frac{13}{15}$ and $\frac{7}{12}$ _____

36. The results of a survey about favorite lunch choices are shown. Which lunch was chosen most often? MCC6.NS.7

_____

Favorite Lunch	
Food	Fraction of Students
Pizza	$\frac{39}{50}$
Hot Dogs	$\frac{3}{25}$
Grilled Cheese	$\frac{1}{10}$

Add and Subtract Unlike Fractions

What You'll Learn

Scan the lesson. List two headings you would use to make an outline of the lesson.

- _____
  _____

- _____
  _____

Essential Question

WHAT happens when you add, subtract, multiply, and divide fractions?

Vocabulary

unlike fractions

Common Core GPS

Content Standards
MCC7.NS.1, MCC7.NS.1d,
MCC7.NS.3, MCC7.EE.3

Mathematical Practices
1, 3, 4

Real-World Link

Time The table shows the fractions of one hour for certain minutes.

1. What fraction of one hour is equal to the sum of 15 minutes and 20 minutes?

   15 minutes   20 minutes

   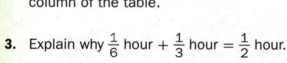

Number of Minutes	Fraction of One Hour	Simplified Fraction
5	$\frac{5}{60}$	
10	$\frac{10}{60}$	
15	$\frac{15}{60}$	
20	$\frac{20}{60}$	
30	$\frac{30}{60}$	

2. Write each fraction of an hour in simplest form in the third column of the table.

3. Explain why $\frac{1}{6}$ hour + $\frac{1}{3}$ hour = $\frac{1}{2}$ hour.

   _____
   _____
   _____

4. Explain why $\frac{1}{12}$ hour + $\frac{1}{2}$ hour = $\frac{7}{12}$ hour.

   _____
   _____

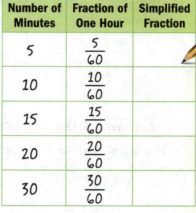

Add or Subtract Unlike Fractions

To add or subtract fractions with different denominators,

- Rename the fractions using the least common denominator (LCD).
- Add or subtract as with like fractions.
- If necessary, simplify the sum or difference.

Before you can add two **unlike fractions**, or fractions with different denominators, rename one or both of the fractions so that they have a common denominator.

Example

1. Find $\frac{1}{2} + \frac{1}{4}$.

Method 1 Use a number line.

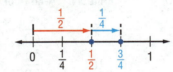

Divide the number line into fourths since the LCD is 4.

Method 2 Use the LCD.

The least common denominator of $\frac{1}{2}$ and $\frac{1}{4}$ is 4.

$\frac{1}{2} + \frac{1}{4} = \frac{1 \times 2}{2 \times 2} + \frac{1 \times 1}{4 \times 1}$ Rename using the LCD, 4.

$= \frac{2}{4} + \frac{1}{4}$ Add the fractions.

$= \frac{3}{4}$ Simplify.

Using either method, $\frac{1}{2} + \frac{1}{4} = \frac{3}{4}$.

Got It? Do these problems to find out.

Add. Write in simplest form.

    a. $\frac{1}{6} + \frac{2}{3}$ b. $\frac{9}{10} + \left(-\frac{1}{2}\right)$

    c. $\frac{1}{4} + \frac{3}{8}$ d. $-\frac{1}{3} + \left(-\frac{1}{4}\right)$

Work Zone

STOP and Reflect

Circle the pairs of fractions that are unlike fractions.

$\frac{1}{3}$ and $\frac{5}{3}$ $\frac{1}{7}$ and $\frac{1}{5}$ $\frac{5}{9}$ and $\frac{4}{11}$

Show your work.

a. _____

b. _____

c. _____

d. _____

Example

2. Find $\left(-\dfrac{3}{4} + \dfrac{5}{9}\right) + \dfrac{7}{4}$.

$$\left(-\dfrac{3}{4} + \dfrac{5}{9}\right) + \dfrac{7}{4} = \left(\dfrac{5}{9} + \left(-\dfrac{3}{4}\right)\right) + \dfrac{7}{4} \qquad \text{Commutative Property of Addition}$$

$$= \dfrac{5}{9} + \left(-\dfrac{3}{4} + \dfrac{7}{4}\right) \qquad \text{Associative Property of Addition}$$

$$= \dfrac{5}{9} + 1 \text{ or } 1\dfrac{5}{9} \qquad \text{Simplify.}$$

Got It? Do these problems to find out.

e. $\dfrac{2}{5} + \left(\dfrac{4}{7} + \dfrac{3}{5}\right)$

f. $\left(-\dfrac{3}{10} + \dfrac{5}{8}\right) + \dfrac{23}{10}$

e. _____

f. _____

Example

3. Find $-\dfrac{2}{3} - \dfrac{1}{2}$.

Method 1 Use a number line.

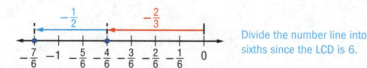

Divide the number line into sixths since the LCD is 6.

Method 2 Use the LCD.

$$-\dfrac{2}{3} - \dfrac{1}{2} = -\dfrac{2 \times 2}{3 \times 2} - \dfrac{1 \times 3}{2 \times 3} \qquad \text{Rename using the LCD, 6.}$$

$$= -\dfrac{4}{6} - \dfrac{3}{6} \qquad \text{Simplify.}$$

$$= \dfrac{-4}{6} - \dfrac{3}{6} \qquad \text{Rewrite } -\dfrac{4}{6} \text{ as } \dfrac{-4}{6}.$$

$$= \dfrac{-4 - 3}{6} \text{ or } \dfrac{-7}{6} \qquad \text{Subtract the numerators. Simplify.}$$

Check by adding $-\dfrac{7}{6} + \dfrac{1}{2} = -\dfrac{7}{6} + \dfrac{3}{6} = -\dfrac{4}{6}$ or $-\dfrac{2}{3}$ ✓

Using either method, $-\dfrac{2}{3} - \dfrac{1}{2} = -\dfrac{7}{6}$ or $-1\dfrac{1}{6}$.

> **Check for Reasonableness**
> Estimate the difference.
> $-\dfrac{2}{3} - \dfrac{1}{2} \approx -\dfrac{1}{2} - \dfrac{1}{2}$ or -1
> Compare $-\dfrac{7}{6}$ to the estimate.
> $-\dfrac{7}{6} \approx -1$. So, the answer is reasonable.

Got It? Do these problems to find out.

Subtract. Write in simplest form.

g. $\dfrac{5}{8} - \dfrac{1}{4}$

h. $\dfrac{3}{4} - \dfrac{1}{3}$

i. $\dfrac{1}{2} - \left(-\dfrac{2}{5}\right)$

g. _____

h. _____

i. _____

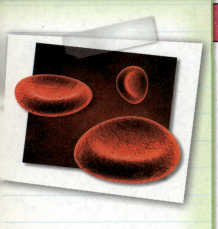

Choose an Operation

Add or subtract unlike fractions to solve real-world problems.

 Example

4. **STEM** Use the table to find the fraction of the total population that has type A or type B blood.

Blood Type Frequencies				
ABO Type	O	A	B	AB
Fraction	$\frac{11}{25}$	$\frac{21}{50}$	$\frac{1}{10}$	$\frac{1}{25}$

To find the fraction of the total population, add $\frac{21}{50}$ and $\frac{1}{10}$.

$$\frac{21}{50} + \frac{1}{10} = \frac{21 \times 1}{50 \times 1} + \frac{1 \times 5}{10 \times 5}$$ Rename using the LCD, 50.

$$= \frac{21}{50} + \frac{5}{50}$$ Add the fractions.

$$= \frac{26}{50} \text{ or } \frac{13}{25}$$ Simplify.

So, $\frac{13}{25}$ of the population has type A or type B blood.

Guided Practice

Add or subtract. Write in simplest form. (Examples 1–3)

1. $\frac{3}{5} + \frac{1}{10} =$ _____

2. $-\frac{5}{6} + \left(-\frac{4}{9}\right) =$ _____

3. $\left(\frac{7}{8} + \frac{3}{11}\right) + \frac{1}{8} =$ _____

 Show your work.

4. $\frac{4}{5} - \frac{3}{10} =$ _____

5. $\frac{3}{8} - \left(-\frac{1}{4}\right) =$ _____

6. $\frac{3}{4} - \frac{1}{3} =$ _____

7. Cassandra cuts $\frac{5}{16}$ inch off the top of a photo and $\frac{3}{8}$ inch off the bottom. How much shorter is the total height of the photo now? Explain. (Example 4)

_____

_____

8. 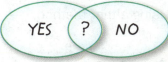 **Building on the Essential Question** Compare adding unlike fractions and adding like fractions.

_____

_____

_____

Rate Yourself!

Are you ready to move on? Shade the section that applies.

YES   ?   NO

For more help, go online to access a Personal Tutor. Tutor

FOLDABLES Time to update your Foldable!

Independent Practice

Go online for Step-by-Step Solutions

Add or subtract. Write in simplest form. (Examples 1–3)

1 $\frac{1}{6} + \frac{3}{8} =$ __13/24__

$\frac{4}{24} + \frac{9}{24} = \frac{13}{24}$

2. $-\frac{1}{15} + \left(-\frac{3}{5}\right) =$ __$-\frac{2}{3}$__

$-\frac{1}{15} + \left(-\frac{9}{15}\right)$

3. $\left(\frac{15}{8} + \frac{2}{5}\right) + \left(-\frac{7}{8}\right) =$ _____

4. $\left(-\frac{7}{10}\right) - \frac{2}{5} =$ _____

5. $\frac{7}{9} - \frac{1}{3} =$ _____

6. $-\frac{7}{12} + \frac{7}{10} =$ _____

$-\frac{35}{60} + \frac{42}{60} = \frac{7}{60}$

7. $-\frac{4}{9} - \frac{2}{15} =$ _____

8. $\frac{5}{8} + \frac{11}{12} =$ _____

9. $\frac{7}{9} + \frac{5}{6} =$ _____

CCGPS **Justify Conclusions** **Choose an operation to solve each problem. Explain your reasoning. Then solve the problem. Write in simplest form.** (Example 4)

10. Mrs. Escalante was riding a bicycle on a bike path. After riding $\frac{2}{3}$ of a mile, she discovered that she still needed to travel $\frac{3}{4}$ of a mile to reach the end of the path. How long is the bike path?

_____

_____

11 Four students were scheduled to give book reports in 1 hour. After the first report, $\frac{2}{3}$ hour remained. The next two reports took $\frac{1}{6}$ hour and $\frac{1}{4}$ hour. What fraction of the hour remained?

_____

_____

12. One hundred sixty cell phone owners were surveyed.

a. What fraction of owners prefers using their cell phone for text messaging or playing games? Explain.

__5/8 becaue $\frac{1}{4} + \frac{3}{8} = 5/8$__

b. What fraction of owners prefers using their phone to take pictures or text message?

_____

$\frac{8}{12} + \frac{9}{12} = \frac{17}{12}$

How do you use a cell phone?

Taking pictures $\frac{3}{8}$

Playing games $\frac{1}{4}$

$\frac{3}{8}$ Text messaging

13. Pepita and Francisco each spend an equal amount of time on homework. The table shows the fraction of time they spend on each subject. Complete the table by determining the missing fraction for each student.

Homework	Fraction of Time	
	Pepita	Francisco
Math		$\frac{1}{2}$
English	$\frac{2}{3}$	
Science	$\frac{1}{6}$	$\frac{3}{8}$

14. Chelsie saves $\frac{1}{5}$ of her allowance and spends $\frac{2}{3}$ of her allowance at the mall. What fraction of her allowance remains? Explain.

_____

H.O.T. Problems   Higher Order Thinking

15. **Persevere with Problems** Fractions whose numerators are 1, such as $\frac{1}{2}$ or $\frac{1}{3}$, are called *unit fractions*. Describe a method you can use to add two unit fractions mentally. _____

_____

_____

_____

16. **Use a Counterexample** Provide a counterexample to the following statement.

> *The sum of three fractions with odd numerators is never $\frac{1}{2}$.*

_____

Georgia Test Practice

17. Which of the following is the prime factorization of the least common denominator of $\frac{7}{12} + \frac{11}{18}$?

Ⓐ 2×3

Ⓑ 2×3^2

Ⓒ $2^2 \times 3^2$

Ⓓ $2^3 \times 3$

Extra Practice

Add or subtract. Write in simplest form.

18. $\dfrac{5}{8} + \dfrac{1}{4} =$ ___ $\dfrac{7}{8}$ ___

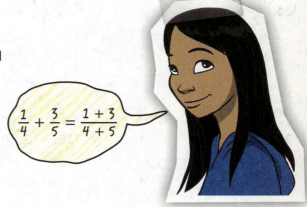

$$\dfrac{5}{8} + \dfrac{1}{4} = \dfrac{5}{8} + \dfrac{1 \times 2}{4 \times 2}$$
$$= \dfrac{5}{8} + \dfrac{2}{8}$$
$$= \dfrac{7}{8}$$

Homework Help

19. $\dfrac{4}{5} - \dfrac{1}{6} =$ _____

20. $\dfrac{5}{6} - \left(-\dfrac{2}{3}\right) =$ _____

21. $\dfrac{3}{10} - \left(-\dfrac{1}{4}\right) =$ _____

22. $-\dfrac{2}{3} + \left(\dfrac{3}{4} + \dfrac{5}{3}\right) =$ _____

23. $-\dfrac{7}{8} + \dfrac{1}{3} =$ _____

Choose an operation to solve each problem. Explain your reasoning. Then solve the problem. Write in simplest form.

24. Ebony is building a shelf to hold the two boxes shown. What is the least width she should make the shelf?

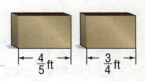

_____

_____

25. Makayla bought $\dfrac{1}{4}$ pound of ham and $\dfrac{5}{8}$ pound of turkey. How much more turkey did she buy? _____

_____

26. **CCGPS** **Persevere with Problems** Find the sum of $\dfrac{\frac{3}{4}}{8}$ and $\dfrac{\frac{1}{3}}{4}$. Write in simplest form.

_____

27. **CCGPS** **Find the Error** Theresa is finding $\dfrac{1}{4} + \dfrac{3}{5}$. Find her mistake and correct it. Explain your answer.

_____

_____

_____

_____

$$\dfrac{1}{4} + \dfrac{3}{5} = \dfrac{1+3}{4+5}$$

$$\dfrac{3}{15} - \dfrac{10}{15} = \dfrac{-7}{15}$$

28. The table gives the number of hours Orlando spent at football practice.

Day	Time (h)
Monday	$\frac{1}{2}$
Tuesday	$\frac{3}{4}$
Thursday	$\frac{1}{3}$
Friday	$\frac{5}{6}$

How many more hours did he practice on Friday than on Thursday?

Ⓐ $\frac{1}{3}$

Ⓑ $\frac{1}{2}$

Ⓒ $\frac{5}{6}$

Ⓓ $1\frac{1}{6}$

29. Brett has $\frac{5}{6}$ of his weekly allowance left to spend. He has budgeted $\frac{1}{8}$ of his allowance to save for a new video game. How much of his weekly allowance will he have left after putting the savings away?

Ⓕ $\frac{4}{7}$

Ⓖ $\frac{3}{8}$

Ⓗ $\frac{7}{12}$

Ⓘ $\frac{17}{24}$

30. Felicia needs 1 cup of flour. She only has a $\frac{2}{3}$-cup measure and a $\frac{3}{4}$-cup measure. Which method will bring her closest to having the amount of flour she needs?

Ⓐ Fill the $\frac{2}{3}$-cup measure twice.

Ⓑ Fill the $\frac{3}{4}$-cup measure twice.

Ⓒ Fill the $\frac{2}{3}$-cup measure once.

Ⓓ Fill the $\frac{3}{4}$-cup measure once.

Write each improper fraction as a mixed number. MCC5.NF.3

31. $\frac{7}{5} =$ _____

32. $\frac{14}{3} =$ _____

33. $\frac{101}{100} =$ _____

34. $\frac{22}{9} =$ _____

35. $\frac{77}{10} =$ _____

36. $\frac{23}{8} =$ _____

Divide. MCC6.NS.2

37. $364 \div 14 =$ _____

38. $4\overline{)5,206} =$ _____

39. $\frac{216}{8} =$ _____

Add and Subtract Mixed Numbers

What You'll Learn

Scan the lesson. List two real-world scenarios in which you would add or subtract mixed numbers.

- _____
- _____

 Essential Question

WHAT happens when you add, subtract, multiply, and divide fractions?

 Common Core GPS

Content Standards
MCC7.NS.1, MCC7.NS.1d, MCC7.NS.3, MCC7.EE.3

Mathematical Practices
1, 3, 4

 Real-World Link

Hockey Junior and adult hockey sticks are shown below.

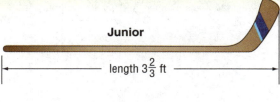

Junior

length $3\frac{2}{3}$ ft

Adult

length $4\frac{5}{6}$ ft

1. Use the expression $4\frac{5}{6} - 3\frac{2}{3}$ to find how much longer the adult hockey stick is than the junior hockey stick.

   Rename the fractions using the LCD, 6.   Subtract the fractions. Then subtract the whole numbers.

   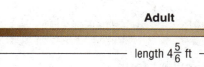

   $4\frac{5}{6} - \boxed{}\frac{\boxed{}}{\boxed{}} = \boxed{}\frac{\boxed{}}{\boxed{}}$

2. Explain how to find $3\frac{7}{10} - 2\frac{2}{5}$. Then use your conjecture to find the difference.

   _____
   _____
   _____

Add and Subtract Mixed Numbers

To add or subtract mixed numbers, first add or subtract the fractions. If necessary, rename them using the LCD. Then add or subtract the whole numbers and simplify if necessary.

Sometimes when you subtract mixed numbers, the fraction in the first mixed number is less than the fraction in the second mixed number. In this case, rename one or both fractions in order to subtract.

Tutor

Examples

1. Find $7\frac{4}{9} + 10\frac{2}{9}$. Write in simplest form.

Estimate $7 + 10 = 17$

$$7\frac{4}{9}$$ Add the whole numbers and fractions separately.
$$+ \ 10\frac{2}{9}$$
$$\overline{17\frac{6}{9}} \text{ or } 17\frac{2}{3}$$ Simplify.

Check for Reasonableness $17\frac{2}{3} \approx 17$ ✔

2. Find $8\frac{5}{6} - 2\frac{1}{3}$. Write in simplest form.

Estimate $9 - 2 = 7$

$$
\begin{array}{ccc}
8\frac{5}{6} & \rightarrow & 8\frac{5}{6} \\
-2\frac{1}{3} & \rightarrow & -2\frac{2}{6}
\end{array}
$$
Rename the fraction using the LCD. Then subtract.

$$6\frac{3}{6} \text{ or } 6\frac{1}{2}$$ Simplify.

Check for Reasonableness $6\frac{1}{2} \approx 7$ ✔

Show your work.

Got It?   Do these problems to find out.

Add or subtract. Write in simplest form.

a. $6\frac{1}{8} + 2\frac{5}{8}$ b. $5\frac{1}{5} + 2\frac{3}{10}$ c. $1\frac{5}{9} + 4\frac{1}{6}$

d. $5\frac{4}{5} - 1\frac{3}{10}$ e. $13\frac{7}{8} - 9\frac{3}{4}$ f. $8\frac{2}{3} - 2\frac{1}{2}$

a. _____

b. _____

c. _____

d. _____

e. _____

f. _____

Example

3. Find $2\frac{1}{3} - 1\frac{2}{3}$.

Method 1   Rename Mixed Numbers

Estimate $2 - 1\frac{1}{2} = \frac{1}{2}$

Since $\frac{1}{3}$ is less than $\frac{2}{3}$, rename $2\frac{1}{3}$ before subtracting.

Change 1 to $\frac{3}{3}$.

$$2\frac{1}{3} \qquad = \qquad 1\frac{3}{3} + \frac{1}{3} \text{ or } 1\frac{4}{3}$$

$$2\frac{1}{3} \quad \rightarrow \quad 1\frac{4}{3} \qquad \text{Rename } 2\frac{1}{3} \text{ as } 1\frac{4}{3}.$$
$$-1\frac{2}{3} \quad \rightarrow \quad -1\frac{2}{3} \qquad \text{Subtract the whole numbers and then the fractions.}$$
$$\overline{\phantom{-1\frac{2}{3}} \quad\quad \frac{2}{3}}$$

Check for Reasonableness $\frac{2}{3} \approx \frac{1}{2}$ ✔

Method 2   Write as Improper Fractions

$$2\frac{1}{3} \quad \rightarrow \quad \frac{7}{3} \qquad \text{Write } 2\frac{1}{3} \text{ as } \frac{7}{3}.$$
$$-1\frac{2}{3} \quad \rightarrow \quad -\frac{5}{3} \qquad \text{Write } 1\frac{2}{3} \text{ as } \frac{5}{3}.$$
$$\overline{\phantom{-1\frac{2}{3}} \quad\quad \frac{2}{3}} \qquad \text{Simplify.}$$

So, $2\frac{1}{3} - 1\frac{2}{3} = \frac{2}{3}$.

Using either method, the answer is $\frac{2}{3}$.

Got It? Do these problems to find out.

Subtract. Write in simplest form.

g. $7 - 1\frac{1}{2}$ **h.** $5\frac{3}{8} - 4\frac{11}{12}$ **i.** $11\frac{2}{5} - 2\frac{3}{5}$

j. $8 - 3\frac{3}{4}$ **k.** $3\frac{1}{4} - 1\frac{3}{4}$ **l.** $16 - 5\frac{5}{6}$

> **Fractions Greater Than One**
>
> An improper fraction has a numerator that is greater than or equal to the denominator. Examples of improper fractions are $\frac{5}{4}$ and $2\frac{6}{5}$.

g. _____

h. _____

i. _____

j. _____

k. _____

l. _____

Choose an Operation

Add or subtract unlike fractions to solve real-world problems.

Real World

Example

4. An urban planner is designing a skateboard park. The length of the skateboard park is $120\frac{1}{2}$ feet. The length of the parking lot is $40\frac{1}{3}$ feet. What will be the length of the park and the parking lot combined?

$$120\frac{1}{2} + 40\frac{1}{3} = 120\frac{3}{6} + 40\frac{2}{6}$$ Rename $\frac{1}{2}$ as $\frac{3}{6}$ and $\frac{1}{3}$ as $\frac{2}{6}$.

$$= 160 + \frac{5}{6}$$ Add the whole numbers and fractions separately.

$$= 160\frac{5}{6}$$ Simplify.

The total length is $160\frac{5}{6}$ feet.

Guided Practice

Add or subtract. Write in simplest form. (Examples 1–3)

1. $8\frac{1}{2} + 3\frac{4}{5} =$ _____

2. $7\frac{5}{6} - 3\frac{1}{6} =$ _____

3. $11 - 6\frac{3}{8} =$ _____

4. A hybrid car's gas tank can hold $11\frac{9}{10}$ gallons of gasoline. It contains $8\frac{3}{4}$ gallons of gasoline. How much more gasoline is needed to fill the tank? (Example 4) _____

5. **Building on the Essential Question** How can you subtract mixed numbers when the fraction in the first mixed number is less than the fraction in the second mixed number? _____

_____

_____

_____

Rate Yourself!

How confident are you about adding and subtracting mixed numbers? Shade the ring on the target.

For more help, go online to access a Personal Tutor.

Name _____ My Homework _____

Add or subtract. Write in simplest form. (Examples 1–3)

1. $2\frac{1}{9} + 7\frac{4}{9} =$ _____

2. $8\frac{5}{12} + 11\frac{1}{4} =$ _____

3. $10\frac{4}{5} - 2\frac{1}{5} =$ _____

Show your work.

4. $9\frac{4}{5} - 2\frac{3}{10} =$ _____

5. $11\frac{3}{4} - 4\frac{1}{3} =$ _____

6. $9\frac{1}{5} - 2\frac{3}{5} =$ _____

7. $6\frac{3}{5} - 1\frac{2}{3} =$ _____

8. $14\frac{1}{6} - 7\frac{1}{3} =$ _____

9. $8 - 3\frac{2}{3} =$ _____

CCGPS **Justify Conclusions** For Exercises 10 and 11, choose an operation to solve. Explain your reasoning. Then solve the problem. Write your answer in simplest form. (Example 4)

10. If Juliana and Brody hiked both of the trails listed in the table, how far did they hike?

_____

Trail	Length (mi)
Woodland Park	$3\frac{2}{3}$
Mill Creek Way	$2\frac{5}{6}$

11. The length of Kasey's garden is $4\frac{5}{8}$ feet. Find the width of Kasey's garden if it is $2\frac{7}{8}$ feet shorter than the length.

_____

12. Karen wakes up at 6:00 A.M. It takes her $1\frac{1}{4}$ hours to shower, get dressed, and comb her hair. It takes her $\frac{1}{2}$ hour to eat breakfast, brush her teeth, and make her bed. At what time will she be ready for school? _____

Add or subtract. Write in simplest form.

13. $-3\frac{1}{4} + \left(-1\frac{3}{4}\right) =$ _____

14. $\dfrac{3\frac{1}{2}}{5} + \dfrac{4\frac{2}{3}}{2} =$ _____

15. $6\frac{1}{3} + 1\frac{2}{3} + 5\frac{5}{9} =$ _____

16. $3\frac{1}{4} + 2\frac{5}{6} - 4\frac{1}{3} =$ _____

🔥 H.O.T. Problems Higher Order Thinking

17. 🔴**CCGPS** **Model with Mathematics** Write a real-world problem that could be represented by the expression $5\frac{1}{2} - 3\frac{7}{8}$. Then solve your problem.

_____

_____

_____

_____

18. 🔴**CCGPS** **Persevere with Problems** A string is cut in half. One of the halves is thrown away. One fifth of the remaining half is cut away and the piece left is 8 feet long. How long was the string initially? Justify your answer.

_____

_____

_____

Georgia Test Practice

19. For a party, Makenna bought $3\frac{1}{3}$ pounds of white grapes. Angelo bought $2\frac{3}{4}$ pounds of red grapes. How many more pounds of grapes did Makenna buy than Angelo?

  Ⓐ $\frac{5}{12}$ lb   Ⓒ $5\frac{5}{12}$ lb

  Ⓑ $\frac{7}{12}$ lb   Ⓓ $6\frac{1}{12}$ lb

Extra Practice

Add or subtract. Write in simplest form.

20. $6\frac{1}{4} - 2\frac{3}{4} = $ _3\frac{1}{2}_

$$6\frac{1}{4} - 2\frac{3}{4} = 5\frac{5}{4} - 2\frac{3}{4}$$
$$= 3\frac{2}{4}$$
$$= 3\frac{1}{2}$$

 Homework Help

21. $8\frac{3}{8} + 10\frac{1}{3} = $ _____

22. $13 - 5\frac{5}{6} = $ _____

23. $3\frac{2}{7} + 4\frac{3}{7} = $ _____

24. $4\frac{3}{10} - 1\frac{3}{4} = $ _____

25. $12\frac{1}{2} - 6\frac{5}{8} = $ _____

CCGPS **Justify Conclusions** Choose an operation to solve. Explain your reasoning. Then solve the problem. Write your answer in simplest form.

26. The length of Alana's hair was $9\frac{3}{4}$ inches. After her haircut, the length was $6\frac{1}{2}$ inches. How many inches did she have cut?

_____

27. Emeril used a total of $7\frac{1}{4}$ cups of flour to make three pastries. He used $2\frac{1}{4}$ cups of flour for the first and $2\frac{1}{3}$ cups for the second. How much flour did Emeril use for the third pastry?

_____

28. Margarite made the jewelry shown. If the necklace is $10\frac{5}{8}$ inches longer than the bracelet, how long is the necklace?

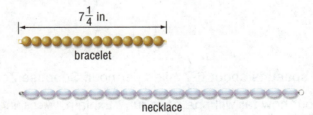

$7\frac{1}{4}$ in.

bracelet

necklace

_____

29. Find the perimeter of the figure. Write your answer in simplest form.

_____

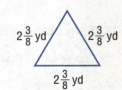

$2\frac{3}{8}$ yd $2\frac{3}{8}$ yd

$2\frac{3}{8}$ yd

30. Suppose you want to place a shelf that is $30\frac{1}{3}$ inches long in the center of a wall that is $45\frac{3}{4}$ inches wide. About how far from each edge of the wall should you place the shelf? _____

31. The distance from home plate to the pitcher's mound is 60 feet 6 inches and from home plate to second base is 127 feet $3\frac{3}{8}$ inches. Find the distance from the pitcher's mound to second base.

Ⓐ 68 ft $3\frac{1}{4}$ in.

Ⓑ 67 ft $8\frac{3}{4}$ in.

Ⓒ 67 ft $2\frac{5}{8}$ in.

Ⓓ 66 ft $9\frac{3}{8}$ in.

32. A recipe for party mix calls for $4\frac{3}{4}$ cups of cereal. The amount of peanuts needed is $1\frac{2}{3}$ cups less than the amount of cereal needed. How many cups of peanuts and cereal are needed?

Ⓕ $3\frac{1}{12}$ cups

Ⓖ $6\frac{1}{2}$ cups

Ⓗ $7\frac{5}{6}$ cups

Ⓘ $8\frac{1}{2}$ cups

ⒸⒸⒼⓅⓈ Common Core Review

Round each mixed number to its nearest whole number. Then estimate each product. MCC5.NF.4

33. $5\frac{1}{4} \times 7\frac{2}{3} \approx \boxed{} \times \boxed{} \approx \boxed{}$

34. $1\frac{1}{11} \times 8\frac{14}{15} \approx \boxed{} \times \boxed{} \approx \boxed{}$

35. $4\frac{3}{4} \times 11\frac{2}{9} \approx \boxed{} \times \boxed{} \approx \boxed{}$

36. $\frac{1}{20} \times \frac{19}{20} \approx \boxed{} \times \boxed{} \approx \boxed{}$

37. Zoe's average running speed is about $6\frac{4}{5}$ miles per hour. Suppose Zoe runs for $1\frac{3}{4}$ hours. About how far will she have run? Explain. MCC5.NF.4

_____

38. Sam ate about $3\frac{5}{6}$ slices of pizza. There were 12 slices of pizza in the box. About how many slices are left? MCC5.NF.1 _____

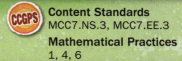

Case #1 Science Experiment

Casey drops a ball from a height of 12 feet. It hits the ground and bounces up half as high as it fell. This is true for each successive bounce.

What is the height the ball reaches after the fourth bounce?

Content Standards
MCC7.NS.3, MCC7.EE.3
Mathematical Practices
1, 4, 6

Understand *What are the facts?*
Casey dropped the ball from a height of 12 feet. It bounces up half as high for each successive bounce.

Plan *What is your strategy to solve this problem?*
Draw a diagram to show the height of the ball after each bounce.

Solve *How can you apply the strategy?*

The ball reaches a height of _____ foot after the fourth bounce.

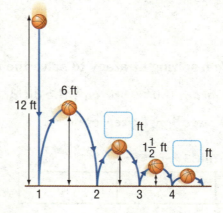

Check *Does the answer make sense?*
Use division to check. $12 \div 2 = 6$, $6 \div 2 = 3$, $3 \div 2 = 1.5$, $1.5 \div 2 = 0.75$.

Analyze the Strategy

Be Precise If the ball is dropped from 12 feet and bounces up $\frac{2}{3}$ as high on each successive bounce, what is the height of the fourth bounce?

Mr. Garcia has driven 60 miles, which is $\frac{2}{3}$ of the way to his sister's house.

How much farther does he have to drive to get to his sister's house?

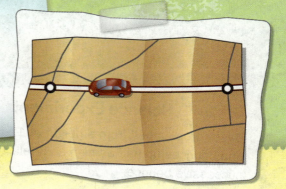

 # Understand

Read the problem. What are you being asked to find?

I need to find _____.

What information do you know?

Mr. Garcia has driven _____ of the way to his sister's house. This is

equal to _____.

Is there any information that you do _not_ need to know?

I do not need to know _____.

Plan

Choose a problem-solving strategy.

I will use the _____ strategy.

Solve

Use your problem-solving strategy to solve the problem.

Use the bar diagram that represents the distance to his sister's house.

Fill in two of the sections to represent $\frac{2}{3}$.

| ┠──────── 60 miles ────────┨ |

[ ] of the 3 parts = 60.

Each part is [ ] miles. The

distance to his sister's house

is 60 + [ ] = [ ].

So, Mr. Garcia has _____ miles left to drive.

Check

Use information from the problem to check your answer.

_____

Case #3 Fractions

Marta ate a quarter of a whole pie. Edwin ate $\frac{1}{4}$ of what was left. Cristina then ate $\frac{1}{3}$ of what was left.

What fraction of the pie remains?

Case #4 Games

Eight members of a chess club are having a tournament. In the first round, every player will play a chess game against every other player.

How many games will be in the first round of the tournament?

Case #5 Distance

Alejandro and Pedro are riding their bikes to school. After 1 mile, they are $\frac{4}{5}$ of the way there.

How much farther do they have to go?

Circle a strategy below to solve the problem.

• Act it out.

• Make a model.

• Look for a pattern.

Case #6 Seats

The number of seats in the first row of a concert hall is 6. The second row has 9 seats, the third row has 12 seats, and the fourth row has 15 seats.

How many seats will be in the eighth row?

Mid-Chapter Check

Vocabulary Check

1. Define *rational number*. Give some examples of rational numbers written in different forms. (Lessons 3 and 4)

   _____

   _____

   _____

2. Fill in the blank in the sentence below with the correct term. (Lesson 1)

   Repeating decimals can be represented using _____.

Skills Check and Problem Solving

Add or subtract. Write in simplest form. (Lessons 3–5)

3. $\frac{5}{8} + \frac{3}{8} =$ _____

4. $-\frac{1}{9} + \frac{2}{9} =$ _____

5. $-\frac{11}{15} - \frac{1}{15} =$ _____

6. $2\frac{5}{9} + 1\frac{2}{3} =$ _____

7. $8\frac{3}{4} - 2\frac{5}{12} =$ _____

8. $5\frac{1}{6} - 1\frac{1}{3} =$ _____

9. The table at the right shows the fraction of each state that is water. Order the states from least to greatest fraction of water. (Lesson 2)

   _____

What Part is Water?	
Alaska	$\frac{3}{41}$
Michigan	$\frac{40}{97}$
Wisconsin	$\frac{1}{6}$

10. The maximum height of an Asian elephant is 9.8 feet. What mixed number represents this height? (Lesson 1) _____

11. **Georgia Test Practice** The table shows the weight of a newborn infant for its first year. During which three-month period was the infant's weight gain the greatest? (Lesson 5)

    Ⓐ 0–3 months   Ⓒ 6–9 months

    Ⓑ 3–6 months   Ⓓ 9–12 months

Month	Weight (lb)
0	$7\frac{1}{4}$
3	$12\frac{1}{2}$
6	$16\frac{5}{8}$
9	$19\frac{4}{5}$
12	$23\frac{3}{20}$

Multiply Fractions

What You'll Learn

Scan the lesson. Predict two things you will learn about multiplying fractions.

- _____
_____

- _____
_____

Essential Question

WHAT happens when you add, subtract, multiply, and divide fractions?

Common Core GPS

Content Standards
MCC7.NS.2, MCC7.NS.2a, MCC7.NS.2c, MCC7.NS.3, MCC7.EE.3

Mathematical Practices
1, 3, 4

Real-World Link

Lunch There are 12 students at the lunch table. Two thirds of the students ordered a hamburger for lunch. One half of those students that ordered a hamburger put cheese on it.

 Step 1 Draw an X through the students that did not order a hamburger.

 Step 2 Draw a C on the students that ordered cheese on their hamburger.

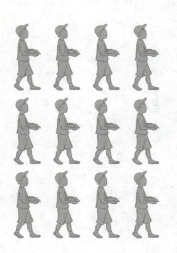

Didn't I order cheese with that?

1. What fraction of the students at the lunch table ordered a cheeseburger? Write in simplest form. _____

2. What is $\frac{1}{2}$ of $\frac{2}{3}$? Write in simplest form. _____

3. Write your own word problem that involves fractions that can be solved using a diagram like the one above.

_____
_____

Multiply Fractions

Words To multiply fractions, multiply the numerators and multiply the denominators.

Examples Numbers

$$\frac{1}{2} \times \frac{2}{3} = \frac{1 \times 2}{2 \times 3} \text{ or } \frac{2}{6}$$

Algebra

$$\frac{a}{b} \cdot \frac{c}{d} = \frac{a \cdot c}{b \cdot d} \text{ or } \frac{ac}{bd}, \text{ where } b, d \neq 0$$

When multiplying two fractions, write the product in simplest form. The numerator and denominator of either fraction may have common factors. If this is the case, you can simplify before multiplying.

Examples

Multiply. Write in simplest form.

1. $\frac{1}{2} \times \frac{1}{3}$

$\frac{1}{2} \times \frac{1}{3} = \frac{1 \times 1}{2 \times 3}$ ← Multiply the numerators.
← Multiply the denominators.

$= \frac{1}{6}$ Simplify.

2. $2 \times \left(-\frac{3}{4}\right)$

$2 \times \left(-\frac{3}{4}\right) = \frac{2}{1} \times \left(\frac{-3}{4}\right)$ Write 2 as $\frac{2}{1}$ and $-\frac{3}{4}$ as $\frac{-3}{4}$.

$= \frac{2 \times (-3)}{1 \times 4}$ ← Multiply the numerators.
← Multiply the denominators.

$= \frac{-6}{4}$ or $-1\frac{1}{2}$ Simplify.

3. $\frac{2}{7} \times \left(-\frac{3}{8}\right)$

$\frac{2}{7} \times \left(-\frac{3}{8}\right) = \frac{\overset{1}{2}}{7} \times \left(-\frac{3}{\underset{4}{8}}\right)$ Divide 2 and 8 by their GCF, 2.

$= \frac{1 \times (-3)}{7 \times 4}$ or $-\frac{3}{28}$ Multiply.

Got It? Do these problems to find out.

Multiply. Write in simplest form.

a. $\frac{3}{5} \times \frac{1}{2}$ **b.** $\frac{2}{3} \times (-4)$ **c.** $-\frac{1}{3} \times \left(-\frac{3}{7}\right)$

Work Zone

GCF
In Example 3, GCF stands for the greatest of the common factors of two or more numbers.
Example: The GCF of 8 and 2 is 2.

a. _____

b. _____

c. _____

Multiply Mixed Numbers

When multiplying by a mixed number, you can rename the mixed number as an improper fraction. You can also multiply mixed numbers using the Distributive Property and mental math.

Example

4. Find $\frac{1}{2} \times 4\frac{2}{5}$. Write in simplest form.

Estimate $\frac{1}{2} \times 4 = 2$

Method 1 Rename the mixed number.

$$\frac{1}{2} \times 4\frac{2}{5} = \frac{1}{\underset{1}{2}} \times \frac{\overset{11}{22}}{5}$$ Rename $4\frac{2}{5}$ as an improper fraction, $\frac{22}{5}$.

Divide 2 and 22 by their GCF, 2.

$$= \frac{1 \times 11}{1 \times 5}$$ Multiply.

$$= \frac{11}{5}$$ Simplify.

$$= 2\frac{1}{5}$$ Simplify.

Method 2 Use mental math.

The mixed number $4\frac{2}{5}$ is equal to $4 + \frac{2}{5}$.

So, $\frac{1}{2} \times 4\frac{2}{5} = \frac{1}{2}\left(4 + \frac{2}{5}\right)$. Use the Distributive Property to multiply, then add mentally.

$$\frac{1}{2}\left(4 + \frac{2}{5}\right) = 2 + \frac{1}{5}$$ Think Half of 4 is 2 and half of 2 fifths is 1 fifth.

$$= 2\frac{1}{5}$$ Rewrite the sum as a mixed number.

Check for Reasonableness $2\frac{1}{5} \approx 2$ ✔

So, $\frac{1}{2} \times 4\frac{2}{5} = 2\frac{1}{5}$.

Using either method, the answer is $2\frac{1}{5}$.

> **Simplifying**
> If you forget to simplify before multiplying, you can always simplify the final answer. However, it is usually easier to simplify before multiplying.

Got It? Do these problems to find out.

Multiply. Write in simplest form.

d. $\frac{1}{4} \times 8\frac{4}{9}$ **e.** $5\frac{1}{3} \times 3$ **f.** $-1\frac{7}{8} \times \left(-2\frac{2}{5}\right)$

Show your work.

d. _____

e. _____

f. _____

Example

5. Humans sleep about $\frac{1}{3}$ of each day. Let each year equal $365\frac{1}{4}$ days. Determine the number of days in a year the average human sleeps.

Meaning of Multiplication

Recall that one meaning of 3×4 is three groups with 4 in each group. In Example 5, there are $365\frac{1}{4}$ groups with $\frac{1}{3}$ in each group.

Find $\frac{1}{3} \times 365\frac{1}{4}$.

Estimate $\frac{1}{3} \times 360 = 120$

$\frac{1}{3} \times 365\frac{1}{4} = \frac{1}{3} \times \frac{1,461}{4}$ Rename the mixed number as an improper fraction.

$= \frac{1}{\overset{}{3}_{1}} \times \frac{\overset{487}{1,461}}{4}$ Divide 3 and 1,461 by their GCF, 3.

$= \frac{487}{4}$ or $121\frac{3}{4}$ Multiply. Then rename as a mixed number.

Check for Reasonableness $121\frac{3}{4} \approx 120$ ✔

The average human sleeps $121\frac{3}{4}$ days each year.

Guided Practice

Multiply. Write in simplest form. (Examples 1–4)

1. $\frac{2}{3} \times \frac{1}{3} =$ _____

2. $-\frac{1}{4} \times \left(-\frac{8}{9}\right) =$ _____

3. $2\frac{1}{4} \times \frac{2}{3} =$ _____

4. **STEM** The weight of an object on Mars is about $\frac{2}{5}$ its weight on Earth. How much would an $80\frac{1}{2}$-pound dog weigh on Mars? (Example 5) _____

5. **Building on the Essential Question** How is the process of multiplying fractions different from the process of adding fractions?

_____

_____

_____

Rate Yourself!

How well do you understand multiplying fractions? Circle the image that applies.

Clear   Somewhat Clear   Not So Clear

For more help, go online to access a Personal Tutor.

FOLDABLES Time to update your Foldable!

Independent Practice

Go online for Step-by-Step Solutions

Multiply. Write in simplest form. (Examples 1–4)

1. $\dfrac{3}{4} \times \dfrac{1}{8} =$ _____

2. $\dfrac{2}{5} \times \dfrac{2}{3} =$ _____

3. $-9 \times \dfrac{1}{2} =$ _____

Show your work.

4. $-\dfrac{1}{5} \times \left(-\dfrac{5}{6}\right) =$ _____

5. $\dfrac{2}{3} \times \dfrac{1}{4} =$ _____

6. $-\dfrac{1}{12} \times \dfrac{2}{5} =$ _____

7. $\dfrac{2}{5} \times \dfrac{15}{16} =$ _____

8. $\dfrac{4}{7} \times \dfrac{7}{8} =$ _____

9. $\left(-1\dfrac{1}{2}\right) \times \dfrac{2}{3} =$ _____

10. The width of a vegetable garden is $\dfrac{1}{3}$ times its length. If the length of the garden is $7\dfrac{3}{4}$ feet, what is the width in simplest form? (Example 5)

_____

11. One evening, $\dfrac{2}{3}$ of the students in Rick's class watched television. Of those students, $\dfrac{3}{8}$ watched a reality show. Of the students that watched the show, $\dfrac{1}{4}$ of them recorded the show. What fraction of the students in Rick's class watched and recorded a reality TV show?

_____

Write each numerical expression. Then evaluate the expression.

12. one half of negative five eighths

_____

13. one third of eleven sixteenths

_____

Lesson 6 Multiply Fractions   **131**

14. CCGPS **Model with Mathematics** Refer to the graphic novel frame below.

a. The height of the closet is 96 inches, and Aisha would like to have 4 rows of cube organizers. What is the most the height of each cube organizer can be?

_____

b. Aisha would like to stack 3 shoe boxes on top of each other at the bottom of the closet. The height of each shoe box is $4\frac{1}{2}$ inches. What is the total height of the 3 boxes?

_____

 H.O.T. Problems Higher Order Thinking

15. CCGPS **Model with Mathematics** Write a real-world problem that involves finding the product of $\frac{3}{4}$ and $\frac{1}{8}$. _____

_____

_____

16. CCGPS **Persevere with Problems** Two positive improper fractions are multiplied. Is the product *sometimes*, *always*, or *never* less than 1? Explain.

_____

_____

 Georgia Test Practice

17. Two-thirds of the students in Levi's homeroom class study Spanish. Of these, one fourth study algebra. What fraction of the students in Levi's homeroom class study both Spanish and algebra?

Ⓐ $\frac{1}{6}$

Ⓒ $\frac{3}{6}$

Ⓑ $\frac{5}{12}$

Ⓓ $\frac{11}{12}$

Extra Practice

Multiply. Write in simplest form.

18. $\frac{4}{5} \times (-6) =$ $-4\frac{4}{5}$

$\frac{4}{5} \times (-6) = \frac{4}{5} \times \left(-\frac{6}{1}\right)$

Homework Help ➤

$= \frac{4 \times (-6)}{5 \times 1}$

$= \frac{-24}{5}$ or $-4\frac{4}{5}$

19. $-\frac{4}{9} \times \left(-\frac{1}{4}\right) =$ _____

20. $3\frac{1}{3} \times \left(-\frac{1}{5}\right) =$ _____

21. $\frac{1}{3} \times \frac{3}{4} =$ _____

22. $\frac{4}{9} \times \left(-\frac{1}{8}\right) =$ _____

23. $\frac{5}{6} \times 2\frac{3}{5} =$ _____

24. Each DVD storage case is about $\frac{1}{5}$ inch thick. What will be the height in simplest form of 12 cases sold together?

_____

25. Mark left $\frac{3}{8}$ of a pizza in the refrigerator. On Friday, he ate $\frac{1}{2}$ of what was left of the pizza. What fraction of the entire pizza did he eat on Friday?

_____

Multiply. Write in simplest form.

26. $\left(\frac{1}{4}\right)^2 =$ _____

27. $\left(-\frac{2}{3}\right)^3 =$ _____

28. $\dfrac{1\frac{1}{3}}{\frac{1}{4}} \times \dfrac{\frac{2}{5}}{\frac{1}{2}} =$ _____

29. **CCGPS** **Justify Conclusions** Alano wants to make one and a half batches of the pasta salad recipe shown at the right. How much of each ingredient will Alano need? Explain how you solved the problem.

_____

_____

_____

Pasta Salad Recipe	
Ingredient	**Amount**
Broccoli	$1\frac{1}{4}$ c
Cooked pasta	$3\frac{3}{4}$ c
Salad dressing	$\frac{2}{3}$ c
Cheese	$1\frac{1}{3}$ c

30. Philip rode his bicycle at $9\frac{1}{2}$ miles per hour. If he rode for $\frac{3}{4}$ of an hour, how many miles in simplest form did he cover? _____

Georgia Test Practice

31. Of the dolls in Marjorie's doll collection, $\frac{1}{5}$ have red hair. Of these, $\frac{3}{4}$ have green eyes. What fraction of Marjorie's doll collection has both red hair and green eyes?

- Ⓐ $\frac{2}{9}$
- Ⓑ $\frac{3}{20}$
- Ⓒ $\frac{4}{9}$
- Ⓓ $\frac{19}{20}$

32. Which description gives the relationship between a term and n, its position in the sequence?

Position	1	2	3	4	5	n
Value of Term	$\frac{1}{4}$	$\frac{1}{2}$	$\frac{3}{4}$	1	$1\frac{1}{4}$	

- Ⓕ Subtract 4 from n.
- Ⓖ Add $\frac{1}{4}$ to n.
- Ⓗ Multiply n by $\frac{1}{4}$.
- Ⓘ Divide n by $\frac{1}{4}$.

33. Short Response Determine if the product of 2 and $\frac{3}{4}$ is greater than or less than 2? _____

Common Core Review

For each multiplication sentence, write two related division sentences. MCC5.NBT.5

34. $3 \times 4 = 12$

_____

_____

35. $\frac{1}{6} \times \frac{1}{3} = \frac{1}{18}$

_____

_____

36. $2\frac{2}{5} \times 4\frac{1}{2} = 10\frac{4}{5}$

_____

_____

37. $5\frac{5}{8} \times 1\frac{1}{5} = 6\frac{3}{4}$

_____

_____

Solve. MCC5.MD.1

38. Madelyn is building a computer desk. She has $8\frac{2}{3}$ feet of wood. How many inches of wood does Madelyn have?

(*Hint:* 12 inches = 1 foot) _____

39. Victor made punch for a birthday party. He used $10\frac{1}{2}$ cups of soda. How many pints of soda did Victor use?

(*Hint:* 2 cups = 1 pint) _____

Convert Between Systems

What You'll Learn

Scan the lesson. List two real-world scenerios in which you would convert measurments.

- _____
  _____

- _____
  _____

Essential Question

HOW do you convert between measurement systems?

Common Core GPS

Content Standards
MCC7.RP.3, MCC7.NS.2, MCC7.NS.3

Mathematical Practices
1, 3, 4, 5, 6

 Real-World Link

5K Race To raise money for a health organization, the Matthews family is participating in a 5K race. A 5K race is 5 kilometers.

1. How many meters long is the race?

   5 kilometers = ☐ meters

2. One mile is approximately 1.6 kilometers. About how many miles is the race?

   5 kilometers ≈ ☐ miles

3. A kilometer is a unit of length in the metric measurement system. A mile is a measure of length in the customary measurement system. Write the following units of length under the correct measurement system.

   centimeter, foot, inch, meter, millimeter, yard

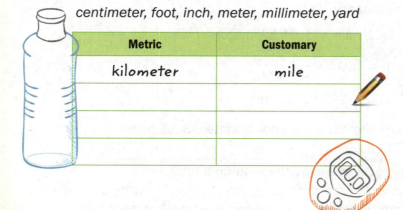

Metric	Customary
kilometer	mile

Convert Between Measurement Systems

You can multiply by fractions to convert between customary and metric units. The table below lists common customary and metric relationships.

Customary and Metric Relationships			
Type of Measure	**Customary**	→	**Metric**
Length	1 inch (in.)	≈	2.54 centimeters (cm)
	1 foot (ft)	≈	0.30 meter (m)
	1 yard (yd)	≈	0.91 meter (m)
	1 mile (mi)	≈	1.61 kilometers (km)
Weight/Mass	1 pound (lb)	≈	453.6 grams (g)
	1 pound (lb)	≈	0.4536 kilogram (kg)
	1 ton (T)	≈	907.2 kilograms (kg)
Capacity	1 cup (c)	≈	236.59 milliliters (mL)
	1 pint (pt)	≈	473.18 milliliters (mL)
	1 quart (qt)	≈	946.35 milliliters (mL)
	1 gallon (gal)	≈	3.79 liters (L)

Examples

1. **Convert 17.22 inches to centimeters. Round to the nearest hundredth if necessary.**

Since 2.54 centimeters ≈ 1 inch, multiply by $\frac{2.54 \text{ cm}}{1 \text{ in.}}$.

$17.22 ≈ 17.22$ in. $\cdot \frac{2.54 \text{ cm}}{1 \text{ in.}}$ Multiply by $\frac{2.54 \text{ cm}}{1 \text{ in.}}$. Divide out common units.

$≈ 43.7388$ cm   Simplify.

So, 17.22 inches is approximately 43.74 centimeters.

2. **Convert 5 kilometers to miles. Round to the nearest hundredth if necessary.**

Since 1 mile ≈ 1.61 kilometers, multiply by $\frac{1 \text{ mi}}{1.61 \text{ km}}$.

$5 \text{ km} ≈ 5 \text{ km} \cdot \frac{1 \text{ mi}}{1.61 \text{ km}}$ Multiply by $\frac{1 \text{ mi}}{1.61 \text{ km}}$. Divide out common units.

$≈ \frac{5 \text{ mi}}{1.61}$ or 3.11 mi   Simplify.

So, 5 kilometers is approximately 3.11 miles.

Got It? Do these problems to find out.

Show your work.

Complete. Round to the nearest hundredth if necessary.

a. 6 yd ≈ ■ m   b. 1.6 cm ≈ ■ in.   c. 17 m ≈ ■ yd

a. _____

b. _____

c. _____

Examples

3. **Convert 828.5 milliliters to cups. Round to the nearest hundredth if necessary.**

Since 1 cup ≈ 236.59 milliliters, multiply by $\frac{1\ c}{236.59\ mL}$.

$828.5\ mL ≈ 828.5\ \cancel{mL} \cdot \frac{1\ c}{236.59\ \cancel{mL}}$ *Multiply by $\frac{1\ c}{236.59\ mL}$ and divide out common units.*

$≈ \frac{828.5\ c}{236.59}$ or 3.50 c   *Simplify.*

So, 828.5 milliliters is approximately 3.50 cups.

> **Dimensional Analysis**
>
> Recall that dimensional analysis is the process of including units of measurement when you compute.

4. **Convert 3.4 quarts to milliliters. Round to the nearest hundredth if necessary.**

Since 946.35 milliliters ≈ 1 quart, multiply by $\frac{946.35\ mL}{1\ qt}$.

$3.4\ qt ≈ 3.4\ \cancel{qt} \cdot \frac{946.35\ mL}{1\ \cancel{qt}}$ *Multiply by $\frac{946.35}{1\ qt}$. Divide out common units.*

$≈ 3{,}217.59\ mL$ *Simplify.*

So, 3.4 quarts is approximately 3,217.59 milliliters.

5. **Convert 4.25 kilograms to pounds. Round to the nearest hundredth if necessary.**

Since 1 pound ≈ 0.4536 kilogram, multiply by $\frac{1\ lb}{0.4536\ kg}$.

$4.25\ kg ≈ 4.25\ \cancel{kg} \cdot \frac{1\ lb}{0.4536\ \cancel{kg}}$ *Multiply by $\frac{1\ lb}{0.4536\ kg}$. Divide out common units.*

$≈ \frac{4.25\ lb}{0.4536}$ or 9.37 lb   *Simplify.*

So, 4.25 kilograms is approximately 9.37 pounds.

Got It? Do these problems to find out.

Complete. Round to the nearest hundredth if necessary.

d. 7.44 c ≈ ■ mL

e. 22.09 lb ≈ ■ kg

f. 35.85 L ≈ ■ gal

Show your work.

d. _____

e. _____

f. _____

Example

6. **An Olympic-size swimming pool is 50 meters long. About how many feet long is the pool?**

Since 1 foot ≈ 0.30 meter, use the ratio $\frac{1 \text{ ft}}{0.30 \text{ m}}$.

$50 \text{ m} \approx 50 \text{ m} \cdot \frac{1 \text{ ft}}{0.30 \text{ m}}$ Multiply by $\frac{1 \text{ ft}}{0.30 \text{ m}}$.

$\approx 50 \text{ m} \cdot \frac{1 \text{ ft}}{0.30 \text{ m}}$ Divide out common units, leaving the desired unit, feet.

$\approx \frac{50 \text{ ft}}{0.30}$ or 166.67 ft   Divide.

An Olympic-size swimming pool is about 166.67 feet long.

Guided Practice

Complete. Round to the nearest hundredth if necessary. (Examples 1 – 5)

1. 3.7 yd ≈ _____ m

2. 11.07 pt ≈ _____ mL

3. 650 lb ≈ _____ kg

Show your work.

4. About how many feet does a team of athletes run in a 1,600-meter relay race? (Example 6) _____

5. Raheem bought 3 pounds of bananas. About how many kilograms did he buy? (Example 6) _____

6. **Building on the Essential Question** How can you use dimensional analysis to convert between measurement systems?

_____

_____

_____

_____

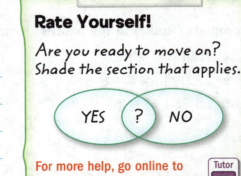

Rate Yourself!

Are you ready to move on? Shade the section that applies.

YES   ?   NO

For more help, go online to access a Personal Tutor.

Independent Practice

Go online for Step-by-Step Solutions eHelp

Complete. Round to the nearest hundredth if necessary. (Examples 1 – 5)

1. 5 in. ≈ _____ cm

 Show your work.

2. 2 qt ≈ _____ mL

3 58.14 kg ≈ _____ lb

4. 4 L ≈ _____ gal

5. 10 mL ≈ _____ c

6. 63.5 T ≈ _____ kg

7. 4.725 m ≈ _____ ft

8. 3 T ≈ _____ kg

9. 680.4 g ≈ _____ lb

10. A notebook computer has a mass of 2.25 kilograms. About how many pounds does the notebook weigh? (Example 6)

_____

11. A glass bottle holds 3.75 cups of water. About how many milliliters of water can the bottle hold? (Example 6)

_____

12. A Cabbage Palmetto has a height of 80 feet. What is the approximate height of the tree in meters? (Example 6)

_____

Persevere with Problems Determine the greater amount for each situation.

13 Which box is greater, a 1.5-pound box of raisins or a 650-gram box of raisins?

14. Which is greater a 2.75-gallon container of juice or a 12-liter container of juice?

H.O.T. Problems Higher Order Thinking

15. **Reason Inductively** One gram of water has a volume of 1 milliliter. What is the volume of the water if it has a mass of 1 kilogram?

16. **Persevere with Problems** The distance from Earth to the Sun is approximately 93 million miles. About how many gigameters is this? Round to the nearest hundredth. *(Hint: In 1 gigameter there are about 621,118.01 miles.)*

 Be Precise Order each set of measures from greatest to least.

17. 1.2 cm, 0.6 in., 0.031 m, 0.1 ft

18. 2 lb, 891 g, 1 kg, 0.02 T

19. $1\frac{1}{4}$ c, 0.4 L, 950 mL, 0.7 gal

20. 4.5 ft, 48 in., 1.3 m, 120 cm

Georgia Test Practice

21. A store sells poster board. The table shows the colors and sizes in-stock. Which of the following metric approximations is the same as the measures of the green poster board?

Ⓐ 2.8 cm by 3.6 cm

Ⓑ 2.8 m by 3.6 m

Ⓒ 28 cm by 36 cm

Ⓓ 28 m by 36 m

Poster Board	
Color	**Size (in.)**
white	11 × 14 16 × 20
green	11 × 14
blue	16 × 20

Extra Practice

Complete. Round to the nearest hundredth if necessary.

22. 15 cm ≈ _5.91_ in.

23. 350 lb ≈ _158.76_ kg

24. 17 mi ≈ _____ km

Homework Help →

$$15 \text{ cm} \approx 15 \text{ cm} \cdot \frac{1 \text{ in.}}{2.54 \text{ cm}}$$
$$\approx 15 \text{ cm} \cdot \frac{1 \text{ in.}}{2.54 \text{ cm}}$$
$$\approx \frac{15 \text{ in.}}{2.54} \approx 5.91 \text{ in.}$$

$$350 \text{ lb} \approx 350 \text{ lb} \cdot \frac{0.4536 \text{ kg}}{1 \text{ lb}}$$
$$\approx 350 \text{ lb} \cdot \frac{0.4536 \text{ kg}}{1 \text{ lb}}$$
$$\approx 158.76 \text{ kg}$$

25. 32 gal ≈ _____ L

26. 50 mL ≈ _____ fl oz

27. 19 kg ≈ _____ lb

28. The Willis Tower has a height of 1,451 feet. What is the estimated height of the building in meters? _____

29. Which is greater, a bottle containing 64 fluid ounces or a bottle containing 2 liters of water? _____

30. **CCGPS** **Use Math Tools** A bakery uses 900 grams of peaches in a cobbler. About how many pounds of peaches does the bakery use in a cobbler?

_____

Determine which quantity is greater.

31. 3 gal, 10 L _____

32. 14 oz, 0.4 kg _____

33. 4 mi, 6.2 km _____

34. Velocity is a rate usually expressed in feet per second or meters per second. How can the units help you calculate velocity using the distance a car traveled and the time recorded? _____

_____

35. The diagram shows the length of a fork from the cafeteria.

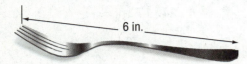

6 in.

Which of the following measurements is approximately equal to the length of the fork?

- Ⓐ 2.4 cm
- Ⓑ 15.2 cm
- Ⓒ 24 cm
- Ⓓ 152 cm

36. The table shows the flying speeds of various birds.

Bird	Speed (km/h)
Spur-winged goose	142
Mallard duck	105

About how fast does the Spur-winged goose travel in miles per hour?

- Ⓕ 229 miles per hour
- Ⓖ 156 miles per hour
- Ⓗ 88 miles per hour
- Ⓘ 71 miles per hour

CCGPS Common Core Review

Convert. Round to the nearest tenth if necessary. MCC5.MD.1

37. 17 ft = _____ yd

38. 82 in. = _____ ft

39. 3 mi = _____ ft

40. A skyscraper is 0.484 kilometer tall. What is the height of the skyscraper in meters? MCC5.MD.1 _____

Multiply. Write in simplest form. MCC7.NS.2a

41. $\frac{1}{3} \times \frac{3}{1} =$ _____

42. $\frac{1}{4} \times 8 =$ _____

43. $\frac{4}{13} \times \frac{65}{4} =$ _____

44. $-\frac{7}{8} \times \left(-\frac{8}{7}\right) =$ _____

45. $-6\frac{2}{5} \times \left(-\frac{5}{32}\right) =$ _____

46. $\frac{1}{5} \times (-10) =$ _____

Divide Fractions

What You'll Learn

Scan the lesson. Predict two things you will learn about dividing fractions.

- _____
  _____
- _____
  _____

Essential Question

WHAT happens when you add, subtract, multiply, and divide fractions?

Common Core GPS

Content Standards
MCC7.NS.2, MCC7.NS.2c, MCC7.NS.3, MCC7.EE.3

Mathematical Practices
1, 3, 4, 5

Real-World Link

Oranges Deandre has three oranges and each orange is divided evenly into fourths. Complete the steps below to find $3 \div \frac{1}{4}$.

Step 1   Draw three oranges. The first one is drawn for you.

Step 2   Imagine you cut each orange into fourths.
Draw the slices for each orange.

So $3 \div \frac{1}{4} = 12$. Deandre will have ☐ orange slices.

1. Find $3 \div \frac{1}{2}$. Use a diagram. _____

2. What is true about $3 \div \frac{1}{2}$ and 3×2? _____

Divide Fractions

Watch

Work Zone

Words   To divide by a fraction, multiply by its multiplicative inverse, or reciprocal.

Examples

Numbers

$$\frac{7}{8} \div \frac{3}{4} = \frac{7}{8} \cdot \frac{4}{3}$$

Algebra

$$\frac{a}{b} \div \frac{c}{d} = \frac{a}{b} \cdot \frac{d}{c}, \text{ where } b, c, d \neq 0$$

Dividing 3 by $\frac{1}{4}$ is the same as multiplying 3 by the reciprocal of $\frac{1}{4}$, which is 4.

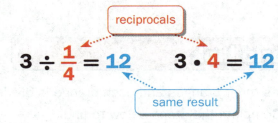

reciprocals

$$3 \div \frac{1}{4} = 12 \qquad 3 \cdot 4 = 12$$

same result

STOP and Reflect

What is the reciprocal of $\frac{2}{3}$? of 15? of $-\frac{4}{9}$? Write your answers below.

Is this pattern true for any division expression?

Consider $\frac{7}{8} \div \frac{3}{4}$, which can be rewritten as $\dfrac{\frac{7}{8}}{\frac{3}{4}}$.

$$\frac{\frac{7}{8}}{\frac{3}{4}} = \frac{\frac{7}{8} \times \frac{4}{3}}{\frac{3}{4} \times \frac{4}{3}}$$

Multiply the numerator and denominator by the reciprocal of $\frac{3}{4}$, which is $\frac{4}{3}$.

$$= \frac{\frac{7}{8} \times \frac{4}{3}}{1} \qquad \frac{3}{4} \times \frac{4}{3} = 1$$

$$= \frac{7}{8} \times \frac{4}{3}$$

So, $\frac{7}{8} \div \frac{3}{4} = \frac{7}{8} \times \frac{4}{3}$. The pattern is true in this case.

Examples

Tutor

1. Find $\frac{1}{3} \div 5$.

$$\frac{1}{3} \div 5 = \frac{1}{3} \div \frac{5}{1}$$ A whole number can be written as a fraction over 1.

$$= \frac{1}{3} \times \frac{1}{5}$$ Multiply by the reciprocal of $\frac{5}{1}$, which is $\frac{1}{5}$.

$$= \frac{1}{15}$$ Multiply.

2. Find $\frac{3}{4} \div \left(-\frac{1}{2}\right)$. Write in simplest form.

Estimate $1 \div \left(-\frac{1}{2}\right) = \boxed{}$

$$\frac{3}{4} \div \left(-\frac{1}{2}\right) = \frac{3}{4} \cdot \left(-\frac{2}{1}\right)$$ Multiply by the reciprocal of $-\frac{1}{2}$, which is $-\frac{2}{1}$.

$$= \frac{3}{\underset{2}{4}} \cdot \left(-\frac{\overset{1}{2}}{1}\right)$$ Divide 4 and 2 by their GCF, 2.

$$= -\frac{3}{2} \text{ or } -1\frac{1}{2}$$ Multiply.

Check for Reasonableness $-1\frac{1}{2} \approx -2$ ✔

Got It? Do these problems to find out.

Divide. Write in simplest form.

a. $\frac{3}{4} \div \frac{1}{4}$

b. $-\frac{4}{5} \div \frac{8}{9}$

c. $-\frac{5}{6} \div \left(-\frac{2}{3}\right)$

Divide Mixed Numbers

To divide by a mixed number, first rename the mixed number as a fraction greater than one. Then multiply the first fraction by the reciprocal, or multiplicative inverse, of the second fraction.

Example

Tutor

3. Find $\frac{2}{3} \div 3\frac{1}{3}$. Write in simplest form.

$$\frac{2}{3} \div 3\frac{1}{3} = \frac{2}{3} \div \frac{10}{3}$$ Rename $3\frac{1}{3}$ a fraction greater than one.

$$= \frac{2}{3} \cdot \frac{3}{10}$$ Multiply by the reciprocal of $\frac{10}{3}$, which is $\frac{3}{10}$.

$$= \frac{\overset{1}{2}}{3} \cdot \frac{\overset{1}{3}}{\underset{5}{10}}$$ Divide out common factors.

$$= \frac{1}{5}$$ Multiply.

Got It? Do these problems to find out.

Divide. Write in simplest form.

d. $5 \div 1\frac{1}{3}$

e. $-\frac{3}{4} \div 1\frac{1}{2}$

f. $2\frac{1}{3} \div 5$

Show your work.

a. _____

b. _____

c. _____

d. _____

e. _____

f. _____

4. The side pieces of a butterfly house are $8\frac{1}{4}$ inches long. How many side pieces can be cut from a board measuring $49\frac{1}{2}$ inches long?

To find how many side pieces can be cut, divide $49\frac{1}{2}$ by $8\frac{1}{4}$.

Estimate Use compatible numbers. $48 \div 8 = 6$

$$49\frac{1}{2} \div 8\frac{1}{4} = \frac{99}{2} \div \frac{33}{4}$$ Rename the mixed numbers as fractions greater than one.

$$= \frac{99}{2} \cdot \frac{4}{33}$$ Multiply by the reciprocal of $\frac{33}{4}$, which is $\frac{4}{33}$.

$$= \frac{\overset{3}{\cancel{99}}}{\underset{1}{\cancel{2}}} \cdot \frac{\overset{2}{\cancel{4}}}{\underset{1}{\cancel{33}}}$$ Divide out common factors.

$$= \frac{6}{1} \text{ or } 6$$ Multiply.

So, 6 side pieces can be cut.

Check for Reasonableness Compare to the estimate. $6 = 6$ ✔

Guided Practice

 Check

Divide. Write in simplest form. (Examples 1–3)

1. $\frac{1}{8} \div \frac{1}{3} =$ _____

2. $-3 \div \left(-\frac{6}{7}\right) =$ _____

3. $-\frac{7}{8} \div \frac{3}{4} =$ _____

 Show your work.

4. On Saturday, Lindsay walked $3\frac{1}{2}$ miles in $1\frac{2}{5}$ hours. What was her walking pace in miles per hour? Write in simplest form. (Example 4) _____

5. **Building on the Essential Question** How is dividing fractions related to multiplying? _____

_____

_____

Rate Yourself!

Are you ready to move on? Shade the section that applies.

I have a few questions.

I'm ready to move on.

I have a lot of questions.

For more help, go online to access a Personal Tutor.

Tutor

FOLDABLES Time to update your Foldable!

Name _____ My Homework _____

Divide. Write in simplest form. (Examples 1 – 3)

1. $\dfrac{3}{8} \div \dfrac{6}{7} =$ _____

2. $-\dfrac{2}{3} \div \left(-\dfrac{1}{2}\right) =$ _____

3 $\dfrac{1}{2} \div 7\dfrac{1}{2} =$ _____

4. $6 \div \left(-\dfrac{1}{2}\right) =$ _____

5. $-\dfrac{4}{9} \div (-2) =$ _____

6. $\dfrac{2}{3} \div 2\dfrac{1}{2} =$ _____

7 Cheryl is organizing her movie collection. If each movie case is $\dfrac{3}{4}$ inch wide, how many movies can fit on a shelf $5\dfrac{1}{4}$ feet wide? (Example 4)

_____

8. Use the table to solve. Write your answers in simplest form.

a. How many times as heavy is the Golden Eagle as the Red-Tailed Hawk? _____

b. How many times as heavy is the Golden Eagle as the Northern Bald Eagle? _____

Bird	Maximum Weight (lb)
Golden Eagle	$13\dfrac{9}{10}$
Northern Bald Eagle	$9\dfrac{9}{10}$
Red-Tailed Hawk	$3\dfrac{1}{2}$

9. CCGPS **Model with Mathematics** Draw a model of the verbal expression below and then evaluate the expression. Explain how the model shows the division process.

one half divided by two fifths _____

 Show your work.

_____
_____
_____
_____

Copy and Solve For Exercises 10 and 11, show your work on a separate piece of paper.

10. **CCGPS** **Multiple Representations** Jorge recorded the distance that five of his friends live from his house in the table shown.

   a. **Numbers** Tye lives about how many times farther away than Jamal?

   b. **Algebra** The mean is the sum of the data divided by the number of items in the data set. Write and solve an equation to find the mean number of miles that Jorge's friends live from his house. Write your answer in simplest form.

   c. **Model** Draw a bar diagram that can be used to find how many more miles Lon travels than Lucia to get to Jorge's house.

Student	Miles
Lucia	$5\frac{1}{2}$
Lon	$8\frac{2}{3}$
Sam	$12\frac{5}{6}$
Jamal	$2\frac{7}{9}$
Tye	$17\frac{13}{18}$

11. Tara bought a dozen folders. She took $\frac{1}{3}$ of the dozen and then divided the remaining folders equally among her four friends. What fraction of the dozen did each of her four friends receive? How many folders was this per person?

H.O.T. Problems

12. **CCGPS** **Find the Error** Blake is finding $\frac{4}{5} \div \frac{6}{7}$. Find his mistake and correct it.

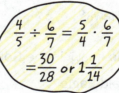

$$\frac{4}{5} \div \frac{6}{7} = \frac{5}{4} \cdot \frac{6}{7}$$
$$= \frac{30}{28} \text{ or } 1\frac{1}{14}$$

13. **CCGPS** **Persevere with Problems** If $\frac{5}{6}$ is divided by a certain fraction $\frac{a}{b}$, the result is $\frac{1}{4}$. What is the fraction $\frac{a}{b}$? _____

Georgia Test Practice

14. Which procedure would you use to find $\frac{2}{3} \div \frac{7}{9}$?

   Ⓐ Multiply the first fraction by the reciprocal of the second fraction.

   Ⓑ Multiply the second fraction by the reciprocal of the first fraction.

   Ⓒ Multiply by the least common multiple of 3 and 9.

   Ⓓ Multiply by the greatest common factor of 3 and 9.

Extra Practice

Divide. Write in simplest form.

15. $\dfrac{5}{9} \div \dfrac{5}{6} = \dfrac{2}{3}$

$$\dfrac{5}{9} \div \dfrac{5}{6} = \dfrac{5}{9} \times \dfrac{6}{5}$$

$$= \dfrac{\overset{1}{\cancel{5}}}{\underset{3}{\cancel{9}}} \times \dfrac{\overset{2}{\cancel{6}}}{\underset{1}{\cancel{5}}}$$

$$= \dfrac{1 \times 2}{3 \times 1}$$

$$= \dfrac{2}{3}$$

Homework Help

16. $-5\dfrac{2}{7} \div \left(-2\dfrac{1}{7}\right) =$ _____

17. $-5\dfrac{1}{5} \div \dfrac{2}{3} =$ _____

18. Vinh bought $4\dfrac{1}{2}$ gallons of ice cream to serve. If a pint is $\dfrac{1}{8}$ of a gallon, how many pint-sized servings can be made? _____

19. William has $8\dfrac{1}{4}$ cups of fruit juice. If he divides the juice into $\dfrac{3}{4}$ cup servings, how many servings will he have? _____

20. CCGPS **Justify Conclusions** So far, a storm has traveled 35 miles in $\dfrac{1}{2}$ hour. If it is currently 5:00 P.M. and the storm is 105 miles away from you, at what time will the storm reach you? Explain how you solved the problem.

_____

_____

_____

21. Find $\dfrac{1\frac{2}{3}}{9} \div \dfrac{1\frac{1}{9}}{3}$. Write in simplest form. _____

22. CCGPS **Use Math Tools** Write the letter of each statement below in the section of any operation to which the statement applies.

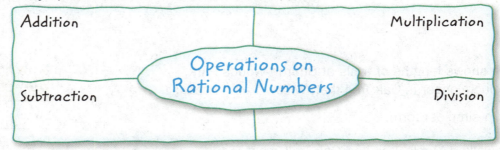

A Use a common denominator.

B Multiply by the multiplicative inverse.

C Write the result in simplest form.

23. Which expression represents the least value?

Ⓐ $298 + \frac{1}{2}$

Ⓑ $298 - \frac{1}{2}$

Ⓒ $298 \times \frac{1}{2}$

Ⓓ $298 \div \frac{1}{2}$

24. How many times as great is the weight of the large box of peanuts than the small box of peanuts?

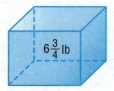

Ⓕ 4

Ⓖ 5

Ⓗ 6

Ⓘ 7

Common Core Review

Add or subtract. Write in simplest form. MCC5.NF.2

25. $\frac{1}{5} + \frac{1}{4} =$ _____

26. $\frac{1}{3} - \frac{1}{6} =$ _____

27. $\frac{4}{9} + \frac{2}{7} =$ _____

28. $\frac{11}{15} - \frac{3}{20} =$ _____

29. The cheerleaders made spirit buttons for the basketball team. They used blue and red ribbons. How much total ribbon did they use? MCC5.NF.2

_____

Ribbon	
Blue	**Red**
$\frac{3}{8}$ ft	$\frac{3}{8}$ ft

30. How much longer is a $2\frac{1}{2}$-inch-long piece of string than a $\frac{2}{5}$-inch-long piece of string? MCC5.NF.2 _____

31. The table shows lengths of trails at Sharon Woods Park.

a. How much longer is Oak Trail than Willow Trail? MCC5.NF.2

Write in simplest form. _____

b. If you walked Maple Trail and Oak Trail, what is the total distance you walked in simplest form? _____

Trail	Length of Trail
Willow	$\frac{1}{8}$ mi
Oak	$\frac{3}{4}$ mi
Maple	$\frac{1}{16}$ mi

21ST CENTURY CAREER
in Fashion Design

Fashion Designer

Do you enjoy reading fashion magazines, keeping up with the latest trends, and creating your own unique sense of style? You might want to consider a career in fashion design. Fashion designers create new designs for clothing, accessories, and shoes. In addition to being creative and knowledgeable about current fashion trends, fashion designers need to be able to take accurate measurements and calculate fit by adding, subtracting, and dividing measurements.

College & Career
READINESS

Explore college and careers at **ccr.mcgraw-hill.com**

Is This the Career for You?

Are you interested in a career as a fashion designer? Take some of the following courses in high school.

- ◆ **Algebra**
- ◆ **Art**
- ◆ **Digital Design**
- ◆ **Geometry**

Find out how math relates to a career in Fashion Design.

A Flair for Fashion!

Use the information in the table to solve each problem. Write in simplest form.

1. For size 8, does Dress Style A or B require more fabric? Explain. _____
   _____

2. How many yards of fabric are needed to make Style A in sizes 8 and 14? _____

3. Estimate how many yards of fabric are needed to make Style B in each of the sizes shown. Then find the actual amount of fabric. _____

4. For Style B, how much more fabric is required for size 14 than for size 12? _____

5. A designer has half the amount of fabric needed to make Style A in size 10. How much fabric does she have? _____

6. A bolt has $12\frac{1}{8}$ yards of fabric left on it. How many dresses in Style B size 12 could be made? How much fabric is left over?
   _____

Amount of Fabric Needed (yards)				
Dress Style	Size 8	Size 10	Size 12	Size 14
A	$3\frac{3}{8}$	$3\frac{1}{2}$	$3\frac{3}{4}$	$3\frac{7}{8}$
B	$3\frac{1}{4}$	$3\frac{1}{2}$	$3\frac{7}{8}$	4

Career Project

It's time to update your career portfolio! Use blogs and webpages of fashion designers to answer some of these questions: Where did they go to school? What was their first job? What do they say is the most difficult part about being a fashion designer? What inspires them to create their designs? What advice do they have for new designers?

_____
_____
_____

Suppose you are an employer hiring a fashion designer. What question would you ask a potential employee?

- _____
- _____

Vocabulary Check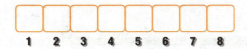

Unscramble each of the clue words. After unscrambling each of the terms, use the numbered letters to find a vocabulary term that relates to all of the other terms.

RAB TONNOTIA

☐☐☐ ☐☐☐☐☐☐☐☐
　　1　　　　7

TAMTINRINGE

☐☐☐☐☐☐☐☐☐☐☐
　　　　3

GIEPEATNR

☐☐☐☐☐☐☐☐☐
　　　4

KIEL STAFCOIRN

☐☐☐☐ ☐☐☐☐☐☐☐☐
　　　　　　　5

LUKIEN

☐☐☐☐☐☐
6　8

NOMMOC
NIOAREOMNDT

☐☐☐☐☐☐ ☐☐☐☐☐☐☐☐☐☐☐
　　　　　　　　　　　2

☐☐☐☐☐☐☐☐
1　2　3　4　5　6　7　8

Complete each sentence using one of the unscrambled words above.

1. The process of using a line over the repeating digits of a decimal is called _____ .

2. Fractions with different denominators are called _____ fractions.

3. The least common multiple of the denominators is called the least _____ .

4. The decimal form of a fraction is a(n) _____ decimal.

5. A _____ decimal is a decimal in which the repeating digit is zero.

6. Fractions with the same denominator are called _____ .

Use Your FOLDABLES

Use your Foldable to help review the chapter.

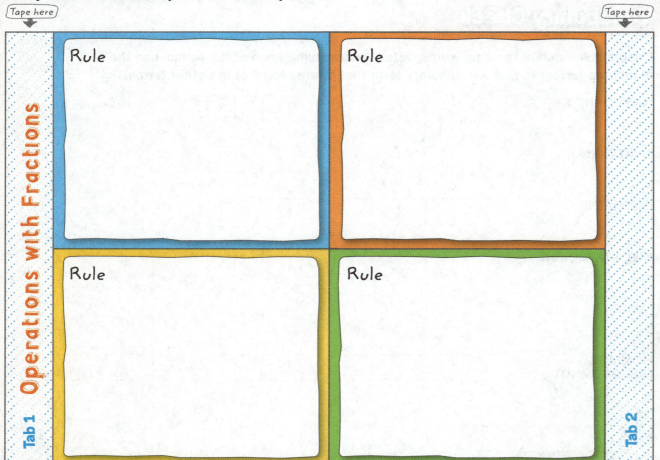

Tape here

Tape here

Operations with Fractions

Tab 1

Tab 2

Rule

Rule

Rule

Rule

Got it?

Circle the correct term or number to complete each sentence.

1. $\frac{1}{5}$ and $\left(\frac{1}{3}, \frac{3}{5}\right)$ are like fractions.

2. To add like fractions, add the (numerators, denominators).

3. To add unlike fractions, rename the fractions using the least common (numerator, denominator).

4. The reciprocal of $\frac{1}{3}$ is (−3, 3).

5. To divide by a fraction, (multiply, divide) by its reciprocal.

6. The least common denominator of $\frac{1}{5}$ and $\frac{1}{10}$ is (10, 50).

Problem Solving

1. Jeremy ran a mile in 5 minutes and 8 seconds. Write the time in minutes as a decimal. (Lesson 1) _____

2. Amaya received a $\frac{26}{30}$ on her English test and an 81% on her biology test. On which test did she receive the higher score? Explain. (Lesson 2)

   _____

   _____

3. **CCGPS** **Model with Mathematics** Mrs. Brown made two desserts. The number line below shows the number of cups of sugar she used to make them. Write an addition sentence that shows the amount of sugar Mrs. Brown used. (Lesson 4) _____

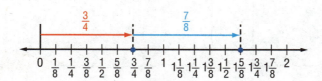

4. Lucas babysat his younger sister $2\frac{1}{2}$ hours on Friday and $3\frac{2}{3}$ hours on Saturday. How much longer did Lucas babysit his younger sister on Saturday than on Friday? (Lesson 5) _____

5. **Financial Literacy** For his birthday, Aiden received a check from his grandmother. The table shows how he spent or saved the money. Two weeks later, Aiden withdrew $\frac{2}{3}$ of the money he had deposited into his savings account. What fraction in simplest form of the original check did Aiden withdraw? Explain. (Lesson 6)

Fraction of Check	How Spent or Saved
$\frac{2}{5}$	Spent on baseball cards
$\frac{1}{4}$	Spent on a CD
$\frac{7}{20}$	Deposited into savings account

   _____

   _____

6. **STEM** The world's largest bird is the ostrich, whose mass can be as much as 156.5 kilograms. What is the approximate weight in pounds? (Lesson 7)

   _____

7. An ounce is $\frac{1}{16}$ of a pound. How many ounces are in $8\frac{3}{4}$ pounds? (Lesson 8)

   _____

Reflect

Use what you learned about operations with rational numbers to complete the graphic organizer. Describe a process to perform each operation.

Add

Subtract

Essential Question

WHAT happens when you add, subtract, multiply, and divide fractions?

Multiply

Divide

Answer the Essential Question. WHAT happens when you add, subtract, multipy, and divide fractions?

UNIT 2

CCGPS

Expressions and Equations

Essential Question

HOW can you communicate mathematical ideas effectively?

Chapter 3
Expressions

Algebraic expressions can be used to represent real-world situations. In this chapter, you will apply the properties of operations to simplify and evaluate algebraic expressions.

Chapter 4
Equations and Inequalities

An equation is a mathematical sentence stating that two expressions are equal. In this chapter, you will use the properties of equality to solve equations algebraically. Then you will apply what you learn to solve inequalities.

Chapter 3
Expressions

 Essential Question

HOW can you use numbers and symbols to represent mathematical ideas?

 Common Core GPS

Content Standards
MCC7.EE.1, MCC7.EE.2, MCC7.NS.3

Mathematical Practices
1, 2, 3, 4, 5, 6, 7

 Math in the Real World

Meerkats live in burrows. Because meerkats have sharp claws, they are able to dig at the rate of 1 foot per second.

Suppose a meerkat digs for 3 seconds. Cross out the expression that does not represent the underground distance dug by the meerkat.

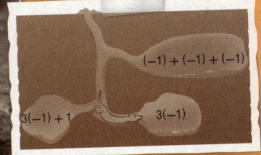

$(-1) + (-1) + (-1)$

$3(-1) + 1$

$3(-1)$

 **FOLDABLES** Study Organizer

 1 Cut out the correct Foldable from the FL pages in the back of this book.

2 Place your Foldable on the Key Concept page toward the end of this chapter.

3 Use the Foldable throughout this chapter to help you learn about expressions.

What Tools Do You Need?

Vocabulary

Additive Identity Property	define a variable	Multiplicative Property of Zero
algebra	Distributive Property	
algebraic expression	equivalent expressions	property
arithmetic sequence	factor	sequence
Associative Property	factored form	simplest form
coefficient	like terms	term
Commutative Property	linear expression	variable
constant	monomial	
counterexample	Multiplicative Identity Property	

Review Vocabulary

Order of Operations The order of operations is a four-step process used to evaluate numerical expressions.

1. Evaluate the expressions inside grouping symbols.
2. Evaluate all powers.
3. Multiply and divide in order from left to right.
4. Add and subtract in order form left to right.

Use the order of operations to evaluate $3 + 5^2(4 + 4)$. Write each step in the organizer below.

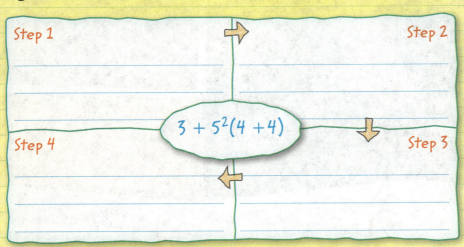

Step 1

Step 2

$3 + 5^2(4 + 4)$

Step 4

Step 3

Play it online!

Hiroshi, Caitlyn, and Dario in
Too Many Texts

Dario, why didn't you respond to my text last night?

Oh, sorry about that - I think I might have gone over my limit this month.

You know, you can check how many text messages you've sent online. Do you want to use my computer?

That's a great idea!

Oh, NO! What's THIS going to cost me?

Your plan:
250 text messages
= $5.00

Messages sent to date:
275

Uh-oh, sounds like you *did* go over the limit!

Hiroshi! Have you been paying attention to ANY of this?

Yes! I have the solution for him -- unlimited text messaging!

Your Turn! You will solve this problem in the chapter.

Try the Quick Check below.
Or, take the Online Readiness Quiz.

CCGPS **Quick Review**

Common Core Review MCC6.EE.2c, MCC7.NS.2c

Example 1

Evaluate 2^5.

$2^5 = 2 \cdot 2 \cdot 2 \cdot 2 \cdot 2$
$= 32$

Example 2

Write $3 \cdot 3 \cdot 3 \cdot 3 \cdot 3 \cdot 3 \cdot 3$ in exponential form.

3 is the base. It is used as a factor 7 times. So, the exponent is 7.

$3 \cdot 3 \cdot 3 \cdot 3 \cdot 3 \cdot 3 \cdot 3 = 3^7$

Example 3

Find $4(-2)$.

$4(-2) = -8$

The integers have different signs. The product is negative.

Example 4

Find $-5(-8)$.

$-5(-8) = 40$

The integers have the same signs. The product is positive.

Quick Check

Exponents **Evaluate each expression.**

1. $2^4 =$ _____

2. $3^3 =$ _____

3. $4^2 =$ _____

 Show your work.

4. Write $4 \cdot 4 \cdot 4 \cdot 4$ in exponential form. _____

Integer Operations **Multiply.**

5. $5(-10) =$ _____

6. $-9(-4) =$ _____

7. $-5^2 =$ _____

How Did You Do?

Which problems did you answer correctly in the Quick Check?
Shade those exercise numbers below.

 ① ② ③ ④ ⑤ ⑥ ⑦

Algebraic Expressions

What You'll Learn

Scan the text on the following two pages. Write two facts you learned about algebraic expressions.

- _____
- _____

Essential Question

HOW can you use numbers and symbols to represent mathematical ideas?

Vocabulary

variable
algebraic expression
algebra
coefficient
define a variable

Common Core GPS

Content Standards
Preparation for MCC7.EE.1 and MCC7.EE.2

Mathematical Practices
1, 2, 3, 4

Vocabulary Start-Up

A **variable** is a symbol that represents an unknown quantity. An **algebraic expression**, such as $n + 2$, is an expression that contains variables, numbers, and at least one operation.

Variable ·······> $n + 2$

Write each of the following phrases in the correct section of the Venn diagram: *contains an operation, has variables and numbers, has only numbers.*

Characteristics of Expressions

numerical expression   algebraic expression

Brrr...!

Real-World Link

The expression $(F - 32) \times \dfrac{5}{9}$ can be used to convert a temperature from Fahrenheit to Celsius. In this algebraic expression, the variable _____ represents the temperature in degrees Fahrenheit.

Evaluate an Algebraic Expression

The branch of mathematics that involves expressions with variables is called **algebra**. In algebra, the multiplication sign is often omitted.

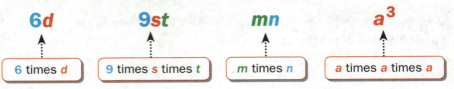

$6d$	$9st$	mn	a^3
6 times d	9 times s times t	m times n	a times a times a

The numerical factor of a multiplication expression that contains a variable is called a **coefficient**. So, 6 is the coefficient of $6d$.

Expressions like $\frac{y}{2}$ can be written as $y \div 2$ or $y \times \frac{1}{2}$.

Examples

Watch | Tutor

Order of Operations
1. Evaluate the expressions inside grouping symbols.
2. Evaluate all powers.
3. Multiply and divide in order from left to right.
4. Add and subtract in order from left to right.

1. Evaluate $2(n + 3)$ if $n = -4$.

$2(n + 3) = 2(-4 + 3)$ Replace n with -4.

$= 2(-1)$ Evaluate inside the parentheses.

$= -2$ Multiply.

2. Evaluate $8w - 2v$ if $w = 5$ and $v = 3$.

$8w - 2v = 8(5) - 2(3)$ Replace w with 5 and v with 3.

$= 40 - 6$ Do all of the multiplication first.

$= 34$ Subtract 6 from 40.

a. _____

b. _____

3. Evaluate $4y^3 + 2$ if $y = 3$.

$4y^3 + 2 = 4(3)^3 + 2$ Replace y with 3.

$= 4(27) + 2$ Evaluate the power.

$= 110$ Multiply, then add.

c. _____

Show your work.

Got It? Do these problems to find out.

d. _____

Evaluate each expression if $c = 8$ and $d = -5$.

a. $c - 3$ **b.** $15 - c$ **c.** $3(c + d)$

e. _____

d. $2c - 4d$ **e.** $d - c^2$ **f.** $2d^2 + 5d$

f. _____

Example

4. Athletic trainers use the formula $\dfrac{3(220 - a)}{5}$, where a is a person's age, to find their minimum training heart rate. Find Latrina's minimum training heart rate if she is 15 years old.

$$\dfrac{3(220 - a)}{5} = \dfrac{3(220 - 15)}{5}$$ Replace a with 15.

$$= \dfrac{3(205)}{5}$$ Subtract 15 from 220.

$$= \dfrac{615}{5}$$ Multiply 3 and 205.

$$= 123$$ Divide 615 by 5.

Latrina's minimum training heart rate is 123 beats per minute.

Got It? Do these problems to find out.

g. To find the area of a triangle, use the formula $\dfrac{bh}{2}$, where b is the base and h is the height. What is the area in square inches of a triangle with a height of 6 inches and base of 8 inches?

Fractions

The fraction bar is a grouping symbol. Evaluate the expressions in the numerator and denominator separately before dividing.

Show your work.

9. _____

Write Expressions

To translate a verbal phrase into an algebraic expression, the first step is to define a variable. When you **define a variable**, you choose a variable to represent an unknown quantity.

Examples

5. Marisa wants to buy a DVD player that costs $150. She already saved $25 and plans to save an additional $10 each week. Write an expression that represents the total amount of money Marisa has saved after any number of weeks.

Words	savings of $25 plus ten dollars each week
Variable	Let w represent the number of weeks.
Expression	25 + 10 · w

$25 + 10w$ represents the total saved after any number of weeks.

6. Refer to Example 5. Will Marisa have saved enough money to buy the $150 DVD player in 11 weeks? Use the expression $25 + 10w$.

$$25 + 10w = 25 + 10(\mathbf{11}) \qquad \text{Replace } w \text{ with 11.}$$
$$= 25 + 110 \qquad \text{Multiply.}$$
$$= 135 \qquad \text{Add.}$$

Marisa will have saved $135 after 11 weeks. Since $135 < $150, Marisa will not have enough money to buy the DVD player.

 Show your work.

Got It? Do this problem to find out.

h. _____

h. An MP3 player costs $70 and song downloads cost $0.85 each. Write an expression that represents the cost of the MP3 player and x number of downloaded songs. Then find the total cost if 20 songs are downloaded.

Guided Practice

 Check ✓

Evaluate each expression if $m = 2$, $n = 6$, and $p = -4$. (Examples 1–4)

1. $3m + 4p$ _____

2. $n^2 + 5$ _____

3. $6p^3$ _____

Show your work.

4. A Web site charges $0.99 to download a game and a $12.49 membership fee. Write an expression that gives the total cost in dollars to download g games. Then find the cost of downloading 6 games. (Examples 5 and 6)

_____

5. **Building on the Essential Question** Tell whether the statement below is *sometimes*, *always*, or *never* true. Justify your reasoning.

The expressions $x - 3$ and $y - 3$ represent the same value.

_____

_____

Rate Yourself!

How well do you understand algebraic expressions? Circle the image that applies.

 Clear

 Somewhat Clear

 Not So Clear

For more help, go online to access a Personal Tutor.

Independent Practice

Go online for Step-by-Step Solutions

Evaluate each expression if $d = 8$, $e = 3$, $f = 4$, and $g = -1$. (Examples 1 – 3)

1. $2(d + 9)$ _____

Show your work.

2. $\dfrac{d}{4}$ _____

3 $\dfrac{ef}{4}$ _____

4. $4f + d$ _____

5. $\dfrac{5d - 25}{5}$ _____

6. $d^2 + 7$ _____

7. $\dfrac{d - 4}{2}$ _____

8. $10(e + 7)$ _____

9. $\dfrac{2g}{2}$ _____

10. The expression $5n + 2$ can be used to find the total cost in dollars of bowling where n is the number of games bowled and 2 represents the cost of shoe rental. How much will it cost Vincent to bowl 3 games? (Example 4)

_____

11. **CCGPS** **Reason Abstractly** A car rental company's fees are shown. Suppose you rent a car using Option 2. Write an expression that gives the total cost in dollars for driving m miles. Then find the cost for driving 150 miles. (Examples 5 and 6)

_____

Car Rental Prices	
Option 1	**Option 2**
$19.99 per day	$50 fee
$0.17 per mi	$0.17 per mi

12. Refer to Exercise 11. Suppose you rent a car using Option 1. Write an expression that gives the total cost in dollars to rent a car for d days and m miles. Then find the cost for renting a car for 2 days and driving 70 miles. (Examples 5 and 6)

_____

Evaluate each expression if $x = 3.2$, $y = 6.1$, and $z = 0.2$.

13. $x + y - z$ _____

14. $14.6 - (x + y + z)$ _____

15. $xz + y^2$ _____

H.O.T. Problems   Higher Order Thinking

16. **CCGPS** **Reason Abstractly** Write an algebraic expression with the variable x that has a value of 3 when evaluated.

_____

17. **CCGPS** **Model with Mathematics** Write a real-world problem that can be represented by the expression $5x + 10$.

_____

_____

_____

18. **CCGPS** **Persevere with Problems** To find the total number of diagonals for any given polygon, you can use the expression $\frac{n(n - 3)}{2}$, where n is the number of sides of the polygon.

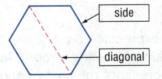

a. Determine the minimum value that n could be. _____

b. Make a table of four possible values of n. Then complete the table by evaluating the expression for each value of n.

n	value

c. Check by drawing the diagonals of a pentagon and counting the diagonals.

Georgia Test Practice

19. Which expression below can be used to find the number of inches in any number of feet f?

Ⓐ $f + 12$

Ⓒ $\frac{12}{f}$

Ⓑ $12f$

Ⓓ $12f - 3$

Extra Practice

Evaluate each expression if $d = 8$, $e = 3$, $f = 4$, and $g = -1$.

20. $10 - e$ *7*

$10 - e$
$10 - 3 = 7$

21. $\dfrac{16}{f}$ *4*

$\dfrac{16}{f}$
$\dfrac{16}{4} = 4$

22. $4e^2$ _____

23. $8g - f$ _____

24. $\dfrac{(5 + g)^2}{2}$ _____

25. $e^2 - 4$ _____

26. The expression $\dfrac{w}{30}$, where w is a person's weight in pounds, is used to find the approximate number of quarts of blood in the person's body. How many quarts of blood does a 120-pound person have?

_____

27. **CCGPS** **Model with Mathematics** Refer to the graphic novel at the beginning of the chapter and the frame below. Let n represent the number of text messages. Evaluate the expression $0.15(n - 250) + 5$ to find the cost of

275 text messages. _____

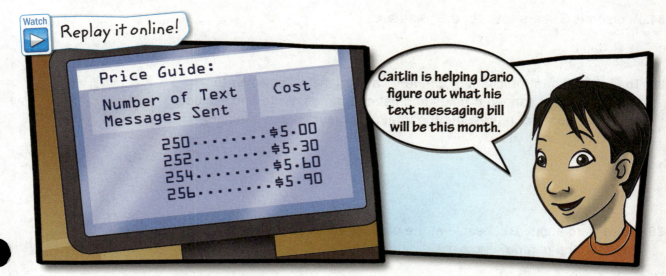

Georgia Test Practice

28. Which expression could be used to find the cost of buying b books and m magazines?

School Book Fair Prices	
Item	**Cost**
Magazines	$4.95
Paperback books	$7.95

Ⓐ $7.95b + 4.95m$ Ⓒ $12.9(b + m)$
Ⓑ $7.95b - 4.95m$ Ⓓ $12.9(bm)$

29. Tonya has x quarters, y dimes, and z nickels in her pocket. Which of the following expressions gives the total amount of change she has in her pocket?

Ⓕ $\$0.25x + \$0.05y + \$0.10z$
Ⓖ $\$0.25x + \$0.10y + \$0.05z$
Ⓗ $\$0.05x + \$0.25y + \$0.10z$
Ⓘ $\$0.10x + \$0.05y + \$0.25z$

30. Short Response What is the value of the expression below if c is 3 and d is -6? _____

$$4c - 5d$$

Common Core Review

Define a variable and write each phrase as an algebraic expression. MCC6.EE.2

31. 8 feet less than the height _____

32. Sarah worked 8 more hours than Paida. _____

33. Kumar has twice the number of goals as Jacob. _____

34. Addison is 3 years younger than Nathan. _____

35. The table shows the costs of different camping activities. Over the summer, Maura canoed 4 times and fished 3 times. Write and evaluate an expression that represents the total cost Maura spent canoeing and fishing. MCC5.OA.1

Camping Activity Costs	
Activity	**Cost**
Canoeing	$8
Fishing	$5

_____

36. There were about 10^5 people at the parade. About how many people attended the parade? MCC6.EE.1

_____

What You'll Learn

Write the math and the real-world definitions of sequence.

- math definition _____

  _____

- real-world definition _____

Essential Question

HOW can you use numbers and symbols to represent mathematical ideas?

Vocabulary

sequence
term
arithmetic sequence

Common Core GPS

Content Standards
Preparation for MCC7.EE.1 and MCC7.EE.2

Mathematical Practices
1, 2, 3, 4

Vocabulary Start-Up

A **sequence** is an ordered list of numbers. Each number in a sequence is called a **term**. In an **arithmetic sequence**, each term is found by adding the same number to the previous term.

Complete the graphic organizer below.

Numbers
Continue each sequence.

1, 3, 5, 7, ☐ , ...

1, 1.5, 2, ☐ , ☐ , ☐ , ...

Words
Describe each sequence.
Add ☐ to the previous term.

_____

Real-World Link

Horseback Riding The number of students who went on each horseback riding trip is shown. Do the numbers represent the terms of an arithmetic sequence? Explain.

Trip	1	2	3	4	5
Number of Students	15	16	18	21	25

_____

_____

Describe and Extend Sequences

In an arithmetic sequence, the terms can be whole numbers, fractions, or decimals.

Examples

Tutor

1. **Describe the relationship between the terms in the arithmetic sequence 8, 13, 18, 23, … . Then write the next three terms in the sequence.**

8, 13, 18, 23, …
+5 +5 +5 ◁⋯⋯ Each term is found by adding 5 to the previous term.

Continue the pattern to find the next three terms.

$$23 + 5 = 28 \qquad 28 + 5 = 33 \qquad 33 + 5 = 38$$

The next three terms are 28, 33, and 38.

2. **Describe the relationship between the terms in the arithmetic sequence 0.4, 0.6, 0.8, 1.0, … . Then write the next three terms in the sequence.**

0.4, 0.6, 0.8, 1.0, …
+0.2 +0.2 +0.2 ◁⋯⋯ Each term is found by adding 0.2 to the previous term.

Show your work.

Continue the pattern to find the next three terms.

$$1.0 + 0.2 = 1.2 \qquad 1.2 + 0.2 = 1.4 \qquad 1.4 + 0.2 = 1.6$$

The next three terms are 1.2, 1.4, and 1.6.

Got It? Do these problems to find out.

Describe the relationship between the terms in each arithmetic sequence. Then write the next three terms in the sequence.

a. 0, 13, 26, 39, …

b. 4, 7, 10, 13, …

c. 1.0, 1.3, 1.6, 1.9, …

d. 2.5, 3.0, 3.5, 4.0, …

a. _____

b. _____

c. _____

d. _____

Write an Algebraic Expression

Watch

In a sequence, each term has a specific position within the sequence. Consider the sequence 2, 4, 6, 8,…

1st position
3rd position
2, 4, 6, 8,…
2nd position
4th position

Notice that as the position number increases by 1, the value of the term increases by 2.

Position	Operation	Value of Term
1	$1 \cdot 2 = 2$	2
2	$2 \cdot 2 = 4$	4
3	$3 \cdot 2 = 6$	6
4	$4 \cdot 2 = 8$	8

+1 · +2
+1 · +2
+1 · +2

> **Arithmetic Sequences**
> When looking for a pattern between the position number and each term in the sequence, it is often helpful to make a table.

You can also write an algebraic expression to represent the relationship between any term in a sequence and its position in the sequence. In this case, if n represents the position in the sequence, the value of the term is $2n$.

 Example

 Tutor

3. The greeting cards that Meredith makes are sold in boxes at a gift store. The first week, the store sold 5 boxes. Each week, the store sells five more boxes. The pattern continues. What algebraic expression can be used to find the total number of boxes sold at the end of the 100th week? What is the total?

Position	Operation	Value of Term
1	$1 \cdot 5$	5
2	$2 \cdot 5$	10
3	$3 \cdot 5$	15
n	$n \cdot 5$	$5n$

Each term is 5 times its position. So, the expression is $5n$.

$5n$ Write the expression.

$5(100) = 500$ Replace n with 100.

At the end of 100 weeks, 500 boxes will have been sold.

Got It? Do this problem to find out.

e. If the pattern continues, what algebraic expression can be used to find the number of circles used in any figure? How many circles will be in the 50th figure?

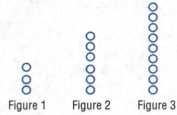

Figure 1   Figure 2   Figure 3

Show your work.

e. _____

Guided Practice

Describe the relationship between the terms in each arithmetic sequence. Then write the next three terms in each sequence. (Examples 1 and 2)

1. 0, 9, 18, 27, …

Show your work.

_____

_____

2. 4, 9, 14, 19, …

_____

_____

3. 1, 1.1, 1.2, 1.3, …

_____

_____

4. Hannah has a doll collection. The table shows the number of dolls she bought the first three years. Suppose this pattern continues. Write an algebraic expression to find the number of dolls in her collection after *n* years? How many dolls will Hannah collect during the 25th year? (Example 3)

Year	Number of Dolls
1	6
2	12
3	18

_____

5. 🇪 **Building on the Essential Question** Explain why the following sequence is considered an arithmetic sequence.

$$5, 9, 13, 17, 21, …$$

_____

_____

_____

Rate Yourself!

How confident are you about sequences? Check the box that applies.

For more help, go online to access a Personal Tutor.

Tutor

Independent Practice

Go online for Step-by-Step Solutions

Describe the relationship between the terms in each arithmetic sequence. Then write the next three terms in each sequence. (Examples 1 and 2)

1. 0, 7, 14, 21, …

 Show your work.

2. 1, 7, 13, 19, …

3 26, 34, 42, 50, …

4. 0.1, 0.4, 0.7, 1.0, …

5. 2.4, 3.2, 4.0, 4.8, …

6. 2.0, 3.1, 4.2, 5.3, …

7 Refer to the table shown. If the pattern continues, what algebraic expression can be used to find the plant's height for any month? What will be the plant's height at 12 months? (Example 3)

Month	Height (in.)
1	3
2	6
3	9

8. **CCGPS** **Model with Mathematics** Explain how the number of text messages Dario sent and the cost form an arithmetic sequence. Then write an expression to find Dario's text messaging bill if he sends *n* number of text messages over 250.

Watch ▶ Replay it online!

Let's go back online and try to find a rule so he will know how much his bill will be.

His mom will thank us.

Remember my texting fiasco? How can I know what my bill will be each month?

9. 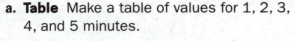 **Multiple Representations** Kendra is stacking boxes of tissues for a store display. She stacks 3 boxes the first minute, 6 boxes the second minute, and 9 boxes the third minute. Suppose the pattern continues for parts **a–d**.

   a. **Table** Make a table of values for 1, 2, 3, 4, and 5 minutes.

   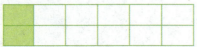

   b. **Symbols** Write an expression to find the *n*th term in the sequence.

   _____

   c. **Graph** Graph the table of values from part **a** on the coordinate plane. Let *x* represent the number of minutes and *y* represent the number of boxes. Then describe the graph.

   _____

   _____

   _____

   d. **Numbers** How many boxes will be displayed after 45 minutes?

   _____

   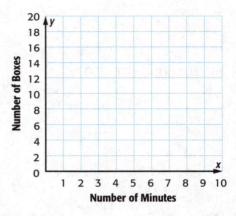

H.O.T. Problems Higher Order Thinking

10. CCGPS **Justify Conclusions** Write five terms of an arithmetic sequence and describe the rule for finding the terms.

_____

_____

CCGPS **Persevere with Problems** Not all sequences are arithmetic. But, there is still a pattern. Describe the relationship between the terms in each sequence. Then write the next three terms in the sequence.

11. 1, 2, 4, 7, 11, …   **12.** 0, 2, 6, 12, 20, …

_____   _____

_____   _____

 Georgia Test Practice

13. What is the rule for the following sequence?

        4.1, 4.6, 5.1, 5.6, 6.1,…

   Ⓐ Add 5 to the previous term.   Ⓒ Multiply the previous term by 5.

   Ⓑ Add 0.5 to the previous term.   Ⓓ Divide the previous term by 5.

Extra Practice

Describe the relationship between the terms in each arithmetic sequence. Then write the next three terms in each sequence.

14. 19, 31, 43, 55, …

12 is added to the previous term; 67, 79, 91

15. 6, 16, 26, 36, …

10 is added to the previous term; 46, 56, 66

16. 33, 38, 43, 48, …

_____

_____

17. 4.5, 6.0, 7.5, 9.0, …

_____

_____

18. 1.2, 3.2, 5.2, 7.2, …

_____

_____

19. 4.6, 8.6, 12.6, 16.6, …

_____

_____

20. 18, 33, 48, 63, …

_____

_____

21. 20, 45, 70, 95, …

_____

_____

22. 38, 61, 84, 107, …

_____

_____

23. **Reason Abstractly** Refer to the figures for parts **a.** and **b.**

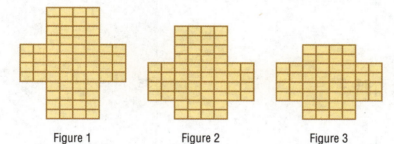

Figure 1   Figure 2   Figure 3

a. Describe the relationship between the figures and the number of

rectangles shown. _____

b. If the pattern continues, how many rectangles will be in the next

2 figures? _____

The terms of an arithmetic sequence can be related by subtraction. Write the next three terms of each sequence.

24. 32, 27, 22, 17, …

_____

25. 45, 42, 39, 36, …

_____

26. 10.5, 10, 9.5, 9, …

_____

Georgia Test Practice

27. Which sequence follows the rule $3n - 2$, where n represents the position of a term in the sequence?

Ⓐ 21, 18, 15, 12, 9, …

Ⓑ 3, 6, 9, 12, 15, …

Ⓒ 1, 7, 10, 13, 16, …

Ⓓ 1, 4, 7, 10, 13, …

28. Which expression can be used to find the nth term in this sequence?

Position	1	2	3	4	5	n
Value of Term	2	5	10	17	26	■

Ⓕ $n^2 + 1$

Ⓖ $2n + 1$

Ⓗ $n + 1$

Ⓘ $2n^2 + 2$

29. Short Response What expression can be used to find the nth term in the sequence 5, 7, 9, 11, …?

_____

 ## Common Core Review

Evaluate. MCC6.EE.1

30. $1^4 =$ _____

31. $3^3 =$ _____

32. $8^2 =$ _____

33. $10^4 =$ _____

34. $5^1 =$ _____

35. $7^5 =$ _____

36. Jayden goes to the batting cage. He purchases three tokens and rents a helmet. If he spends a total of $6.50, how much is each token? MCC6.EE.6

_____

Batting Cage Prices	
Tokens	■
Helmet Rental	$2

HOW can geometric figures be used to model numerical patterns?

CCGPS **Content Standards**
Preparation for MCC7.EE.2
Mathematical Practices
1, 3

Fences A fencing company uses 4 planks of wood for one section of fence, 7 planks for two sections, and 10 planks of wood for three sections. The fence sections are represented using the toothpicks shown. Determine how many planks would be used to create 5 sections of fence.

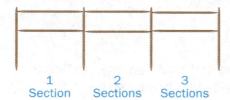

1 Section   2 Sections   3 Sections

Investigation

Step 1 Find a pattern in the table. Then fill in the number of planks that would be in 4 and 5 sections of fencing.

Number of Sections	Number of Planks
1	4
2	7
3	10
4	
5	

Step 2 Check your work by using toothpicks to show 5 fence sections. Draw the result in the space below.

So, there will be [ ] planks in 5 sections fencing.

Collaborate

Work with a partner. Complete the table. You can use toothpicks to continue each pattern if needed.

1.

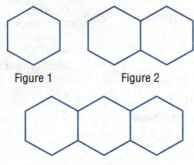

Figure 1   Figure 2

Figure 3

Figure Number	Number of Toothpicks
1	6
2	11
3	16
4	
5	

2. Refer to Exercise 1. Write an expression that could be used to find the number of toothpicks that would be needed for any figure.

3. Use your expression from Exercise 2 to find the number of toothpicks that would be needed to create Figure 10. Explain.

Reflect

4. **CCGPS** **Reason Abstractly** Refer back to the Investigation. Write an expression that could be used to find the number of planks in any number of sections.

5. **CCGPS** **Justify Conclusions** Use the expression in Exercise 4 to find the number of planks that would be needed to create 10 sections of fencing. Explain.

6. **Inquiry** HOW can geometric figures be used to model numerical patterns?

Properties of Operations

What You'll Learn

Scan the lesson. List two headings you would use to make an outline of the lesson.

- _____
- _____

Essential Question

HOW can you use numbers and symbols to represent mathematical ideas?

Vocabulary

Commutative Property
Associative Property
property
Additive Identity Property
Multiplicative Identity Property
Multiplicative Property of Zero
counterexample

Common Core GPS

Content Standards
MCC7.EE.1, MCC7.EE.2
Mathematical Practices
1, 3, 4, 5, 7

Real-World Link

Driving Miss Ricardo drives up and down her street to complete different errands. Some of the places on her street are shown below. The number of blocks between the places are also shown.

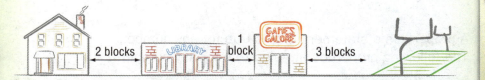

2 blocks — 1 block — 3 blocks

1. Suppose Miss Ricardo drives from home to the game store and back. Write an expression for each distance.

   from home to
   the game store: _____

   from the game
   store to home: _____

2. Circle the property that is illustrated in Exercise 1.

   Commutative   Associative

3. On Monday, Miss Ricardo drives from home, stops at the library, and then drives to the football field. On Tuesday, she drives from home, stops at the game store, and then drives to the football field. Write an expression for each distance.

   Monday: _____   Tuesday: _____

4. Circle the property that is illustrated in Exercise 3.

   Commutative   Associative

Properties of Operations

Watch

Words The **Commutative Property** states that the order in which numbers are added or multiplied does not change the sum or product.

	Addition	Multiplication
Symbols	$a + b = b + a$	$a \cdot b = b \cdot a$
Examples	$6 + 1 = 1 + 6$	$7 \cdot 3 = 3 \cdot 7$

Words The **Associative Property** states that the way in which numbers are grouped when they are added or multiplied does not change the sum or product.

	Addition	Multiplication
Symbols	$a + (b + c) = (a + b) + c$	$a \cdot (b \cdot c) = (a \cdot b) \cdot c$
Examples	$2 + (3 + 8) = (2 + 3) + 8$	$3 \cdot (4 \cdot 5) = (3 \cdot 4) \cdot 5$

A **property** is a statement that is true for any number. The following properties are also true for any numbers.

Property	Words	Symbols	Examples
Additive Identity	When 0 is added to any number, the sum is the number.	$a + 0 = a$ $0 + a = a$	$9 + 0 = 9$ $0 + 9 = 9$
Multiplicative Identity	When any number is multiplied by 1, the product is the number.	$a \cdot 1 = a$ $1 \cdot a = a$	$5 \cdot 1 = 5$ $1 \cdot 5 = 5$
Multiplicative Property of Zero	When any number is multiplied by 0, the product is 0.	$a \cdot 0 = 0$ $0 \cdot a = 0$	$8 \cdot 0 = 0$ $0 \cdot 8 = 0$

Example

Tutor

1. **Name the property shown by the statement $2 \cdot (5 \cdot n) = (2 \cdot 5) \cdot n$.**

The order of the numbers and variable did not change, but their grouping did. This is the Associative Property of Multiplication.

Show your work.

Got It? Do these problems to find out.

a. _____

b. _____

a. $42 + x + y = 42 + y + x$ **b.** $3x + 0 = 3x$

You may wonder if any of the properties apply to subtraction or division. If you can find a <mark>counterexample</mark>, an example that shows that a conjecture is false, the property does not apply.

Example

2. **State whether the following conjecture is *true* or *false*. If *false*, provide a counterexample.**

   Division of whole numbers is commutative.

   Write two division expressions using the Commutative Property.

   $15 \div 3 \overset{?}{=} 3 \div 15$ State the conjecture.

   $5 \neq \dfrac{1}{5}$ Divide.

   The conjecture is false. We found a counterexample. That is, $15 \div 3 \neq 3 \div 15$. So, division is *not* commutative.

Got It? Do this problem to find out.

Show your work.

c. The difference of two different whole numbers is always less than both of the two numbers.

c. _____

Example

3. **Alana wants to buy a sweater that costs $38, sunglasses that costs $14, a pair of jeans that costs $22, and a T-shirt that costs $16. Use mental math to find the total cost before tax.**

   Write an expression for the total cost. You can rearrange the numbers using the properties of math. Look for sums that are multiples of ten.

   $38 + 14 + 22 + 16$

   $= 38 + 22 + 14 + 16$ Commutative Property of Addition

   $= (38 + 22) + (14 + 16)$ Associative Property of Addition

   $= 60 + 30$ Add.

   $= 90$ Simplify.

   The total cost of the items is $90.

Got It? Do this problem to find out.

Show your work.

d. Lance made four phone calls from his cell phone today. The calls lasted 4.7, 9.4, 2.3, and 10.6 minutes. Use mental math to find the total amount of time he spent on the phone.

d. _____

Examples

Simplify each expression. Justify each step.

4. $(7 + g) + 5$

$(7 + g) + 5 = (g + 7) + 5$	Commutative Property of Addition
$= g + (7 + 5)$	Associative Property of Addition
$= g + 12$	Simplify.

5. $(m \cdot 11) \cdot m$

$(m \cdot 11) \cdot m = (11 \cdot m) \cdot m$	Commutative Property of Multiplication
$= 11 \cdot (m \cdot m)$	Associative Property of Multiplication
$= 11m^2$	Simplify.

Got It? Do this problem to find out.

e. $4 \cdot (3c \cdot 2)$

Simplify Algebraic Expressions

To simplify an expression is to perform all possible operations.

 Show your work.

e. _____

Guided Practice

Check

Name the property shown by each statement. (Example 1)

1. $3m \cdot 0 \cdot 5m = 0$ _____

2. $7c + 0 = 7c$ _____

3. State whether the following conjecture is *true* or *false*. If *false*, provide a counterexample. (Example 2)

Subtraction of whole numbers is associative.

_____

4. Simplify $9c + (8 + 3c)$. Justify each step. (Examples 3–5)

_____

_____

_____

5.  **Building on the Essential Question** Explain the difference between the Commutative and Associative

Properties. _____

_____

_____

_____

Rate Yourself!

Are you ready to move on?
Shade the section that applies.

YES ? NO

For more help, go online to access a Personal Tutor.

Tutor

Independent Practice

Go online for Step-by-Step Solutions

Name the property shown by each statement. (Example 1)

1. $a + (b + 12) = (b + 12) + a$

_____

2. $(5 + x) + 0 = 5 + x$

_____

3. $16 + (c + 17) = (16 + c) + 17$

_____

4. $d \cdot e \cdot 0 = 0$

_____

5. **CCGPS** **Use a Counterexample** State whether the conjecture is true or false. If false, provide a counterexample. (Example 2)

Division of whole numbers is associative.

_____

6. Darien ordered a soda for $2.75, a sandwich for $8.50, and a dessert for $3.85. Sales tax was $1.15. Use mental math to find the total amount of the bill. Explain. (Example 3) _____

_____

_____

Simplify each expression. Justify each step. (Examples 4 and 5)

7. $15 + (12 + 8a)$

_____

_____

_____

_____

8. $(5n \cdot 9) \cdot 2n$

_____

_____

_____

_____

9. $3x \cdot (7 \cdot x)$

_____

_____

_____

_____

_____

_____

10. $(4m \cdot 2) \cdot 5m$

_____

_____

_____

_____

_____

_____

11. Simplify the expression $(7 + 47 + 3)[5 \cdot (2 \cdot 3)]$. Use properties to justify each step.

_____

_____

_____

 H.O.T. Problems Higher Order Thinking

12. CCGPS **Model with Mathematics** Write about something you do every day that is commutative. Then write about another situation that is not commutative.

_____

_____

_____

13. CCGPS **Find the Error** Blake is simplifying $4 \cdot (5 \cdot m)$. Find his mistake and correct it.

_____

_____

_____

_____

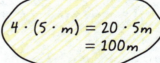

$$4 \cdot (5 \cdot m) = 20 \cdot 5m$$
$$= 100m$$

14. CCGPS **Identify Structure** Does the Associative Property *always*, *sometimes*, or *never* hold for subtraction? Explain your reasoning using examples and counterexamples.

_____

_____

_____

_____

Georgia Test Practice

15. Which equation is an example of the Commutative Property?

Ⓐ $4 \cdot 1 = 4$

Ⓑ $16 + 0 = 16$

Ⓒ $w + (3 + 2) = w + (2 + 3)$

Ⓓ $d(9 \cdot f) = (d \cdot 9)f$

Extra Practice

Name the property shown by each statement.

16. $9(ab) = (9a)b$

Associative (×)

17. $y \cdot 7 = 7y$

_____

18. $1 \times c = c$

_____

19. $5 + (a + 8) = (5 + a) + 8$

_____

20. State whether the conjecture is true or false. If false, provide a counterexample.

Subtraction of whole numbers is commutative.

_____

21. **CCGPS** **Use Math Tools** The times for each leg of a relay for four runners are shown. Use mental math to find the total time for the relay team. Explain.

Runner	Time (s)
Jamal	12.4
Kenneth	11.8
Bryce	11.2
Jorge	12.6

_____

_____

Simplify each expression. Justify each step.

22. $(22 + 19b) + 7$

_____

_____

23. $18 + (5 + 6m)$

_____

_____

24. $11s(4)$

_____

_____

25. $10y(7)$

_____

_____

26. $(9 + 31 + 5)[(7 \cdot 5) \cdot 4]$

_____

_____

_____

27. The equation $15 + 0 = 15$ is an example of which of the following properties?

Ⓐ Multiplicative Property of Zero

Ⓑ Multiplicative Identity

Ⓒ Additive Identity

Ⓓ Associative Property

28. Short Response Simplify the expression below. Show and justify each step.

$$14 + (4p + 46) + 0$$

_____

_____

_____

_____

29. Short Response The table shows the cost of different items at a bakery. Write a numerical expression to find the total cost of a doughnut, muffin, and cookie.

_____

Item	Cost ($)
Doughnut	2.29
Muffin	2.50
Cookie	2.21
Roll	1.15

(CCGPS) Common Core Review

Evaluate each expression if $a = 6$, $b = 15$, and $c = 9$. MCC6.EE.2

30. $a + 2b$ _____

31. $c^2 - 5$ _____

32. $10 + a^3$ _____

33. $8c - 9 + 25$ _____

34. $14 + 8b \div 2$ _____

35. $3^3 \div (3a)$ _____

36. A package of pencils costs $1.25. A new eraser costs $0.45. Write an expression to find the total cost of 3 packages of pencils and 2 erasers. Then find the total cost. MCC6.EE.2

_____

The Distributive Property

What You'll Learn

Scan the lesson. Predict two things you will learn about the Distributive Property.

- _____
  _____
- _____
  _____

Essential Question

HOW can you use numbers and symbols to represent mathematical ideas?

Vocabulary

Distributive Property
equivalent expressions

Common Core GPS

Content Standards
MCC7.EE.1, MCC7.EE.2
Mathematical Practices
1, 3, 4, 5, 7

 **Real-World Link**

School Supplies Jordan buys three notebooks that cost $5 each. He also buys three packages of pens for $6 each.

1. Write an expression that shows the cost of three notebooks added to the cost of three packages of pens.

   $\boxed{} \cdot 5 + \boxed{} \cdot 6$

2. Write an expression that shows three times the cost of one notebook and one package of pens.

   $\boxed{}\left(\boxed{} + \boxed{}\right)$

3. Evaluate both expressions. What do you notice?

   _____

   _____

4. Suppose Jordan buys five notebooks that cost $3 each and five packages of pens that cost $1 each. Circle the expressions that represent Jordan's purchases.

   $5 \cdot 3 + 5 \cdot 1$ $\qquad$ $5 \cdot 3 \cdot 5 \cdot 1$ $\qquad$ $5(3 + 1)$

5. Suppose Jordan buys two rulers that cost $1 each and two folders that cost $1.50 each. Circle the expressions that represent Jordan's purchases.

   $2 + 1 + 2 + 1.50$ $\quad$ $2(1 + 1.50)$ $\qquad$ $2 \cdot 1 + 2 \cdot 1.50$

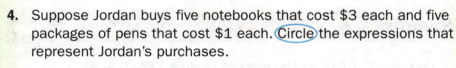

Use the Distributive Property

Words The **Distributive Property** states that to multiply a sum or difference by a number, multiply each term inside the parentheses by the number outside the parentheses.

Symbols $a(b + c) = ab + ac$ $a(b - c) = ab - ac$

Examples $4(6 + 2) = 4 \cdot 6 + 4 \cdot 2$ $3(7 - 5) = 3 \cdot 7 - 3 \cdot 5$

You can model the Distributive Property with algebraic expressions using algebra tiles. The expression $2(x + 2)$ is modeled below.

Model $x + 2$ using algebra tiles.

Double the amount of tiles to represent $2(x + 2)$.

Rearrange the tiles by grouping together the ones with the same shapes.

$$2(x + 2) = 2(x) + 2(2) \qquad \text{Distributive Property}$$
$$= 2x + 4 \qquad \text{Multiply.}$$

The expressions $2(x + 2)$ and $2x + 4$ are **equivalent expressions**. No matter what x is, these expressions have the same value.

Example

 Tutor

Show your work.

1. Use the Distributive Property to evaluate $8(-9 + 4)$.

$$8(-9 + 4) = 8(-9) + 8(4) \qquad \text{Expand using the Distributive Property.}$$
$$= -72 + 32 \text{ or } -40 \qquad \text{Multiply. Then add.}$$

a. _____

b. _____

Got It? Do these problems to find out.

   a. $5(-9 + 11)$ b. $7(10 - 5)$ c. $(12 - 8)9$

c. _____

Examples

Tutor

Use the Distributive Property to rewrite each expression.

2. $4(x + 7)$

$$4(x + 7) = 4(x) + 4(7) \qquad \text{Expand using the Distributive Property.}$$
$$= 4x + 28 \qquad \text{Simplify.}$$

3. $6(p - 5)$

$$6(p - 5) = 6[p + (-5)] \qquad \text{Rewrite } p - 5 \text{ as } p + (-5).$$
$$= 6(p) + 6(-5) \qquad \text{Expand using the Distributive Property.}$$
$$= 6p + (-30) \qquad \text{Simplify.}$$
$$= 6p - 30 \qquad \text{Definition of subtraction}$$

4. $-2(x - 8)$

$$-2(x - 8) = -2[x + (-8)] \qquad \text{Rewrite } x - 8 \text{ as } x + (-8).$$
$$= -2(x) + -2(-8) \qquad \text{Expand using the Distributive Property.}$$
$$= -2x + 16 \qquad \text{Simplify.}$$

5. $5(-3x + 7y)$

$$5(-3x + 7y) = 5(-3x) + 5(7y) \qquad \text{Expand using the Distributive Property.}$$
$$= -15x + 35y \qquad \text{Simplify.}$$

6. $\frac{1}{3}(x - 6)$

$$\frac{1}{3}(x - 6) = \frac{1}{3}[x + (-6)] \qquad \text{Rewrite } x - 6 \text{ as } x + (-6).$$
$$= \frac{1}{3}(x) + \left(\frac{1}{3}(-6)\right) \qquad \text{Expand using the Distributive Property.}$$
$$= \frac{1}{3}x + (-2) \qquad \text{Simplify.}$$
$$= \frac{1}{3}x - 2 \qquad \text{Definition of subtraction}$$

Got It? **Do these problems to find out.**

d. $6(a + 4)$ **e.** $(m + 3n)8$

f. $-3(y - 10)$ **g.** $\frac{1}{2}(w - 4)$

Show your work.

d. _____

e. _____

f. _____

g. _____

Tutor

Example

7. Mr. Ito needs to buy batting helmets for the baseball team. The helmets he plans to buy are **$19.95 each**. Find the total cost if Mr. Ito needs to buy 9 batting helmets for the team.

Rename $19.95 as $20.00 − $0.05. Then use the Distributive Property to find the total cost mentally.

$9($20.00 − $0.05) = 9($20.00) − 9($0.05)$ Distributive Property

$= $180 − 0.45 Multiply.

$= 179.55 Subtract.

The total cost of the helmets is $179.55.

Show your work.

Got It? Do this problem to find out.

h. A sports club rents dirt bikes for $37.50 each. Find the total cost for the club to rent 20 bikes. Justify your answer by using the Distributive Property.

h. _____

Guided Practice

Check ✓

Use the Distributive Property to evaluate or rewrite each expression. (Examples 1–6)

1. $(8 + 11)(−3) =$ _____

2. $−5(2x + 4y) =$ _____

3. $\frac{1}{5}(g − 10) =$ _____

Show your work.

4. A housefly can fly about 6.4 feet per second. At this rate, how far can it fly in 25 seconds? Justify your answer by using the Distributive Property. (Example 7)

_____

5. **Building on the Essential Question** Describe how the formula to find the perimeter of a rectangle is an application of the Distributive Property. _____

_____

_____

_____

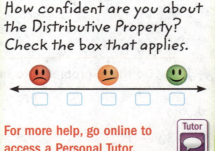

Rate Yourself!

How confident are you about the Distributive Property? Check the box that applies.

For more help, go online to access a Personal Tutor.

Name _____ My Homework _____

Go online for Step-by-Step Solutions

Use the Distributive Property to evaluate each expression. (Example 1)

1. $3(5 + 6) =$ _____

2. $(6 + 4)(-12) =$ _____

3 $-6(9 - 4) =$ _____

 Show your work.

4. $5(-6 + 4) =$ _____

5. $4(8 - 7) =$ _____

6. $(5 - 7)(-3) =$ _____

CCGPS Identify Structure **Use the Distributive Property to rewrite each expression.** (Examples 2–6)

7. $3(-4x + 8) =$ _____

8. $4(x - 6y) =$ _____

9. $6(5 - q) =$ _____

10. $\frac{1}{2}(c - 8) =$ _____

11. $-3(5 - b) =$ _____

12. $(d + 2)(-7) =$ _____

13 Amelia bought roast beef for $6.85 per pound. Find the total cost if Amelia bought 4 pounds of roast beef. Justify your answer by using the Distributive Property. (Example 7)

_____

14. The table shows the different prices of items at a movie theater.

  a. Suppose Mina and two of her friends go to the movies. Write an expression that could be used to find the total cost for them to go to the movies and buy one of each item.

  _____

  b. What is the total cost for all three people?

  _____

Movie Theater Prices	
Item	**Cost ($)**
box of candy	2.25
drink	3.25
popcorn	4.50
ticket	7.50

CCGPS **Use Math Tools** Find each product mentally. Justify your answer.

15. $9 \cdot 35 =$ _____

16. $8 \cdot 28 =$ _____

17. $112 \cdot 6 =$ _____

18. $85 \cdot 8 =$ _____

19. $4 \cdot 122 =$ _____

20. $12 \cdot 64 =$ _____

H.O.T. Problems Higher Order Thinking

21. **CCGPS** **Reason Abstractly** Write an expression, that when using the Distributive Property, can be simplified to $12a + 18b - 6c$.

_____

22. **CCGPS** **Identify Structure** Use the Distributive Property to rewrite the expression $7bx + 7by$ as an equivalent expression.

_____

23. **CCGPS** **Persevere with Problems** Use the Distributive Property to write an equivalent expression for the expression $(a + b)(2 + y)$.

_____

Georgia Test Practice

24. Which of the following expressions is equivalent to the expression below?

$$5a + 5b$$

Ⓐ $5ab$

Ⓑ $5(a + b)$

Ⓒ $5a + b$

Ⓓ $a + 5b$

Extra Practice

Use the Distributive Property to evaluate each expression.

25. $(3 + 6)(-8) = \underline{-72}$

$3 \cdot (-8) + 6(-8) =$

$-24 + (-48) = -72$

Homework Help

26. $4(11 - 5) = $ _____

27. $(12 - 4)(-5)$ _____

Use the Distributive Property to rewrite each expression.

28. $-8(a + b) = $ _____

29. $(2b + 8)5 = $ _____

30. $(p + 7)(-2) = $ _____

31. **CCGPS** **Justify Conclusions** Theresa is planning on making a fleece blanket for her nephew. She learns that the fabric she wants to use is $7.99 per yard. Find the total cost of 4 yards of fabric. Justify your answer by using the Distributive Property.

_____

_____

32. You are ordering T-shirts with your school's mascot printed on them. Each T-shirt costs $4.75. The printer charges a setup fee of $30 and $2.50 to print each shirt. Write two expressions to represent the total cost of printing n T-shirts.

_____

_____

Use the Distributive Property to rewrite each expression.

33. $0.5x(y - z)$

$= $ _____

34. $-6a(2b + 5c)$

$= $ _____

35. $-4m(3n - 6p)$

$= $ _____

36. $3(2y + 4z)$

$= $ _____

37. $-2(3a - 2b)$

$= $ _____

38. $-6(12p - 8n)$

$= $ _____

39. Write two equivalent expressions for the area of the figure.

_____

$x + 4$

16

40. Celeste is going to summer camp. The table below shows the cost of items she will need to purchase with the camp logo.

Item	Cost ($)
T-shirt	8.00
Shorts	4.50
Socks	2.25

Celeste needs to buy four of each item. Which expression below *cannot* be used to find the total cost of the items?

Ⓐ 4(14.75)

Ⓑ 4(8) + 4(4.50) + 4(2.25)

Ⓒ 4(8.00) + 4.50 + 2.25

Ⓓ 4(8.00 + 4.50 + 2.25)

41. Which property is demonstrated in the equation below?

$$4x + 32 = 4(x + 8)$$

Ⓕ Associative Property of Addition

Ⓖ Commutative Property of Addition

Ⓗ Distributive Property

Ⓘ Multiplicative Identity

42. Which equation is an example of the Distributive Property?

Ⓐ $5(2 + y) = 5(2) + 5y$

Ⓑ $(5 + 2) + y = 5 + (2 + y)$

Ⓒ $(5 + 2) + y = (2 + 5) + y$

Ⓓ $(5 + 2) + y = y + (5 + 2)$

43. Short Response The table shows the number of seniors, adults, and children going on a group trip to an aquarium. The tickets are $14.95 per person. Find the total cost of the tickets. Justify your answer by using the Distributive Property.

Type of Ticket	Tickets Purchased
Senior	7
Adult	11
Child	12

_____

_____

Evaluate each expression if $x = 9$ and $y = 3$. MCC6.EE.2c

44. $x + y - 58$ _____

45. $y^3 + x^3$ _____

46. $y^4 - 128 =$ _____

47. In the expression below, identify the coefficient and the variable. MCC6.EE.2

$$4x + 450$$

coefficient: _____   variable: _____

CCGPS **Content Standards**
MCC7.NS.3
Mathematical Practices
1, 3, 4

Case #1 Mountain Biking

Hoshi wants to purchase a membership to a dirt bike park. The cost depends on the number of people on the membership. It costs $55 for 5 people, $65 for 6 people, and $75 for 7 people.

Find the cost of a membership that includes 8 people.

1 Understand What are the facts?

The cost of a membership depends on the number of people included on the membership.

2 Plan What is your strategy to solve this problem?

Make a table that shows the number of people and the cost.

3 Solve How can you apply the strategy?

Make a table. Find the cost for 8 people.

Number of People (p)	Cost
5	$55
6	$65
7	$75
8	

+10
+10
+10

So, the cost for 8 people is ⬚.

4 Check Does the answer make sense?

The expression $10p + 5$ can be used to represent the situation.

Since $10(8) + 5 = 85$, the solution is reasonable.

Analyze the Strategy Tutor

CCGPS **Justify Conclusions** Hoshi wants to purchase a membership for four people. Explain how the table would change and then solve.

_____

_____

Case #2 Financial Literacy

Latoya is saving money to buy a saxophone. After 1 month, she has $75. After 2 months, she has $120. After 3 months, she has $165. She plans to keep saving at the same rate.

How long will it take Latoya to save enough money to buy a saxophone that costs $300?

 Understand

Read the problem. What are you being asked to find?

I need to find _____

_____.

Underline key words and values. What information do you know?

After 1 month, Latoya has ⬚. After 2 months, she has ⬚.

After 3 months, she has ⬚. She continues to save at the same rate.

Is there any information that you do _not_ need to know?

I do not need to know _____.

 Plan

Choose a problem-solving strategy.

I will use the _____ strategy.

 Solve

Use your problem-solving strategy to solve the problem.

Months	1	2	3	4	5	6
Amount Saved ($)	75	120	165			

+45 +45 +45   +45 +45

Latoya will have $300 saved in _____.

 Check

Use information from the problem to check your answer.

_____

_____

Case #3 Carnivals

For a carnival game, containers are arranged in a triangular display. The top row has 1 container. The second row has 2 containers. The third row has 3 containers. The pattern continues until the bottom row, which has 10 containers.

How many total containers are there?

_____

Case #4 Budget

Tamara earns $2,050 each month. She spends $1,315 of the amount she earns. The rest of the money is deposited in a savings account.

How many months until Tamara has deposited more than $2,500 in her savings account?

_____

Case #5 Toothpicks

Find the number of toothpicks that will be in Figure 8 of the pattern shown.

_____

Figure 1   Figure 2   Figure 3

Circle a strategy below to solve the problem.
- Draw a diagram.
- Act it out.
- Look for a pattern.

Case #6 Algebra

What are the next two numbers in the pattern?

16, 32, 64, 128, 256, _____, _____

Mid-Chapter Check

Vocabulary Check

1. Fill in the blank in the sentence below with the correct term. (Lesson 1)

A _____ is a symbol that represents an unknown quantity.

2. Define *arithmetic sequence*. Then provide an example. (Lesson 2)

_____

_____

Skills Check and Problem Solving

Describe the relationship between the terms in each arithmetic sequence. Then write the next three terms in each sequence. (Lesson 2)

3. 5, 8, 11, 14, …

4. 4, 11, 18, 25, …

5. 5.8, 10.8, 15.8, 20.8, …

Use the Distributive Property to rewrite each expression. (Lesson 4)

6. $4(x + 9) =$ _____

7. $2(x + 5) =$ _____

8. $3(-2x + 4) =$ _____

9. **Identify Structure** What property is shown by the statement $8x + 0 = 8x$? (Lesson 3)

_____

10. Georgia Test Practice A coach spent $201 on baseball bats and baseball gloves. Let *b* represent the number of bats and *g* represent the number of gloves. Which expression represents the number of items that she bought? (Lesson 1)

Ⓐ $b + g$

Ⓑ $b \cdot g$

Ⓒ $2b + 3g$

Ⓓ $3b + 2g$

$35

$48

Simplify Algebraic Expressions

What You'll Learn

Scan the lesson. Write two facts you learned about simplifying algebraic expressions.

- _____
  _____
- _____
  _____

Real-World Link

Music Store Patricia, Hugo, and Sun work at a music store. Each week, Patricia works three more than twice the number of hours that Hugo works. Sun works 2 less hours than Hugo.

1. Let *x* represent the number of hours that Hugo works each week. The number of hours that Hugo, Patricia, and Sun work can be modeled as shown below. Write an expression that represents each person's number of hours.

Hugo's hours	Patricia's hours	Sun's hours
x	x x 1 1 1	x −1 −1
	Twice Three	Hugo Two
	Hugo more	less

Expression: _____   Expression: _____   Expression: _____

2. Model the total number of hours that Patricia and Sun work. Draw the result below. Then write an expression for the drawing.

   Expression: _____

3. Like tiles are tiles that have the same shape. Group like tiles together and remove the zero pairs. Draw the result below. Then write an expression for your drawing.

   Expression: _____

Essential Question

HOW can you use numbers and symbols to represent mathematical ideas?

Vocabulary

term
like terms
constant
simplest form

Common Core GPS

Content Standards
MCC7.EE.1, MCC7.EE.2

Mathematical Practices
1, 2, 3, 4, 6

Identify Parts of an Expression

When addition or subtraction signs separate an algebraic expression into parts, each part is called a **term**. Recall that the numerical factor of a term that contains a variable is called the coefficient of the variable.

Like terms contain the same variables to the same powers. For example, $3x^2$ and $-7x^2$ are like terms. So are $8xy^2$ and $12xy^2$. But $10x^2z$ and $22xz^2$ are *not* like terms. A term without a variable is called a **constant**. Constant terms are also like terms.

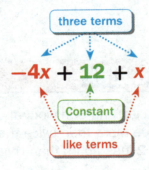

three terms

$$-4x + 12 + x$$

Constant

like terms

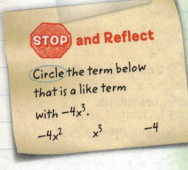

STOP and Reflect

Circle the term below that is a like term with $-4x^3$.

$-4x^2$ x^3 -4

Example

Tutor

1. Identify the terms, like terms, coefficients, and constants in the expression $6n - 7n - 4 + n$.

$6n - 7n - 4 + n = 6n + (-7n) + (-4) + 1n$ Rewrite the expression.

- Terms: $6n, -7n, -4, n$

- Like terms: $6n, -7n, n$ All of these terms have the same variable.

- Coefficients: $6, -7, 1$

- Constants: -4 This is the only term without a variable.

Got It? Do these problems to find out.

Identify the terms, like terms, coefficients, and constants in each expression.

a. $9y - 4 - 11y + 7$ **b.** $3x + 2 - 10 - 3x$

Show your work.

a. _____

b. _____

Simplify Algebraic Expressions

An algebraic expression is in **simplest form** if it has no like terms and no parentheses. Use the Distributive Property to combine like terms.

Examples

2. **Write $4y + y$ in simplest form.**

$4y$ and y are like terms.

$4y + y = 4y + 1y$ Identity Property; $y = 1y$

         $= (4 + 1)y$ or $5y$ Distributive Property; Simplify.

3. **Write $7x - 2 - 7x + 6$ in simplest form.**

$7x$ and $-7x$ are like terms. -2 and 6 are also like terms.

$7x - 2 - 7x + 6 = 7x + (-2) + (-7x) + 6$ Definition of subtraction

                $= 7x + (-7x) + (-2) + 6$ Commutative Property

                $= [7 + (-7)]x + (-2) + 6$ Distributive Property

                $= 0x + 4$ Simplify.

                $= 0 + 4$ or 4 Multiplicative Property of zero and Additive Identity Property of zero.

> **Equivalent Expressions**
>
> To check whether $4y + y$ and $5y$ are equivalent expressions, substitute any value for y and see whether the expressions have the same value.

Show your work.

c. _____

d. _____

e. _____

Got It? Do these problems to find out.

   c. $4z - z$ **d.** $6 - 3n + 3n$ **e.** $2g - 3 + 11 - 8g$

Example

4. **The cost of a jacket j after a 5% markup can be represented by the expression $j + 0.05j$. Simplify the expression. Then determine the total cost of the jacket after the markup, if the original price is $35.**

$j + 0.05j = 1j + 0.05j$ Identity Property; $j = 1j$

          $= (1 + 0.05)j$ Distributive Property

          $= 1.05j$ Simplify.

$1.05j = 1.05(35)$ Replace j with 35 to find the total cost.

        $= 36.75$ Multiply.

So, the cost of the jacket after a 5% markup is $36.75.

Got It? Do this problem to find out.

   f. Write an expression in simplest form for the cost of the jacket in Example 4 if the markup is 8%. Then determine the total cost after the markup.

f. _____

 Example

5. At a concert, you buy some T-shirts for $12.00 each and the same number of CDs for $7.50 each. Write an expression in simplest form that represents the total amount spent.

Let x represent the number of T-shirts and CDs.

$12x + 7.50x$ Write the expression.

$12x + 7.50x = (12 + 7.50)x$ Distributive Property

$= 19.50x$ Simplify.

The expression $\$19.50x$ represents the total amount spent.

Got It? Do this problem to find out.

 Show your work.

g. You have some money. Your friend has $50 less than you. Write an expression in simplest form that represents the total amount of money you and your friend have.

g. _____

Guided Practice

1. Identify the terms, like terms, coefficients, and constants in $5n - 2n - 3 + n$ (Example 1)

2. Write $4p - 7 + 6p + 10$ in simplest form. (Examples 2 and 3)

3. The cost of a game g with 7% sales tax can be represented by the expression $g + 0.07g$. Simplify the expression. Then determine the total cost of the game after sales tax if the original price is $52. (Example 4)

4. You go to a basketball game and buy 3 waters that cost x dollars each and a bag of peanuts for $4.50. Write an expression in simplest form that represents the total amount of money you spent. (Example 5)

5. **Building on the Essential Question** Explain why $2(x - 1) + 3(x - 1) = 5(x - 1)$ is a true statement. Justify your answer using properties.

Rate Yourself!

Are you ready to move on? Shade the section that applies.

YES   ?   NO

For more help, go online to access a Personal Tutor.

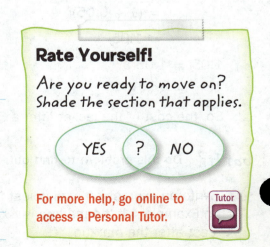

Independent Practice

Go online for Step-by-Step Solutions

Identify the terms, like terms, coefficients, and constants in each expression. (Example 1)

1. $2 + 3a + 9a$

2. $7 - 5x + 1$

3. $9 - z + 3 - 2z$

Write each expression in simplest form. (Examples 2 and 3)

4. $n + 5n =$ _____

5. $12c - c =$ _____

6. $-4j - 1 - 4j + 6 =$ _____

7. The cost of a ticket t to a concert with a 3% sales tax can be represented by the expression $t + 0.03t$. Simplify the expression. Then determine the total cost after the sales tax if the original price is $72. (Example 4)

_____

Write an expression in simplest form that represents the total amount in each situation. (Example 5)

8. You rent x pairs of shoes for $2 each. You buy the same number of drinks for $1.50 each. You also pay $9 for a bowling lane.

_____

9 You watch x minutes of television on Monday, the same amount on Wednesday, and 30 minutes on Friday.

_____

10. In a State Legislature, there were 119 more members in the House of Representatives than in the Senate. If there were m members in the Senate, write an expression to represent the total members in the State

Legislature. _____

11 Elian and his friends paid a total of $7 for tickets to the school football game. While at the game, they bought 5 hot dogs at x dollars each, 4 boxes of popcorn at y dollars each, and 2 pretzels at z dollars each.

a. Write an expression to show the total cost of admission and the snacks.

_____

b. Hot dogs cost $4, popcorn cost $3, and pretzels cost $2. What was

the total cost for admission and snacks? _____

CCGPS **Reason Abstractly** Write an expression in simplest form for the perimeter of each figure.

12.

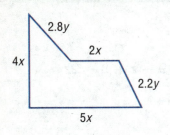

13.

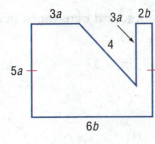

14.

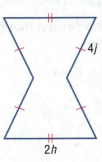

---

15. **CCGPS** **Be Precise** Write an expression that has three terms and simplifies to $4x - 7$. Identify the coefficient(s) and constant(s) in your expression.

_____

_____

16. **CCGPS** **Which One Doesn't Belong?** Identify the expression that is not equivalent to the other three. Explain your reasoning.

| $x - 2 + 3x$ | $4(x - 2)$ | $-2 + 7x - 3x$ | $4x - 2$ |

_____

_____

17. **CCGPS** **Persevere with Problems** Simplify the expression $8x^2 - 2x + 12x - 3$. Show that your answer is true for $x = 2$.

_____

_____

Georgia Test Practice

18. Which of the following expressions is $7a - 3(2a - 4)$ in simplest form?

Ⓐ $a - 12$

Ⓑ $a + 12$

Ⓒ $13a - 12$

Ⓓ $13a + 12$

Extra Practice

Identify the terms, like terms, coefficients, and constants in each expression.

19. $4 + 5y - 6y + y$

terms: 4, 5y, −6y, y

like terms: 5y, −6y, y

coefficients: 5, −6, 1

constant: 4

20. $n + 4n - 7n - 1$

21. $-3d + 8 - d - 2$

Write each expression in simplest form.

22. $5x + 4 + 9x$

= _____

23. $2 + 3d + d$

= _____

24. $-3r + 7 - 3r - 12$

= _____

Write an expression in simplest form that represents the total amount in each situation.

25. You subscribe to m different magazines. Your friend subscribes to 2 fewer than you.

_____

26. Today is your friend's birthday. She is y years old. Her brother is 5 years younger.

_____

27. You spent m minutes studying on Monday. On Tuesday, you studied 15 more minutes than you did on Monday. Wednesday, you studied 30 minutes less than you did on Tuesday. You studied twice as long on Thursday as you did on Monday. On Friday, you studied 20 minutes less than you did on Thursday. Write an expression in simplest form to represent the number of minutes you studied in all.

_____

28. **CCGPS** **Reason Abstractly** Write a real-world situation for $7.50y + 9$.

_____

_____

Simplify each expression.

29. $3(4x - 5) + 4(2x + 6)$

= _____

30. $-8(2a - 3b) - 5(6b - 4a)$

= _____

31. $10(5g + 2h - 3) - 4(3g - 4h + 2)$

= _____

32. Samir has c cards in his baseball card collection. On his birthday, he received 20 more cards than the number of cards already in his collection. Which expression represents the total number of cards now in his collection?

- Ⓐ $c + 20$
- Ⓑ $c - 20$
- Ⓒ $2c + 20$
- Ⓓ $2c - 20$

33. Short Response Simplify the expression below.

$$5(3x + 4y) - 6(2x + 5y)$$

34. The table shows the number of tickets needed and the number of times Patricia participated in different activities at a carnival.

Activity	Tickets	Times Completed
Ring toss	2	a
Dunk tank	4	b
Balloon pop	3	a
Trampoline	5	b

Which expression represents the total number of tickets she used?

- Ⓕ 14
- Ⓗ $2a + 2b$
- Ⓖ $a + b$
- Ⓘ $5a + 9b$

35. Mica spends \$5 for her lunch and \$2 for breakfast each day Monday through Friday. Use the Associative Property to find how much money she spends on lunch and breakfast for 4 weeks. MCC7.EE.1

Define a variable. Then write each phrase as an algebraic expression. MCC6.EE.2

36. Anna has volunteered 9 more hours than Tricia

37. the cost of a pair of jeans is 4 times the cost of a book

Evaluate each expression if $x = 2$, $y = 10$, and $z = 4$. MCC6.EE.2c

38. $5z - 10$ _____

39. $y \div 2 + x$ _____

40. $x^3 + (y \div x)$ _____

Add Linear Expressions

What You'll Learn

Scan the lesson. Predict two things you will learn about adding linear expressions.

- _____
- _____

Essential Question

HOW can you use numbers and symbols to represent mathematical ideas?

Vocabulary

linear expression

Common Core GPS

Content Standards
MCC7.EE.1, MCC7.EE.2
Mathematical Practices
1, 2, 3, 4

Real-World Link

 Tools

Homework Luke has 20 math problems and 11 science questions for homework. Cameron has 23 math problems and 10 science questions for homework.

1. The expression below represents the types of exercises that Luke has for homework.

   20 math problems + 11 science questions

   Complete the expression that represents the types of exercises that Cameron has for homework.

   [   ] math problems + [   ] science questions

2. Write an expression for the total number of math problems and science questions for both boys.

   [   ] math problems + [   ] science questions

3. Suppose Luke has x math problems and 5 science questions for homework and Cameron has x math problems and 6 science questions. The algebra tiles below represent the total number of math problems and science questions for both boys. Write an expression in simplest form that represents the algebra tiles.

   Expression: _____

Add Linear Expressions

A **linear expression** is an algebraic expression in which the variable is raised to the first power. The table below gives some examples of expressions that are linear and some examples of expressions that are not linear.

Linear Expressions	Nonlinear Expressions
$5x$	$5x^2$
$3x + 2$	$3x^3 + 2$
$x - 7$	$x^4 - 7$

You can add linear expression with or without models. Sometimes you will need to use zero pairs.

Examples

Tutor

Add.

1. $(2x + 3) + (x + 4)$

Model each linear expression.

Combine like tiles and write a linear expression for the combined tiles.

So, $(2x + 3) + (x + 4) = 3x + 7$.

2. $(2x - 1) + (x - 5)$

$$
\begin{array}{r}
2x - 1 \\
+\ x - 5 \\
\hline
3x - 6
\end{array}
$$

Arrange like terms in columns.

Add.

So, $(2x - 1) + (x - 5) = 3x - 6$.

Show your work.

Got It? Do these problems to find out.

a. $(3x - 5) + (2x - 3)$

b. $(2x - 4) + (3x - 7)$

a. _____

b. _____

Examples

3. Find $(2x - 3) + (-x + 4)$. Use models if needed.

2x + (−3)   −x + 4

Model each linear expression.

x   +   1

Combine like tiles. Then remove all zero pairs and write a linear expression for the remaining tiles.

So, $(2x - 3) + (-x + 4) = x + 1$.

4. Find $2(x + 3) + (3x + 1)$.

$2(x + 3) + (3x + 1) = (2 \cdot x + 2 \cdot 3) + (3x + 1)$ Use the Distributive Property.

$\qquad\qquad\qquad = (2x + 6) + (3x + 1)$ Simplify.

$$\begin{array}{r} 2x + 6 \\ + 3x + 1 \\ \hline 5x + 7 \end{array}$$

Arrange like terms in columns.

Add.

So, $2(x + 3) + (3x + 1) = 5x + 7$.

5. Find $5(x - 4) + (2x - 7)$.

$5(x - 4) + (2x - 7) = (5 \cdot x - 5 \cdot 4) + (2x - 7)$ Use the Distributive Property.

$\qquad\qquad\qquad = (5x - 20) + (2x - 7)$ Simplify.

$$\begin{array}{r} 5x - 20 \\ + 2x - 7 \\ \hline 7x - 27 \end{array}$$

Arrange like terms in columns.

Add.

So, $5(x - 4) + (2x - 7) = 7x - 27$.

Got It? Do these problems to find out.

Add. Use models if needed.

c. $(x - 1) + (2x + 3)$ **d.** $(x - 4) + (-2x + 1)$

e. $6(x + 7) + (x + 3)$ **f.** $(12x + 19) + 2(x - 10)$

Show your work.

c. _____

d. _____

e. _____

f. _____

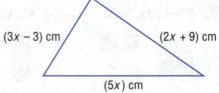

Example

6. Write a linear expression in simplest form to represent the perimeter of the triangle. Find the perimeter if the value of x is 5 centimeters.

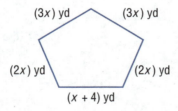

(3x − 3) cm   (2x + 9) cm   (5x) cm

Write a linear expression for the perimeter of the triangle.

$(3x - 3) + (2x + 9) + (5x)$ Write each expression.

$(3x + 2x + 5x) + (-3 + 9)$ Rearrange to combine like terms.

$10x + 6$ Add.

Find the perimeter.

$10x + 6 = 10(5) + 6$ or 56 Replace x with 5. Simplify.

So, the perimeter of the triangle is 56 centimeters.

Got It? Do this problem to find out.

g. A rectangle has side lengths $(x + 4)$ feet and $(2x - 2)$ feet. Write a linear expression in simplest form to represent the perimeter. Find the perimeter if the value of x is 7 feet.

g. _____

Guided Practice

Add. Use models if needed. (Examples 1–5)

1. $(2x + 3) + (x + 1) =$ _____

2. $10(x - 2) + (6x - 6) =$ _____

3. Write a linear expression in simplest form to represent the perimeter of the pentagon. Then find the perimeter if the value of x is 3 yards. (Example 6)

(3x) yd   (3x) yd   (2x) yd   (2x) yd   (x + 4) yd

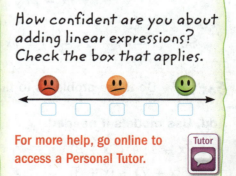

Rate Yourself!

How confident are you about adding linear expressions? Check the box that applies.

For more help, go online to access a Personal Tutor.

4. **Building on the Essential Question** Explain how adding linear expressions is similar to simplifying expressions.

FOLDABLES Time to update your Foldable!

Independent Practice

Go online for Step-by-Step Solutions

Add. Use models if needed. (Examples 1–5)

1. $(4x + 8) + (7x + 3) =$ _____

2. $(-3x + 7) + (-6x + 9) =$ _____

3. $(x - 10) + (3x - 6) =$ _____

4. $(-3x - 7) + (4x + 7) =$ _____

5. $2(x + 14) + (2x - 14) =$ _____

6. $(11x - 8) + 7(x - 1) =$ _____

7. Write a linear expression in simplest form to represent the perimeter of the triangle at the right. Then find the perimeter if the value of x is 10 millimeters. (Example 6)

_____

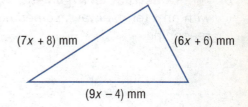

$(7x + 8)$ mm $(6x + 6)$ mm $(9x - 4)$ mm

8. A rectangle has side lengths $(2x - 5)$ meters and $(2x + 6)$ meters. Write a linear expression in simplest form to represent the perimeter. Find the perimeter if the value of x is 12 meters. (Example 6)

_____

9. Find the sum of $(x + 5)$, $(-4x - 2)$, and $(2x - 1)$.

_____

Add.

10. $(-3.5x + 1.7) + (9.1x - 0.3) =$ _____

11. $(0.5x + 15) + (8.2x - 16.6) =$ _____

12. **CCGPS** **Reason Abstractly** The table shows the breakdown of the points scored in last week's basketball game.

	1st Quarter Field Goal Points	2nd Quarter Field Goal Points	3rd Quarter Field Goal Points	4th Quarter Field Goal Points	Total Free Throw Points
Panthers	$2x - 6$	$x + 2$	$2x$	$x - 6$	9

a. Write a linear expression in simplest form to represent the total field goal points scored in the first two quarters.

b. Write a linear expression in simplest form to represent the total points scored in the game.

H.O.T. Problems Higher Order Thinking

13. **CCGPS** **Reason Inductively** Write two linear expressions with a sum of $-5x + 4$.

14. **CCGPS** **Construct an Argument** Will the sum of two linear expressions, each with an x-term, *always, sometimes,* or *never* have an x-term? Explain your reasoning.

15. **CCGPS** **Persevere with Problems** An integer can be represented by x. The next integer can then be represented as $(x + 1)$. Write a linear expression that represents the sum of any two consecutive integers. Show that the sum of any two consecutive integers is always odd.

Georgia Test Practice

16. Which expression below is equivalent to $(9x - 4) + 13(3x - 2)$?

Ⓐ $9x + 26$ Ⓒ $48x - 30$

Ⓑ $39x - 26$ Ⓓ $48x + 30$

Extra Practice

Add. Use models if needed.

17. $(-x + 10) + (-3x + 6) =$ ___$-4x + 16$___

Homework Help →
$$-x + 10$$
$$(+) -3x + 6$$
$$\overline{-4x + 16}$$

18. $(-4x + 3) + (-2x + 8) =$ _____

19. $(-6x + 5) + (4x - 7) =$ _____

20. $(-4x + 5) + (15x - 3) =$ _____

21. $(-5x + 4) + -1(x - 1) =$ _____

22. $17(2x - 5) + (-x + 4) =$ _____

23. Write a linear expression in simplest form to represent the perimeter of the trapezoid at the right. Then find the perimeter if the value of x is 7 yards. _____

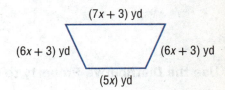

(7x + 3) yd
(6x + 3) yd   (6x + 3) yd
(5x) yd

24. CCGPS **Reason Abstractly** The table shows the points earned by a contestant in four rounds on a game show.

Round 1	Round 2	Round 3	Round 4
2x + 40	5x + 12	100	6x − 10

a. Write a linear expression in simplest form to represent the total points earned by the contestant in rounds 1 and 2.

_____

b. Write a linear expression in simplest form to represent the total points earned in all four rounds.

_____

Show your work.

c. If the value of x is 8, what is the total points earned in all four rounds?

_____

25. Which expression represents the perimeter of the triangle?

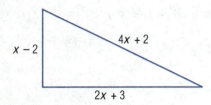

Ⓐ $5x + 6$

Ⓑ $3x + 7$

Ⓒ $6x + 7$

Ⓓ $7x + 3$

26. Karena makes x dollars per hour working at the grocery story. She makes y dollars per hour working at the library. One week she worked 9 hours at the grocery store and 12 hours at the library. Which expression represents her total earnings for that week?

Ⓕ $9 + x + 12 + y$

Ⓖ $(9 + 12)(x + y)$

Ⓗ $9(12)xy$

Ⓘ $9x + 12y$

27. Short Response A square has side lengths $(x - 9)$ meters. Write a linear expression in simplest form to represent the perimeter. _____

CCGPS **Common Core Review**

28. Write an expression in simplest form for the perimeter of the figure.
MCC6.EE.2

_____

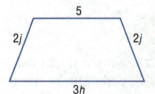

Use the Distributive Property to evaluate each expression. MCC6.EE.3

29. $8(4 + 3) =$ _____

30. $7(9 - 4) =$ _____

31. $(9 + 2)6 =$ _____

32. $5(9 + 8) =$ _____

33. The number of students in each of the seventh grade homerooms that volunteer in the office are shown in the table. Use mental math to find the total number of students who volunteered. Explain. MCC6.EE.3

_____

_____

Office Volunteers	
Homeroom	Number of Students
A	6
B	5
C	4
D	8

Subtract Linear Expressions

What You'll Learn

Scan the lesson. Predict two things you will learn about subtracting linear expressions.

- _____
- _____

Essential Question

HOW can you use numbers and symbols to represent mathematical ideas?

Common Core GPS

Content Standards
MCC7.EE.1, MCC7.EE.2

Mathematical Practices
1, 2, 3, 4

 Real-World Link Watch ▶

Dog Sledding The Iditarod is a dog sledding race over 1,150 miles across Alaska. The table shows two winning times.

Iditarod				
	Days	**Hours**	**Minutes**	**Seconds**
Race 1	9	11	46	48
Race 2	9	5	8	41

1. What is the difference in hours, minutes, and seconds between the two races?

   [ ] h   [ ] min   [ ] s

2. Explain how you could find the difference in times between any two races, given the days, hours, minutes, and seconds.

   _____

   _____

3. Describe another situation in which finding the difference involves subtracting like units.

   _____

   _____

   _____

   _____

Subtract Linear Expressions

When subtracting linear expressions, subtract like terms. Use zero pairs if needed.

Examples

Subtract. Use models if needed.

1. **(6x + 3) − (2x + 2)**

6x   +   3

Model the linear expression 6x + 3.

4x   +   1

To subtract 2x + 2, remove two x-tiles and two 1-tiles. Then write the linear expression for the remaining tiles.

There are four x-tiles and one 1-tile remaining.

So, (6x + 3) − (2x + 2) = 4x + 1.

2. **(2x − 3) − (x − 2)**

2x   +   (−3)

Model the linear expression 2x − 3.

x   +   (−1)

To subtract x − 2, remove one x-tile and two −1-tiles. Then write the linear expression for the remaining tiles.

There is one x-tile and one −1-tile remaining.

So, (2x − 3) − (x − 2) = x − 1.

  Show your work.

a. _____

b. _____

Got It? Do these problems to find out.

a. (5x − 9) − (2x − 7)   **b.** (6x − 10) − (2x − 8)

Example

3. Find $(-2x - 4) - (2x)$. Use models if needed.

$-2x + (-4)$

Model the linear expression $-2x - 4$.

zero pairs

Since there are no positive x-tiles to remove, add two zero pairs of x-tiles. Remove two positive x-tiles.

So, $(-2x - 4) - (2x) = -4x - 4$.

Got It? Do these problems to find out.

c. $(3x - 2) - (5x - 4)$ **d.** $(4x - 4) - (-2x + 2)$

c. _____

d. _____

Use the Additive Inverse to Subtract

When subtracting integers, add the opposite, or the additive inverse. The same process is used when subtracting linear expressions.

Examples

4. Find $(6x + 5) - (3x + 1)$.

$$\begin{array}{r} 6x + 5 \\ (+) \ -3x - 1 \\ \hline 3x + 4 \end{array}$$

Arrange like terms in columns.
The additive inverse of $3x + 1$ is $(-3x - 1)$.

Additive Inverse
The additive inverse is found by multiplying the linear expression by −1.

5. Find $(-4x - 7) - (-5x - 2)$.

$$\begin{array}{r} -4x - 7 \\ (+) \ 5x + 2 \\ \hline x - 5 \end{array}$$

Arrange like terms in columns.
The additive inverse of $(-5x - 2)$ is $(5x + 2)$.

Got It? Do these problems to find out.

e. $(4x - 3) - (2x + 7)$ **f.** $(5x - 4) - (2x + 3)$

e. _____

f. _____

Example

6. A hat store tracks the sale of college and professional team hats for *m* months. The number of college hats sold is represented by $(6m + 3)$. The number of professional hats sold is represented by $(5m - 2)$. Write an expression to show how many more college hats were sold than professional hats. Then evaluate the expression if *m* equals 10.

Find $(6m + 3) - (5m - 2)$.

$$
\begin{array}{l}
6m + 3 \quad \text{Arrange like terms in columns.} \\
\underline{(+) -5m + 2} \quad \text{The additive inverse of } 5m - 2 \text{ is } (-5m + 2). \\
m + 5
\end{array}
$$

Evaluate the expression if $m = 10$.

$m + 5 = \mathbf{10} + 5$ Substitute 10 for *m*.

$ = 15$ Simplify.

So, 15 more college team hats were sold.

Guided Practice

 Check ✓

Subtract. Use models if needed. (Examples 1–5)

1. $(2x + 4) - (-x + 5) =$ _____

2. $(6x + 9) - (7x - 1) =$ _____

 Show your work.

3. The number of runs scored by the home team at a baseball game is represented by $(x + 7)$. The number of runs scored by the visiting team is represented by $(3x - 7)$. Write an expression to find how many more runs the home team scored than the visiting team. Then evaluate the expression if the value of *x* is 6. (Example 6)

_____

4. **Q** **Building on the Essential Question** How can you use the additive inverse to help you subtract linear expressions?

_____
_____
_____

Rate Yourself!

How well do you understand subtracting linear expressions? Circle the image that applies.

Clear   Somewhat Clear   Not So Clear

For more help, go online to access a Personal Tutor. Tutor

FOLDABLES Time to update your Foldable!

Name _____ My Homework _____

Subtract. Use models if needed. (Examples 1–5)

 1 $(9x + 5) - (4x + 3) =$ _____

2. $(-x + 3) - (x - 5) =$ _____

Show your work. ➡

3. $(3x + 4) - (x + 2) =$ _____

4. $(7x + 5) - (3x + 2) =$ _____

5. $(9x - 8) - (x + 4) =$ _____

6. $(9x - 12) - (5x - 7) =$ _____

7. CCGPS **Reason Abstractly** The number of customers in a store on the first day is represented by $(6x - 3)$. The number of customers on the second day is represented by $(x - 1)$. Write an expression to find how many more customers visited the store on the first day. Then evaluate the expression if x is equal to 50. (Example 6)

_____

8. The perimeter of the garden shown is $6x + 2$ units. Find the length of the missing side.

_____

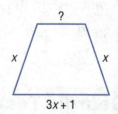

9 The cost for shipping a package that weighs x pounds from Boise to Los Angeles is shown at the right. How much more does Shipping Central charge than Globe Delivery?

_____

Company	Cost ($)
Shipping Central	$3x + 3.50$
Globe Delivery	$2x + 2.99$

10. Find the difference in the given lengths of the polygons. _____

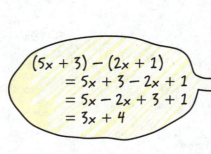

(7x + 2) units

(6x − 5) units

11. **CCGPS** **Find the Error** Theresa is finding $(5x + 3) − (2x + 1)$. Find her mistake and correct it.

_____

_____

_____

_____

_____

_____

$$(5x + 3) − (2x + 1)$$
$$= 5x + 3 − 2x + 1$$
$$= 5x − 2x + 3 + 1$$
$$= 3x + 4$$

12. **CCGPS** **Reason Inductively** Name two linear expressions whose difference is $5x − 4$.

_____

_____

13. **CCGPS** **Persevere with Problems** One linear expression is subtracted from a second linear expression and the difference is $x − 5$. What is the difference when the second linear expression is subtracted from

the first? _____

✏️ Georgia Test Practice

14. What is $(5x − 7) − (3x − 4)$?

Ⓐ $2x − 3$

Ⓑ $2x + 3$

Ⓒ $2x − 11$

Ⓓ $2x + 11$

Extra Practice

Subtract. Use models if needed.

15. $(-3x - 2) - (7x + 9) =$ _$-10x - 11$_

Homework Help ➡

$$-3x - 2$$
$$\underline{(+) -7x - 9}$$
$$-10x - 11$$

16. $(-2x - 1) - (x - 7) =$ _____

17. $(9x + 5) - (6x - 8) =$ _____

18. $(-8x + 1) - (8x - 1) =$ _____

19. $(4x + 10) - (-3x + 5) =$ _____

20. $(-6x - 11) - (-2x - 4) =$ _____

21. **CCGPS** **Reason Abstractly** The number of questions on a math test is represented $(3x + 1)$. The number of questions on a spelling test is represented by $(x + 12)$. Write an expression to find how many more questions were on the math test. Then evaluate the expression if the value of x is 8.

_____

Subtract.

22. $(5.7x - 0.8) - (4.9x - 1.4) =$ _____

23. $\left(-\dfrac{5}{6}x + 5\dfrac{1}{2}\right) - \left(\dfrac{2}{3}x + 4\right) =$ _____

24. $2(x + 1) - 3x =$ _____

25. $5(x - 3) - x =$ _____

26. What is the additive inverse of $5x - 8$?

Ⓐ $5x - 8$

Ⓑ $5x + 8$

Ⓒ $-5x - 8$

Ⓓ $-5x + 8$

27. Short Response Mei plans to trim a picture to fit into the length of a frame. The picture is $12x + 4$ units long, but the frame is only $7x + 1$ units long. How many units of the picture will Mei have to trim so that it will fit into the frame?

_____

28. Short Response The charges for a large pizza and each topping for two pizzerias are shown.

Write a linear expression that represents how much more a pizza with t toppings would cost at Pizza Palace than at Mario's Pizza. _____

Pizzeria	Pizza ($)	Each Topping ($)
Mario's Pizza	10	1.25
Pizza Palace	12	1.50

Common Core Review

29. Camilla wants to attach a string of lights to the edges of her patio for a party. She does not want the string to go across the edge with the steps. Write a linear expression that represents the length of string in feet she will need. Then find the length if $x = 3$. **MCC7.EE.1**

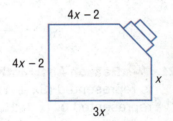

_____

Evaluate each expression if $x = \dfrac{1}{2}$ and $y = \dfrac{3}{4}$. MCC6.EE.3

30. xy _____

31. $x - y$ _____

32. $x + y$ _____

33. x^3 _____

34. $3y + 2x$ _____

35. $x \div y$ _____

Inquiry **HOW do models help you factor linear expressions?**

CCGPS Content Standards
MCC7.EE.1
Mathematical Practices
1, 3

Mosaic Max has enough 1 inch square glass tiles to create a rectangular piece of mosaic art that has an area of 24 square inches. Some of the possible dimensions of the rectangle are listed in the table. Write the two missing possible dimensions.

Length (in.)	Width (in.)
24	1
3	8

Each of the dimensions listed are factors of 24. Sometimes, you know the product and are asked to find the factors. This process is called *factoring*.

Investigation 1

Use algebra tiles to factor 2x + 6.

Step 1 Model the expression 2x + 6.

Step 2 Arrange the tiles into a rectangle with equal rows and columns. The total area of the tiles represents the product. Its length and width represent the factors.

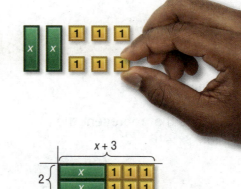

The rectangle has a width of two 1-tiles and a length of one x-tile and three 1-tiles.

So, 2x + 6 = 2(x + ☐).

Investigation 2

Use algebra tiles to factor 2x − 8.

Step 1 | Model the expression 2x − 8.

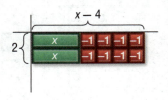

Step 2 | Arrange the tiles into a rectangle with equal rows and columns.

The rectangle has a width of two 1-tiles and a length of one x-tile and four −1-tiles.

So, 2x − 8 = _____.

Investigation 3

Use algebra tiles to factor 3x − 6.

Step 1 | Draw the tiles that represent the expression 3x − 6.

Step 2 | Redraw the tiles into a rectangle with equal rows and columns.

The rectangle has a width of _____ 1-tiles and a length of one x-tile and _____ −1-tiles.

So, 3x − 6 = _____.

Collaborate

Work with a partner. Factor each expression by arranging the appropriate algebra tiles into equal rows and columns. Draw the finished product.

1. $4x + 6 =$ _____

Show your work.

2. $5x + 10 =$ _____

3. $3x + 12 =$ _____

4. $4x - 10 =$ _____

5. $3x - 9 =$ _____

6. $2x - 4 =$ _____

7. $4x + 2 =$ _____

8. $5x - 5 =$ _____

Work with a partner to complete the table. Use algebra tiles if needed.

	Original Expression	Factored Expression	Distributive Property
	$2x + 8$	$2(x + 4)$	$2(x) + 2(4) = 2x + 8$
9.	$4x - 8$	$4(x - \boxed{})$	$4(x) - 4(2) = 4x - 8$
10.	$6x + 2$	$2(\boxed{}x + 1)$	$2(3x) + 2(1) =$
11.	$2x - 10$		$2(x) - 2(5) =$
12.	$8x + 6$		

13. **CCGPS** **Reason Inductively** How is factoring related to using the Distributive Property?

_____

_____

 Reflect

14. **CCGPS** **Construct an Argument** Is the expression $2x - 2$ equivalent to the expression $2(x - 2)$? Explain.

_____

_____

15. **CCGPS** **Justify Conclusions** Explain how you could use algebra tiles to factor $5x + 15$.

_____

_____

_____

16. **Inquiry** HOW do models help you factor linear expressions?

_____

_____

_____

Factor Linear Expressions

What You'll Learn

Scan the lesson. Predict two things you will learn about factoring linear expressions.

- _____

- _____

Essential Question

HOW can you use numbers and symbols to represent mathematical ideas?

Vocabulary

monomial
factor
factored form

Common Core GPS

Content Standards
MCC7.EE.1, MCC7.EE.2
Mathematical Practices
1, 2, 3, 4

Real-World Link

Yard Sale A rectangular yard is being separated into four equal-size sections for different items at a yard sale. The area of the yard is (8x + 12) square meters.

1. How can you find the area of each section of the yard sale?

   _____

   _____

2. What is the area of each section? Explain your answer.

   _____

   _____

   _____

3. The algebra tiles represent the area of the entire yard sale. Fill in the length and width. Write an expression that represents the area in terms of the length and width of the model. _____

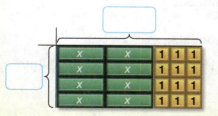

Find the GCF of Monomials

A **monomial** is a number, a variable, or a product of a number and one or more variables.

Monomials	Not Monomials
25, x, 40x	x + 4, 40x + 120

To **factor** a number means to write it as a product of its factors. A monomial can be factored using the same method you would use to factor a number.

The greatest common factor (GCF) of two monomials is the greatest monomial that is a factor of both.

Examples

Tutor

Find the GCF of each pair of monomials.

1. 4x, 12x

$4x = 2 \cdot 2 \cdot x$ Write the prime factorization of 4x and 12x.

$12x = 2 \cdot 2 \cdot 3 \cdot x$ Circle the common factors.

The GCF of 4x and 12x is 2 · 2 · x or 4x.

2. 18a, 20ab

$18a = 2 \cdot 3 \cdot 3 \cdot a$ Write the prime factorization of 18a and 20ab.

$20ab = 2 \cdot 2 \cdot 5 \cdot a \cdot b$ Circle the common factors.

The GCF of 18a and 20ab is 2 · a or 2a.

3. 12cd, 36cd

$12cd = 2 \cdot 2 \cdot 3 \cdot c \cdot d$ Write the prime factorization of 12cd and 36cd.

$36cd = 2 \cdot 2 \cdot 3 \cdot 3 \cdot c \cdot d$ Circle the common factors.

The GCF of 12cd and 36cd is 2 · 2 · 3 · c · d or 12cd.

Show your work.

Got It? Do these problems to find out.

Find the GCF of each pair of monomials.

a. 12, 28c   b. 25x, 15xy   c. 42mn, 14mn

a. _____

b. _____

c. _____

Factor Linear Expressions

You can use the Distributive Property and the work backward strategy to express a linear expression as a product of its factors. A linear expression is in **factored form** when it is expressed as the product of its factors.

$$8x + 4y = 4(2x) + 4(y) \quad \text{The GCF of } 8x \text{ and } 4y \text{ is } 4.$$
$$= 4(2x + y) \quad \text{Distributive Property}$$

Examples

4. **Factor $3x + 9$.**

> **Method 1** Use a model.

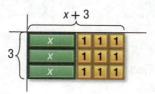

Arrange three x-tiles and nine 1-tiles into equal rows and columns. The rectangle has a width of three 1-tiles, or 3, and a length of one x-tile and three 1-tiles, or $x + 3$.

> **Method 2** Use the GCF.

$$3x = 3 \cdot x \quad \text{Write the prime factorization of } 3x \text{ and } 9.$$
$$9 = 3 \cdot 3 \quad \text{Circle the common factors.}$$

The GCF of $3x$ and 9 is 3. Write each term as a product of the GCF and its remaining factors.

$$3x + 9 = 3(x) + 3(3)$$
$$= 3(x + 3) \quad \text{Distributive Property}$$

So, $3x + 9 = 3(x + 3)$.

5. **Factor $12x + 7y$.**

Find the GCF of $12x$ and $7y$.

$$12x = 2 \cdot 2 \cdot 3 \cdot x$$
$$7y = 1 \cdot 7 \cdot y$$

There are no common factors, so $12x + 7y$ *cannot be factored*.

Got It? Do these problems to find out.

Factor each expression. If the expression cannot be factored, write *cannot be factored*. Use algebra tiles if needed.

    d. $4x - 28$ **e.** $3x + 33y$ **f.** $4x + 35$

Factoring Expressions

To check your factored answers, multiply your factors out. You should get your original expression as a result.

 Show your work.

d. _____

e. _____

f. _____

Example

Tutor

6. The drawing of the garden at the right has a total area of (15x + 18) square feet. Find possible dimensions of the garden.

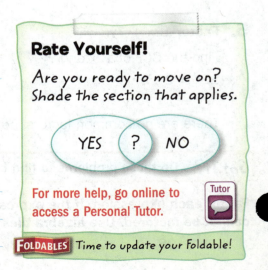

| 15x | 18 |

Factor 15x + 18.

$15x = 3 \cdot 5 \cdot x$ Write the prime factorization of 15x and 18.

$18 = 2 \cdot 3 \cdot 3$ Circle the common factors.

The GCF of 15x and 18 is 3. Write each term as a product of the GCF and its remaining factors.

$15x + 18 = 3(5x) + 3(6)$

$= 3(5x + 6)$ Distributive Property

So, the possible dimensions are 3 feet by (5x + 6) feet.

Guided Practice

Check ✓

Find the GCF of each pair of monomials. (Examples 1–3)

1. 32x, 18 _____

Show your work.

2. 27s, 54st _____

3. 18cd, 30cd _____

Factor each expression. If the expression cannot be factored, write *cannot be factored*. Use algebra tiles if needed. (Examples 4 and 5)

4. 36x + 24 _____

5. 4x + 9 _____

6. 14x − 16y _____

7. Mr. Phen's monthly income can be represented by the expression 25x + 120 where x is the number of hours worked. Factor the expression 25x + 120. (Example 6)

_____

8. ℯ **Building on the Essential Question** Explain how the GCF is used to factor an expression. Use the term *Distributive Property* in your response.

_____

_____

Rate Yourself!

Are you ready to move on? Shade the section that applies.

YES   ?   NO

For more help, go online to access a Personal Tutor.

Tutor

FOLDABLES Time to update your Foldable!

Independent Practice

Go online for Step-by-Step Solutions eHelp

Find the GCF of each pair of monomials. (Examples 1–3)

1. 24, 48m _____

 Show your work.

2. 32a, 48b _____

3 36k, 144km _____

Factor each expression. If the expression cannot be *factored*, write *cannot be factored*. Use algebra tiles if needed. (Examples 4 and 5)

4. 3x + 6 _____

5. 2x − 15 _____

6. 12x + 30y _____

7 The area of a rectangular dance floor is (4x − 8) square units. Factor 4x − 8 to find possible dimensions of the dance floor. (Example 6)

_____

8. The area of a rectangular porch is (9x + 18) square units. Factor 9x + 18 to find possible dimensions of the porch. (Example 6)

_____

9. Six friends visited a museum to see the new holograms exhibit. The group paid for admission to the museum and $12 for parking. The total cost of the visit can be represented by the expression 6x$ + $12. What was the cost of the visit for one person?

_____

10. The diagram represents a flower border that is 3 feet wide surrounding a rectangular sitting area. Write an expression in factored form that represents the area of the flower border.

CCGPS **Reason Abstractly** Write an expression in factored form to represent the total area of each rectangle.

11.

5x	20

_____

12.

7	49x

_____

13.

36	20x	40

_____

14.

18
6x
12

_____

🔥 H.O.T. Problems Higher Order Thinking

15. **CCGPS** **Reason Inductively** Write two monomials whose greatest common factor is 4*m*.

_____

_____

16. **CCGPS** **Find the Error** Jamar is factoring 90x − 15. Find his mistake and correct it.

$$90x - 15 = 15(6x)$$
$$= 9$$

✏️ Georgia Test Practice

17. Which of the following expressions cannot be factored?

Ⓐ 6 + 3x

Ⓑ 7x + 3

Ⓒ 15x + 10

Ⓓ 30x + 40

Extra Practice

Find the GCF of each pair of monomials.

18. 63p, 84 _21_

$63p = 3 \cdot 3 \cdot 7 \cdot p$

$84 = 2 \cdot 2 \cdot 3 \cdot 7$

Homework Help ➡ The GCF of 63p and 84 is 3 · 7 or 21.

19. 30rs, 42rs _6rs_

$30rs = 2 \cdot 3 \cdot 5 \cdot r \cdot s$

$42rs = 2 \cdot 3 \cdot 7 \cdot r \cdot s$

The GCF of 30rs and 42rs is 2 · 3 · r · s or 6rs.

20. 60jk, 45jkm _____

21. 40x, 60x _____

22. 54gh, 72g _____

23. 100xy, 75xyz _____

Factor each expression. If the expression cannot be factored, write *cannot be factored*. Use algebra tiles if needed.

24. 5x + 5 _____

25. 18x + 6 _____

26. 4x − 7 _____

27. 10x − 35 _____

28. 32x + 24y _____

29. 30x − 40 _____

30. James has $120 in his savings account and plans to save $x each month for 6 months. The expression $6x + $120 represents the total amount in the account after 6 months. Factor the expression 6x + 120.

_____

31. A square scrapbooking page has a perimeter of (8x + 20) inches. What is the length of one side of the scrapbooking page?

_____

Copy and Solve Write an expression in factored form that is equivalent to the given expression. Show your work on a separate piece of paper.

32. $\frac{1}{2}x + 4$

33. $\frac{2}{3}x + 6$

34. $\frac{3}{4}x - 24$

35. $\frac{5}{6}x - 30$

36. $\frac{2}{5}x + 16$

37. $\frac{3}{8}x + 18$

Georgia Test Practice

38. Short Response Factor the expression shown below.

$$40x + 15$$

_____

39. Which pair of monomials has a GCF of 4*a*?

Ⓐ 16*a*, 8*a*

Ⓑ 18*a*, 8*a*

Ⓒ 16*ab*, 12*b*

Ⓓ 16*ab*, 12*a*

40. The Venn diagram shows the factors of 12 and 18*x*.

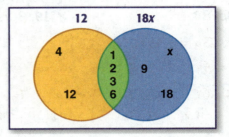

What is the greatest common factor of the two monomials?

Ⓕ 2

Ⓖ 3

Ⓗ 6

Ⓘ 36

Common Core Review

Use the Distributive Property to rewrite each expression. MCC6.EE.1

41. $4(x + 1) =$ _____

42. $3(a + 10) =$ _____

43. $7(2b + 5) =$ _____

44. Wyatt spends \$1.50 for a bag of chips, \$3 for a sandwich, and \$1.50 on a drink each day Monday through Friday. Use the Associative Property to find how much money he spends on lunch and a drink for 2 weeks. MCC7.EE.1

_____

45. The letters P, E, M, D, A, and S form PEMDAS. This is a mnemonic device that can be used to help you remember the order of operations. Each letter stands for something. Complete the organizer. MCC6.EE.3

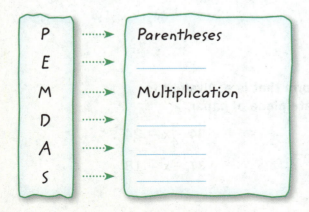

P	······▸	Parentheses
E	······▸	_____
M	······▸	Multiplication
D	······▸	_____
A	······▸	_____
S	······▸	_____

Shark Scientist

Are you fascinated by sharks, especially those that are found around the coasts of the United States? If so, you should consider a career as a shark scientist. Shark scientists use satellite-tracking devices, called tags, to study and track the movements of sharks. By analyzing the data transmitted by the tags, scientists are able to learn more about the biology and ecology of sharks. Their research is helpful in protecting shark populations around the world.

College & Career
READINESS

Explore college and careers at ccr.mcgraw-hill.com

Is This the Career for You?

Are you interested in a career as a shark scientist? Take some of the following courses in high school.

- ◆ Algebra
- ◆ Calculus
- ◆ Physics
- ◆ Statistics

Find out how math relates to a career in Animal Conservation.

Tag, You're It!

The *fork length* of a shark is the length from the tip of the snout to the fork of the tail. Use the information on the note cards to solve each problem.

1. Write an expression to represent the total length of a hammerhead shark that has a fork length of f feet. _____

2. Use the expression from Exercise 1 to find the total length of a hammerhead shark that has a fork length of 11.6 feet. _____

3. Write an expression to represent the average fork length of a tiger shark, given the average fork length s of a sandbar shark. _____

4. Use the expression from Exercise 3 to find the average fork length of a tiger shark if the average fork length of a sandbar shark is 129 centimeters. _____

5. Write an expression to find the average fork length of a white shark with a total length of t centimeters. _____

6. The total length of a white shark is 204 centimeters. Use the expression in Exercise 5 to find the approximate fork length of the white shark. _____

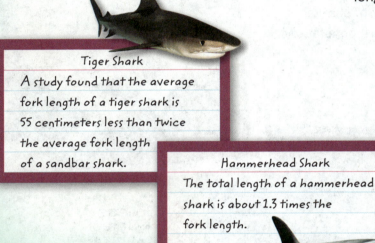

Tiger Shark
A study found that the average fork length of a tiger shark is 55 centimeters less than twice the average fork length of a sandbar shark.

Hammerhead Shark
The total length of a hammerhead shark is about 1.3 times the fork length.

White Shark
The fork length of a white shark is about 5.74 centimeters less than 0.94 times the total length t.

Career Project

It's time to update your career portfolio! Describe the skills that would be necessary for a shark scientist to possess. Determine whether this type of career would be a good fit for you.

_____
_____
_____
_____
_____
_____

List several challenges associated with this career.

- _____
- _____
- _____
- _____
- _____

Vocabulary Check

In the puzzle below, write a vocabulary term for each clue.

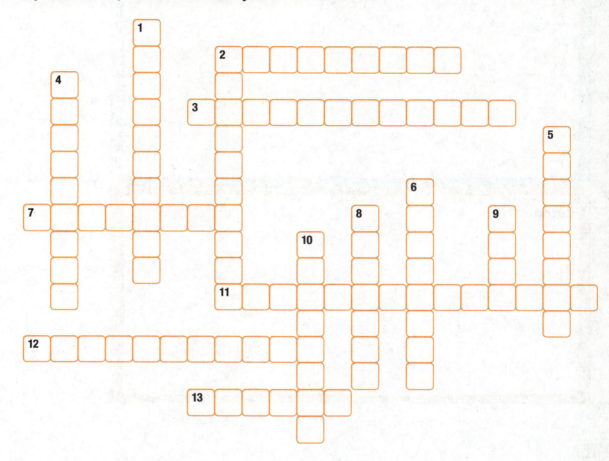

Across

2. a type of expression that contains a variable or variables

3. an algebraic expression that has no like terms and no parentheses is in this form (two words)

7. an ordered list of numbers

11. an example showing a statement is not true

12. the numerical factor of a multiplication expression

13. what is done to a variable to represent an unknown quantity

Down

1. expressions like 4(3 + 2) and 4(3) + 4(2)

2. a sequence in which each term is found by adding the same number

4. terms that include the same variable

5. a letter or symbol

6. a statement that is true for any number or variable

8. a branch of mathematics that uses variables

9. a number in a sequence

10. a term that contains a number only

Use Your FOLDABLES

Use your Foldable to help review the chapter.

Tape here

Linear Expressions

Explanation

Explanation

Got it?

Draw a line to match each expression with its equivalent expression.

1. 3 + 1

2. 4(2 − x)

3. 3x − 2 − x + 6

4. 2(x + 2) + (3x + 1)

5. 3x + 21

a. 8 − 4x

b. 5x + 5

c. 3(x + 7)

d. 1 + 3

e. 2x + 4

Problem Solving

$8.95

$5.75

1. Write an expression that represents the cost in dollars of buying any number of hats h and any number of shirts s. Then find the cost of buying 3 hats and 5 shirts. (Lesson 1)

_____

_____

2. **CCGPS** **Reason Abstractly** Tanya collected $4.50 for the first car washed at a band fundraiser. After the second and third cars were washed, the donations totaled $9 and $13.50, respectively. Suppose this donation pattern continues. Write the next three terms in the sequence. Then write an algebraic expression to find the amount of money earned for the number of cars washed c. (Lesson 2)

Terms: _____

Expression: _____

3. Graham earned 8, 13, 7, 12, and 9 points on his last few homework assignments. Use mental math to find his total number of points. Explain. (Lesson 3)

_____

_____

4. Carlita had some pictures printed for $0.20 per print. Find the total cost if Carlita had 65 pictures printed. Justify your answer by using the Distributive Property. (Lesson 4)

_____

_____

5. The angle measures of a triangle are $(x - 7)°$, $(x)°$, and $(3x + 2)°$. Write an expression in simplest form to represent all of the measures of the angles of the triangle. (Lesson 6)

_____

6. The perimeter of a rectangular garden is shown at the right. What is the perimeter of the garden in factored form? (Lesson 8) _____

_____

$P = (3w + 12)$ ft

Reflect

 Answering the Essential Question

Use what you learned about algebraic expressions to complete the graphic organizer. Then answer the chapter's Essential Question below.

When do you use a variable?

 Essential Question

HOW can you use numbers and symbols to represent mathematical ideas?

How do you know which operation symbol to use?

 Answer the Essential Question. HOW can you use numbers and symbols to represent mathematical ideas?

Chapter 4
Equations and Inequalities

Essential Question

WHAT does it mean to say two quantities are equal?

Common Core GPS

Content Standards
MCC7.EE.3, MCC7.EE.4, MCC7.EE.4a, MCC7.EE.4b

Mathematical Practices
1, 2, 3, 4, 5, 7

Math in the Real World

Driving Suppose you live in a state where you must be at least 16 years of age to obtain a driver's license. Circle the statement that represents this age.

DRIVER LICENSE

NAME: Joan Smith
AGE: $a < 16$
$a = 16$
$a \geq 16$
ADDRESS:
1234 Anyplace Dr.

FOLDABLES
Study Organizer

1 Cut out the correct Foldable from the FL pages in the back of this book.

2 Place your Foldable on the Key Concept page toward the end of this chapter.

3 Use the Foldable to help you learn about equations and inequalities.

Vocabulary

Addition Property
   of Equality

Addition Property
   of Inequality

coefficient

Division Property
   of Equality

Division Property
   of Inequality

equation

equivalent equation

inequality

Multiplication Property of
   Equality

Multiplication Property of
   Inequality

solution

Subtraction Property
   of Equality

Subtraction Property
   of Inequality

two-step equation

two-step inequality

Study Skill: Reading Math

Identify Key Information Have you ever tried to solve a word problem and didn't know where to start. Start by looking for key words in the text and images. Then write the important information in one sentence.

1. Highlight or circle key words in the following real-world problem.

   During a recent Super Bowl, millions of pounds of potato chips and tortilla chips were consumed. The number of pounds of potato chips consumed was 3.1 million pounds more than the number of pounds of tortilla chips. How many pounds of tortilla chips were consumed?

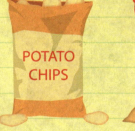

2. Write a sentence that summarizes the information provided. Include information from the text and

   the image. _____

   _____

   _____

12.4 million pounds   ? million pounds

Watch — Play it online!

Seth, Marisol, and Jamar in

Movie Night

NEW RELEASE

Hey guys. Help me pick out some movies for movie night at school.

How much money can we spend?

Don't forget the popcorn.

Student council gave us $100. They want us to pick out as many movies as we can and...

Don't forget the popcorn.

Yes, popcorn. Don't worry, Seth, I won't forget the popcorn.

The DVDs are $19 each. I hope we can get a few different movies. What do you think? A comedy? A thriller? A drama?

...and popcorn?

Yes Seth, and popcorn! Jamar, how much will we need for popcorn?

I think we'll need $39 for popcorn.

Mmmm... popcorn.

Hey! I have a great idea! Let's just skip the movie and have a popcorn party! We can use the $100 and have all kinds of different popcorn! And while we're at it, let's order a pizza!

Seth, I'm beginning to get the idea that you haven't eaten dinner yet.

You got it.

Right. Thinking with your stomach. Let's pick out some movies now.

We have $100, and popcorn is $39, and DVDs cost $19 each. I wonder how many DVDs we can get.

Your Turn! **You will solve this problem in the chapter.**

 **Are You Ready?**

Try the Quick Check below.
Or, take the Online Readiness Quiz.

CCGPS **Quick Review**

Common Core Review MCC6.EE.2a, MCC6.EE.5

Example 1

Write the phrase as an algebraic expression.

Phrase: five dollars more than Jennifer earned

Variable: Let d represent the number of dollars Jennifer earned.

Expression: $d + 5$

Example 2

Is 3, 4, or 5 the solution of the equation $x + 8 = 12$?

Value of x	$x + 8 = 12$	Are both sides equal?
3	$3 + 8 \overset{?}{=} 12$ $11 \neq 12$	no
4	$4 + 8 \overset{?}{=} 12$ $12 = 12$	yes ✓
5	$5 + 8 \overset{?}{=} 12$ $13 \neq 12$	no

The solution is 4 since replacing x with 4 results in a true sentence.

Quick Check

Words and Symbols Write the phrase as an algebraic expression.

1. 3 more runs than the Pirates scored

_____

2. a number decreased by eight

_____

3. ten dollars more than Grace has

_____

 Show your work.

One-Step Equations Identify the solution of each equation from the list given.

4. $8 + w = 17$; 7, 8, 9 _____

5. $d - 12 = 5$; 16, 17, 18 _____

6. $6 = 3y$; 2, 3, 4 _____

7. $7 \div c = 7$; 0, 1, 2 _____

8. $a + 8 = 23$; 13, 14, 15 _____

9. $10 = 45 - n$; 35, 36, 37 _____

 **How Did You Do?**

Which problems did you answer correctly in the Quick Check? Shade those exercise numbers below.

① ② ③ ④ ⑤ ⑥ ⑦ ⑧ ⑨

Inquiry **HOW** can bar diagrams or algebra tiles help you solve an equation?

CCGPS Content Standards MCC7.EE.4, MCC7.EE.4a

Mathematical Practices 1, 2, 3, 5

Buses In a recent year, 15 of the 50 states had a law banning the use of handheld cell phones while driving a school bus. Determine how many states did *not* have this law.

Investigation 1

You can represent this situation with an equation.

Step 1 The bar diagram represents the total number of states and the number of states that have passed a cell phone law. Fill in the missing information.

| ⬚ states |
| states with a law | states that do not have a law |
| ⬚ states | ? |

Step 2 Write an equation from the bar diagram. Let x represent the states that do not have a cell phone law for school bus drivers.

$$15 + x = 50$$

Step 3 Use the *work backward* strategy to solve the equation. Since $15 + x = 50$, $x = 50 - 15$. So, $x = \boxed{}$.

Check $15 + \boxed{} = 50$ ✔

So, $\boxed{}$ states did *not* have a law banning the use of cell phones by bus drivers.

Collaborate

Work with a partner to solve each problem.

1. Draw a bar diagram and write an addition equation to represent the following situation. Then solve the equation.

   The sum of a number and four is equal to 18.

   Equation: _____   Solution: $x =$ _____

2. **CCGPS Use Math Tools** Jack collects postage stamps. He sold 7 of his stamps and had 29 stamps left. Complete the bar diagram below. Then write and solve a subtraction equation to find the number of stamps Jack had at the beginning.

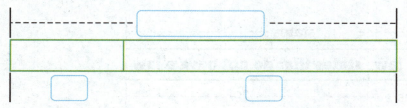

   Equation: _____   Solution: $n =$ _____

   So, Jack had ☐ stamps at the beginning.

3. Suppose Jack sold 15 stamps and had 21 stamps left. How would the bar diagram change?

   _____

   _____

4. **CCGPS Reason Abstractly** Suppose Jack had 40 stamps in the beginning and sold 7 of them. How would the bar diagram change? What equation could you write to represent the situation?

   _____

   _____

Solve $x - 3 = -2$ using algebra tiles.

Remember a 1-tile and −1 tile combine to make a *zero pair*. You can add or subtract zero pairs from either side of an equation without changing its value.

Step 1 Model the equation.

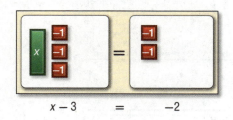

$$x - 3 \qquad = \qquad -2$$

Step 2 Add three 1-tiles to the left side of the mat and _____ 1-tiles to the right side of the mat to form zero pairs on each side of the mat.

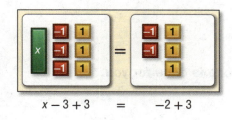

$$x - 3 + 3 \qquad = \qquad -2 + 3$$

Step 3 Remove all of the zero pairs from each side. There is _____ 1-tile on the right side of the mat.

$$x \qquad = \qquad 1$$

Therefore, $x = \boxed{}$.

Check $\boxed{} - 3 = -2$ ✔

Collaborate

CCGPS **Use Math Tools** Work with a partner to solve each equation. Use algebra tiles. Show your work using drawings.

5. $x + 4 = 4$ $x = $ _____

6. $-2 = x + 1$ $x = $ _____

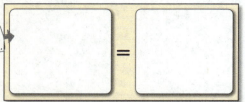

7. $x - 1 = -3$ $x = $ _____

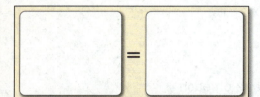

8. $4 = x - 2$ $x = $ _____

Analyze

Work with a partner to complete the table. The first one is done for you.

	Equation	Related Equation
	$x + 3 = 4$	$x = 4 - 3$
9.	$6 + x = 10$	
10.	$x + 3 = -1$	
11.	$6 + x = -7$	

12. **CCGPS** **Construct an Argument** Write a rule that you can use to solve addition equations without using models or a drawing.

_____

_____

Reflect

13. **Inquiry** HOW can bar diagrams or algebra tiles help you solve an equation?

_____

_____

Solve One-Step Addition and Subtraction Equations

What You'll Learn

Scan the lesson. Write the definitions of equation and equivalent equations.

- _____
  _____

- _____
  _____

Vocabulary Start-Up

An **equation** is a sentence stating that two quantities are equal. The value of a variable that makes an equation true is called the **solution** of the equation.

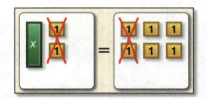

$$x + 2 = 6$$
$$\underline{-2 = -2}$$
$$x = 4$$

The equations $x + 2 = 6$ and $x = 4$ are **equivalent equations** because they have the same solution, 4.

Circle the equations below that are equivalent to $x = 3$. Use algebra tiles if needed.

$x + 3 = 6$	$x + 1 = 6$	$x + 6 = 8$
$x + 3 = 3$	$x + 1 = 4$	$x + 2 = 5$

Real-World Link

Video Games Robyn had some video games, and then she bought 4 more games. Now she has 10 games. This scenario can be described using the equation $x + 4 = 10$.

1. What does x represent in the equation?

   _____

2. Write two different equations that are equivalent to $x + 4 = 10$.

   _____

Essential Question

WHAT does it mean to say two quantities are equal?

Vocabulary

equation
solution
equivalent equation
Subtraction Property of Equality
Addition Property of Equality

Common Core GPS

Content Standards
MCC7.EE.4, MCC7.EE.4a

Mathematical Practices
1, 2, 3, 4, 5

Subtraction Property of Equality

Words   The **Subtraction Property of Equality** states that the two sides of an equation remain equal when you subtract the same number from each side.

Symbols   If $a = b$, then $a - c = b - c$.

You can use bar diagrams and the *work backward* problem-solving strategy to solve equations arithmetically. Or, you can use the properties of equality to solve equations algebraically.

Examples

Tutor

1. Solve $x + 6 = 4$. Check your solution.

$$x + 6 = 4$$ Write the equation.
$$\underline{-6 = -6}$$ Subtraction Property of Equality
$$x = -2$$ Simplify.

Check $x + 6 = 4$ Write the original equation.

$$-2 + 6 \stackrel{?}{=} 4$$ Replace x with -2.

$$4 = 4 \checkmark$$ The sentence is true.

So, the solution is -2.

Solutions

Notice that your new equation, $x = -2$, has the same solution as the original equation, $x + 6 = 4$.

2. Solve $-5 = b + 8$. Check your solution.

$$-5 = b + 8$$ Write the equation.
$$\underline{-8 = -8}$$ Subtraction Property of Equality
$$-13 = b$$ Simplify.

Check $-5 = b + 8$ Write the original equation.

$$-5 \stackrel{?}{=} -13 + 8$$ Replace b with -13.

$$-5 = -5 \checkmark$$ The sentence is true.

So, the solution is -13.

Show your work.

Got It?   Do these problems to find out.

Solve each equation. Check your solution.

a. _____

b. _____

c. _____

a. $y + 6 = 9$ **b.** $x + 3 = 1$ **c.** $-3 = a + 4$

Example

Watch | Tutor

3. An angelfish can grow to be 12 inches long. If an angelfish is 8.5 inches longer than a clown fish, how long is a clown fish?

Words	An angelfish is 8.5 inches longer than a clown fish.
Variable	Let c represent the length of the clown fish.
Equation	$12 \quad = \quad c \quad + \quad 8.5$

$$12 \ = c + 8.5 \qquad \text{Write the equation.}$$
$$\underline{-8.5 = \quad -8.5} \qquad \text{Subtraction Property of Equality}$$
$$3.5 = c \qquad \text{Simplify.}$$

A clown fish is 3.5 inches long.

> **Solve Arithmetically**
> You can use a bar diagram to solve an equation arithmetically.
>
> ├─ angelfish, 12 inches ─┤
> | clown fish | |
> ├── c ──┼── 8.5 inches ──┤
>
> Work backward to solve for c.
> $c = 12 - 8.5 = 3.5$

Got It? Do this problem to find out.

Show your work.

d. The highest recorded temperature in Warsaw, Missouri, is 118°F. This is 158° greater than the lowest recorded temperature. Find the lowest recorded temperature.

d. _____

Addition Property of Equality

Key Concept

Words	The **Addition Property of Equality** states that the two sides of an equation remain equal when you add the same number to each side.
Symbols	If $a = b$, then $a + c = b + c$.

Example

Tutor

4. Solve $x - 2 = 1$. Check your solution.

$$x - 2 = \quad 1 \qquad \text{Write the equation.}$$
$$\underline{+2 = +2} \qquad \text{Addition Property of Equality}$$
$$x \quad = \quad 3 \qquad \text{Simplify.}$$

The solution is 3.   Check $3 - 2 = 1$ ✔

Show your work.

e. _____

f. _____

Got It? Do these problems to find out.

e. $y - 3 = 4$ **f.** $r - 4 = -2$ **g.** $q - 8 = -9$

g. _____

Example

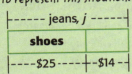

Models

A bar diagram can be used to represent this situation.

├------ jeans, *j* ------┤

| shoes | |

├----$25----┼-$14-┤

j = 25 + 14 = 39

5. **A pair of shoes costs $25. This is $14 less than the cost of a pair of jeans. Find the cost of the jeans.**

Shoes are $14 less than jeans. Let *j* represent the cost of jeans.

$$25 = j - 14 \qquad \text{Write the equation.}$$

$$\underline{+\,14 = \ +\,14} \qquad \text{Addition Property of Equality}$$

$$39 = j \qquad \text{Simplify.}$$

The jeans cost $39.

 Show your work.

Got It? **Do this problem to find out.**

h. _____

h. The average lifespan of a tiger is 17 years. This is 3 years less than the average lifespan of a lion. Write and solve an equation to find the average lifespan of a lion.

Guided Practice

 Check ✓

Solve each equation. Check your solution. (Examples 1, 2, and 4)

1. $n + 6 = 8$

2. $7 = y + 2$

3. $-7 = c - 6$

 Show your work.

4. Orville and Wilbur Wright made the first airplane flights in 1903. Wilbur's flight was 364 feet. This was 120 feet longer than Orville's flight. Write an equation to represent the flights. Use a bar diagram if needed. Then solve to find the length of Orville's flight. (Examples 3 and 5)

_____

5. **Ⓠ Building on the Essential Question** What are two methods for solving a real-world problem that can be represented by an equation?

_____

_____

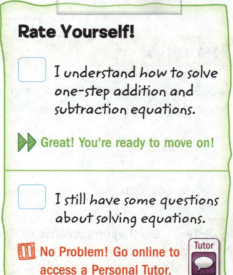

Rate Yourself!

☐ I understand how to solve one-step addition and subtraction equations.

▶▶ Great! You're ready to move on!

☐ I still have some questions about solving equations.

❚❚ No Problem! Go online to access a Personal Tutor.

Name _____ My Homework _____

Independent Practice

Go online for Step-by-Step Solutions

Solve each equation. Check your solution. (Examples 1, 2, and 4)

1. $a + 3 = 10$

Show your work.

2. $y + 5 = -11$

3. $s - 8 = 9$

4. $5 = x + 8$

5. $-2 = p - 1$

6. $14 = s + 7$

Use a bar diagram to solve arithmetically. Then use an equation to solve algebraically. (Examples 3 and 5)

7. Last week Tiffany practiced her bassoon a total of 7 hours. This was 2 hours more than she practiced the previous week. How many hours did Tiffany practice the previous week?

8. In a recent presidential election, Ohio had 20 electoral votes. This is 14 votes less than Texas had. How many electoral votes did Texas have?

9. **CCGPS** **Multiple Representations** Use the table to solve.
  a. **Symbols** The difference in speeds of Son of Beast and The Rattler is 13 miles per hour. If Son of Beast has the greater speed, write and solve a subtraction equation to find its speed.

Tallest Wooden Roller Coasters	Height (feet)	Drop (feet)	Speed (mph)
Son of Beast	218	214	s
El Toro	181	176	70
The Rattler	180	d	65
Colossos	h	159	75

  b. **Diagram** The Rattler has a drop that is 52 feet less than El Toro. Draw a bar diagram to the right and write an equation to find the height of The Rattler.

Show your work.

  c. **Words** Let h represent the height of the Colossos roller coaster. Explain why $h + 10 = 180$ and $h + 48 = 218$ are equivalent equations. Then explain the meaning of the solution.

Copyright © The McGraw-Hill Companies, Inc.

Lesson 1 Solve One-Step Addition and Subtraction Equations **255**

10. The sum of the measures of the angles of a triangle is 180°. Write and solve an equation to find the missing measure.

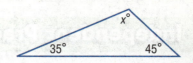

_____

11. The sum of the measures of a quadrilateral is 360°. Write and solve an equation to find the missing measure.

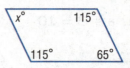

_____

12. CCGPS **Reason Inductively** Write an addition equation and a subtraction equation that have 10 as a solution.

_____

13. CCGPS **Find the Error** Aisha is finding $b + 5 = -8$. Find her mistake and correct it.

_____

_____

_____

$$b + 5 = -8$$
$$ + 5 + 5$$
$$b = -3$$

14. CCGPS **Reason Abstractly** Suppose $x + y = 11$ and the value of x increases by 2. If their sum remains the same, what must happen to the value of y?

_____

✏️ **Georgia Test Practice**

15. The Oriental Pearl Tower in China is 1,535 feet tall. It is 280 feet shorter than the Canadian National Tower in Canada. Which equation can be used to find the height of the Canadian National Tower?

Ⓐ $1,535 + h = 280$

Ⓑ $h = 1,535 - 280$

Ⓒ $1,535 = h - 280$

Ⓓ $280 - h = 1,535$

Extra Practice

Solve each equation. Check your solution.

16. $r + 6 = -3$

Homework Help

$$r + 6 = -3$$
$$\underline{-6 = -6}$$
$$r = -9$$

17. $w - 7 = 11$

18. $k + 3 = -9$

19. $-1 = q - 8$

20. $9 = r + 2$

21. $y + 15 = 11$

CCGPS **Use Math Tools** Use a bar diagram to solve arthimetically. Then use an equation to solve algebraically.

22. Zach is $15\frac{1}{2}$ years old. This is 3 years younger than his brother Lou. How old is Lou?

23. The Miami Heat scored 79 points. This was 13 points less than the Chicago Bulls. How many points did the Chicago Bulls score?

24. The table shows a golfer's scores for four rounds of a recent U.S. Women's Open. Her total score was even with par. What was her score for the third round?

Round	Score
First	−1
Second	−3
Third	s
Fourth	+2

Copy and Solve Solve each equation. Check your solution. Show your work on a separate piece of paper.

25. $a - 3.5 = 14.9$

26. $b + 2.25 = 1$

27. $-\frac{1}{3} = r - \frac{3}{4}$

28. $x - 2.8 = 9.5$

29. $r - 8.5 = -2.1$

30. $z - 9.4 = -3.6$

31. $m + \frac{5}{6} = \frac{11}{12}$

32. $-\frac{5}{6} + c = -\frac{11}{12}$

33. $s - \frac{1}{9} = \frac{5}{18}$

34. Which of the following statements is true concerning the equation $x + 3 = 7$?

Ⓐ To find the value of x, add 3 to each side.

Ⓑ To find the value of x, add 7 to each side.

Ⓒ To find the value of x, find the sum of 3 and 7.

Ⓓ To find the value of x, subtract 3 from each side.

35. Short Response What is the solution to the equation below? _____

$$-8 = x - 15$$

36. The model represents the equation $x - 2 = 5$.

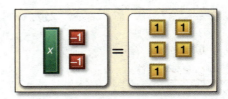

How could you find the value of x?

Ⓕ Add two positive counters to each side of the equation mat.

Ⓖ Add two negative counters to each side of the equation mat.

Ⓗ Add five positive counters to each side of the equation mat.

Ⓘ Add five negative counters to each side of the equation mat.

CCGPS Common Core Review

Multiply or divide. MCC7.NS.2

37. $5(-4) =$ _____

38. $\dfrac{36}{-9} =$ _____

39. $(-10)(-6) =$ _____

40. $\dfrac{-42}{-7} =$ _____

41. $(-3)(12) =$ _____

42. $\dfrac{-54}{2} =$ _____

43. While playing a round of golf, Tina had a score of three under par after the first three holes. Write and solve an equation to find Tina's average score per hole h after three holes. MCC7.NS.3 _____

44. On Friday morning, the temperature dropped 2 degrees per hour for four hours. Write and solve an equation to find the total number of degrees d the temperature dropped on Friday morning. MCC7.NS.3 _____

Inquiry HOW do you know which operation to use when solving an equation?

Content Standards
MCC7.EE.4,
MCC7.EE.4a

Mathematical Practices
1, 2, 3

Money Sakiya tutors students to earn money to buy a new Blu-ray™ player that costs $63. She is able to tutor seven hours in a week. How much should she charge per hour to have enough money by the end of the week?

What do you know? _____

_____

What do you need to find? _____

_____

Investigation

Step 1 Draw a bar diagram that represents the money Sakiya needs to earn and the number of hours she is available to tutor that week.

hour 1	hour 2	hour 3	hour 4			

$\$\boxed{}$

$\boxed{?}$

Step 2 Write an equation from the bar diagram. Let x represent the amount she should charge each hour.

$$7x = 63$$

Step 3 Use the *work backward* strategy to solve the equation. Since

$7x = 63$, $x = 63 \div 7$. So, $x = \boxed{}$.

Check $7 \times \boxed{} = 63$ ✔

So, Sakiya should charge $\boxed{}$ per hour.

Collaborate

Work with a partner to solve the following real-world problems.

1. **Reason Abstractly** Keyani spent $70 for 4 hours of dance classes. How much did she spend per hour of dance class? Complete the bar diagram below and write an equation. Then solve the equation.

Show your work.

hour 1			

_____

2. The screen on Lin's cell phone allows for 8 lines of text per message. The maximum number of characters for each message is 160. How many characters can each line hold? Complete the bar diagram below and write an equation. Then solve the equation.

_____

_____

Analyze

Work with a partner to answer the following question.

3. **CCGPS** **Make a Conjecture** Refer to Exercise 2. Suppose Lin's cell phone allows 4 lines of text and a maximum of 80 characters for each text message. How would the bar diagram and equation change?

_____

_____

Reflect

4. **Inquiry** HOW do you know which operation to use when solving an equation?

_____

_____

Multiplication and Division Equations

What You'll Learn

Scan the lesson. Write the definitions of coefficient and formula.

- _____
- _____

Watch ▶ **Tools** 🔧 **Vocab** abc

Vocabulary Start-Up

The expression 3x means *3 times the value of* x. The numerical factor of a multiplication expression like 3x is called a **coefficient**. So, 3 is the coefficient of x.

The figure below illustrates the multiplication equation $3x = 6$.

Since there are 3 xs, each x is matched with 2.

$$3x = 6 \qquad x = 2$$

The solution of $3x = 6$ is 2.

Write an equation that represents each of the models below. Identify the coefficient in your equation. Then solve.

1.

Equation: _____

Coefficient: ☐

Solution: ☐

2.

Equation: _____

Coefficient: ☐

Solution: ☐

Essential Question

WHAT does it mean to say two quantities are equal?

Vocabulary
abc

coefficient
Division Property of Equality
Multiplication Property of Equality

Common Core GPS

Content Standards
MCC7.EE.4, MCC7.EE.4a

Mathematical Practices
1, 2, 3, 4, 7

Division Property of Equality

Words   The **Division Property of Equality** states that the two sides of an equation remain equal when you divide each side by the same nonzero number.

Symbols   If $a = b$ and $c \neq 0$, then $\dfrac{a}{c} = \dfrac{b}{c}$.

Work Zone

You can use the Division Property of Equality to solve multiplication equations.

Examples

Tutor

1. **Solve $20 = 4x$. Check your solution.**

$20 = 4x$	Write the equation.
$\dfrac{20}{4} = \dfrac{4x}{4}$	Division Property of Equality
$5 = x$	Simplify.

Check	$20 = 4x$	Write the original equation.
	$20 \overset{?}{=} 4(5)$	Replace x with 5.
	$20 = 20$ ✔	This sentence is true.

So, the solution is 5.

- -

2. **Solve $-8y = 24$. Check your solution.**

$-8y = 24$	Write the equation.
$\dfrac{-8y}{-8} = \dfrac{24}{-8}$	Division Property of Equality
$y = -3$	Simplify.

Check	$-8y = 24$	Write the original equation.
	$-8(-3) \overset{?}{=} 24$	Replace y with -3.
	$24 = 24$ ✔	This sentence is true.

So, the solution is -3.

Show your work.

Got It?   Do these problems to find out.

Solve each equation. Check your solution.

a. $30 = 6x$ **b.** $-6a = 36$ **c.** $-9d = -72$

a. _____

b. _____

c. _____

Example

 Tutor

3. **Lelah sent 574 text messages last week. On average, how many messages did she send each day?**

Let m represent the number of messages Lelah sent.

$574 = 7m$ Write the equation. There are 7 days in one week.

$\dfrac{574}{7} = \dfrac{7m}{7}$ Division Property of Equality

$82 = m$ Simplify.

Lelah sent 82 messages on average each day.

Got It?   **Do this problem to find out.**

d. Mrs. Acosta's car can travel an average of 24 miles on each gallon of gasoline. Write and solve an equation to find how many gallons of gasoline she will need for a trip of 348 miles.

> **Solve Arithmetically**
>
> You can use a bar diagram to solve an equation arithmetically.
>
> | text messages in 1 week, 574 |
> | m | m | m | m | m | m | m |
>
> text messages in 1 day
>
> Work backward to solve for m.
>
> $m = 574 \div 7 = 82$

Show your work.

d. _____

Multiplication Property of Equality

Key Concept

Words   The **Multiplication Property of Equality** states that the two sides of an equation remain equal if you multiply each side by the same number.

Symbols   If $a = b$, then $ac = bc$.

You can use the Multiplication Property of Equality to solve division equations.

Example

Tutor

4. Solve $\dfrac{a}{-4} = -9$.

$\dfrac{a}{-4} = -9$ Write the equation.

$\dfrac{a}{-4}(-4) = -9(-4)$ Multiplication Property of Equality

$a = 36$ Simplify.

e. _____

f. _____

Got It?   **Do these problems to find out.**

e. $\dfrac{y}{-3} = -8$ **f.** $\dfrac{m}{5} = -7$ **g.** $30 = \dfrac{b}{-6}$

g. _____

Copyright © The McGraw-Hill Companies, Inc.

Lesson 2 Multiplication and Division Equations   **263**

5. The distance d Tina travels in her car while driving 60 miles per hour for 3 hours is given by the equation $\frac{d}{3} = 60$. How far did she travel?

$$\frac{d}{3} = 60 \qquad \text{Write the equation.}$$

$$\frac{d}{3}(3) = 60(3) \qquad \text{Multiplication Property of Equality}$$

$$d = 180 \qquad \text{Simplify.}$$

Tina traveled 180 miles.

Distance Formula

The distance formula, distance = rate × time, can be written as $d = rt$, $r = \frac{d}{t}$, or $t = \frac{d}{r}$.

Guided Practice

 Check ✓

Solve each equation. Check your solution. (Examples 1, 2, and 4)

1. $6c = 18$

2. $24 = -8x$

3. $7m = -28$

Show your work.

4. $\frac{p}{9} = 9$

5. $\frac{a}{12} = -3$

6. $\frac{n}{-10} = -4$

7. Antonia earns $6 per hour helping her grandmother. Write and solve an equation to find how many hours she needs to work to earn $48. (Example 3) _____

8. A shark can swim at an average speed of 25 miles per hour. At this rate, how far can a shark swim in 2.4 hours? Use $r = \frac{d}{t}$. (Example 5) _____

9. **Building on the Essential Question** How is the process for solving multiplication and division one-step equations like solving one-step addition and subtraction equations?

_____

_____

_____

Rate Yourself!

How confident are you about solving one-step multiplication and division equations? Check the box that applies.

☐ ☐ ☐ ☐ ☐

For more help, go online to access a Personal Tutor.

 Tutor

Independent Practice

Go online for Step-by-Step Solutions

Solve each equation. Check your solution. (Examples 1, 2, and 4)

1. $7a = 49$

2. $-6 = 2x$

3. $-32 = -4b$

4. $\dfrac{u}{6} = 9$

5. $-8 = \dfrac{c}{-10}$

6. $54 = -9d$

7. $-12y = 60$

8. $\dfrac{r}{20} = -2$

9. $\dfrac{g}{10} = -9$

10. Brandy wants to buy a digital camera that costs $300. Suppose she saves $15 each week. In how many weeks will she have enough money for the camera? Use a bar diagram to solve arithmetically. Then use an equation to solve algebraically. (Example 3) _____

11. A race car can travel at a rate of 205 miles per hour. At this rate, how far would it travel in 3 hours? Use $r = \dfrac{d}{t}$. Write an equation and then solve. (Example 5)

_____

12. A certain hurricane travels at 20.88 kilometers per hour. The distance from Cuba to Key West is 145 kilometers. Write and solve a multiplication equation to find about how long it would take the hurricane to travel from Cuba to Key West.

_____

13. **CCGPS** **Multiple Representations** Kennedy saves $5.50 for each hour she works. She needs to save an additional $44 to buy an E-reader. How many more hours does Kennedy need to work to pay for the E-reader?

    a. Diagram Draw a bar diagram that represents the situation.

    Show your work.

    b. Algebra Write an equation that represents the situation.

    c. Words Describe the process you would use to solve your equation. Then solve.

H.O.T. Problems Higher Order Thinking

14. **CCGPS** **Reason Abstractly** Describe a real-world situation in which you would use a division equation to solve a problem. Write your equation and then solve your problem.

Situation: _____

_____

_____

Equation: _____ Solution: _____

15. **CCGPS** **Identify Structure** *True* or *false*. To solve the equation $5x = 20$ you can use the Multiplication Property of Equality. Explain your reasoning.

_____

_____

16. **CCGPS** **Persevere with Problems** Solve $3|x| = 12$. Explain your reasoning.

_____

_____

Georgia Test Practice

17. Which operation would you use to solve $ax = b$ for x?

    Ⓐ Add a to each side.   Ⓒ Multiply each side by a.

    Ⓑ Subtract a from each side.   Ⓓ Divide each side by a.

Extra Practice

Solve each equation. Check your solution.

18. $-4j = 36$

Homework Help →
$$-4j = 36$$
$$\frac{-4j}{-4} = \frac{36}{-4}$$
$$j = -9$$

19. $-4s = -16$

20. $63 = -9d$

21. $\frac{m}{10} = 7$

$$\frac{m}{10} = 7$$
$$\frac{m}{10}(10) = 7(10)$$
$$m = 70$$

22. $\frac{h}{-3} = 12$

23. $\frac{g}{12} = -10$

24. The width of a computer monitor is 1.25 times its height. Find the height of the computer monitor at the right. Use a bar diagram to solve arithmetically. Then use an equation to solve algebraically. _____

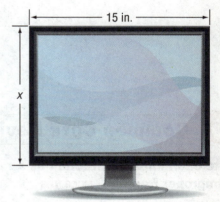

15 in.

x

25. A dragonfly, the fastest insect, can fly a distance of 50 feet at a speed of 25 feet per second. Find the time in seconds. Write the equation in the form $d = rt$, then solve.

_____

26. **CCGPS** **Find the Error** Raul is solving $-6x = 72$. Find his mistake and correct it.

_____

_____

$$-6x = 72$$
$$\frac{-6x}{6} = \frac{72}{6}$$
$$x = 12$$

27. A football player can run 20 yards in 3.4 seconds. Which equation could be used to find y, the number of yards the football player can run in a second?

Ⓐ $20y = 3.4$ Ⓒ $3.4y = 20$

Ⓑ $3.4 - y = 20$ Ⓓ $20 + y = 3.4$

28. Short Response Use the formula $A = bh$ to find the base in inches of a rhombus with a height of 7 inches and an area of 56 square inches. _____

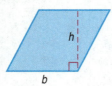

29. The table shows the prices of different satellite radio plans.

Satellite Radio Plans	
Plan	Cost per Month ($)
A	16.50
B	14.35
C	11.99

Suppose Mrs. Freedman paid $99 for x number of months of satellite radio under Plan A. Which operation would you use to determine the number of months for which Mrs. Freedman has prepaid?

Ⓕ Multiply 99 by 16.50.

Ⓖ Divide 99 by 16.50.

Ⓗ Multiply 99 by 11.99.

Ⓘ Divide 99 by 11.99.

CCGPS ## Common Core Review

Write each improper fraction as a mixed number and each mixed number as an improper fraction. MCC5.NF.3

30. $\frac{10}{3} =$ _____

31. $\frac{40}{7} =$ _____

32. $\frac{101}{100} =$ _____

33. $2\frac{2}{7} =$ _____

34. $3\frac{1}{4} =$ _____

35. $10\frac{5}{9} =$ _____

Divide. MCC6.NS.3

36. $6 \div 1.5 =$ _____

37. $3.6 \div 0.4 =$ _____

38. $2.73 \div 1.3 =$ _____

Multiply. Write in simplest form. MCC5.NF.4

39. $\frac{2}{9} \times \frac{7}{5} =$ _____

40. $\frac{3}{4} \times 7 =$ _____

41. $\frac{5}{8} \times \frac{4}{15} =$ _____

Inquiry **HOW can you use bar diagrams to solve equations with rational coefficients?**

CCGPS **Content Standards**
MCC7.EE.4,
MCC7.EE.4a

Mathematical Practices
1, 3

Talent Show Two thirds of Chen's homeroom class plan to participate in the school talent show. If 16 students from the class plan to participate, how many students are in the homeroom class?

What do you know? _____

_____

What do you need to find? _____

_____

Investigation

You can represent the situation above with an equation.

Step 1 Draw a bar diagram that represents the total number of students in the class and how many plan to participate.

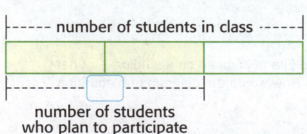

├ ----- number of students in class ------ ┤

├ ----------- ┤ ----------- ┤
number of students
who plan to participate

Step 2 Write an equation from the bar diagram. Let *c* represent the total number of students in the class. _____

Step 3 Find the number of students represented by the sections of the bar. Write that number in each section of the bar in Step 1.

Since each section represents 8 students, there are 8 × 3 or ☐ students in the class.

Check $\frac{2}{3} \times 24 = \frac{2}{3} \times \frac{24}{1}$

$= \frac{48}{3}$ or 16 ✔

Collaborate

Work with a partner to solve the following problem.

1. Eliana is spending $\frac{3}{5}$ of her monthly allowance on a costume for the talent show. She plans to spend $24. Draw a bar diagram to represent the situation. Then write and solve an equation to find the amount of Eliana's monthly allowance.

Equation: _____   Solution: _____

Analyze

Work with a partner to answer the following questions.

2. **CCGPS** **Reason Inductively** Suppose Eliana plans on spending $30 on a costume. How would the diagram and equation be different?

_____

_____

3. **CCGPS** **Make a Conjecture** Suppose Eliana planned on spending $\frac{3}{4}$ of her monthly allowance on a costume. How would the diagram and equation be different?

_____

_____

Reflect

4. **Inquiry** HOW can you use bar diagrams to solve equations with rational coefficients?

_____

_____

_____

Solve Equations with Rational Coefficients

Copyright © The McGraw-Hill Companies, Inc.   Gregory Costanzo/Getty Images

What You'll Learn

Scan the lesson. List two headings you would use to make an outline of the lesson.

- _____
- _____

 Essential Question

WHAT does it mean to say two quantities are equal?

 Common Core GPS

Content Standards
MCC7.EE.4, MCC7.EE.4a

Mathematical Practices
1, 2, 3, 4

Real-World Link

Social Networks Three-fourths of the students in Aaliyah's class belong to a social network. There are 15 students in her class that belong to a social network.

1. Create a bar diagram and shade $\frac{3}{4}$, or 0.75, of it.

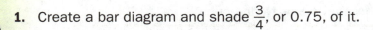
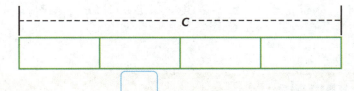

   Label 15 along the bottom to show the amount of the bar that represents 15 students.

2. Based on the diagram, circle the equation that can be used to find c, the number of students in Aaliyah's class.

   $15c = \frac{3}{4}$ $0.75c = 15$ $4c = 15$

3. Based on what you know about solving equations, explain how you could solve the equation you circled in Exercise 2.

   _____

4. How many students are in Aaliyah's class?

   _____

Decimal Coefficients

If the coefficient is a decimal, divide each side by the coefficient.

Show your work.

a. _____

b. _____

c. _____

d. _____

Example

1. Solve $16 = 0.25n$. Check your solution.

$16 = 0.25n$	Write the equation.
$\dfrac{16}{0.25} = \dfrac{0.25n}{0.25}$	Division Property of Equality
$64 = n$	Simplify.

Check $16 = 0.25\boldsymbol{n}$ Write the original equation.

$16 \stackrel{?}{=} 0.25 \cdot \boldsymbol{64}$ Replace n with 64.

$16 = 16$ ✓   This sentence is true.

The solution is 64.

Got It? Do these problems to find out.

a. $6.4 = 0.8m$ **b.** $-2.8p = 4.2$ **c.** $-4.7k = -10.81$

Example

Real World

2. Jaya's coach agreed to buy ice cream for all of the team members. Ice cream cones are $2.40 each. Write and solve an equation to find how many cones the coach can buy with $30.

Let n represent the number of cones the coach can buy.

$2.4n = 30$	Write the equation; $2.40 = 2.4$.
$\dfrac{2.4n}{2.4} = \dfrac{30}{2.4}$	Division Property of Equality
$n = 12.5$	Simplify.

Since the number of ice cream cones must be a whole number, there is enough money for 12 ice cream cones.

Got It? Do this problem to find out.

d. Suppose the ice cream cones cost $2.80 each. How many ice cream cones could the coach buy with $42?

Fraction Coefficients

Recall that two numbers with a product of 1 are called multiplicative inverses, or reciprocals. If the coefficient in a multiplication equation is a fraction, multiply each side by the reciprocal of the coefficient.

Examples

3. Solve $\frac{3}{4}x = \frac{12}{20}$.

$$\frac{3}{4}x = \frac{12}{20}$$ Write the equation.

$$\left(\frac{4}{3}\right) \cdot \frac{3}{4}x = \left(\frac{4}{3}\right) \cdot \frac{12}{20}$$ Multiply each side by the reciprocal of $\frac{3}{4}$, $\frac{4}{3}$.

$$\frac{\overset{1}{\cancel{4}}}{\underset{1}{\cancel{3}}} \cdot \frac{\overset{1}{\cancel{3}}}{\underset{1}{\cancel{4}}}x = \frac{\overset{1}{\cancel{4}}}{\underset{1}{\cancel{3}}} \cdot \frac{\overset{4}{\cancel{12}}}{\underset{5}{\cancel{20}}}$$ Divide by common factors.

$$x = \frac{4}{5}$$ Simplify. Check the solution.

- - - - - - - - - -

4. Solve $-\frac{7}{9}d = 5$. Check your solution.

$$-\frac{7}{9}d = 5$$ Write the equation.

$$\left(-\frac{9}{7}\right) \cdot \left(-\frac{7}{9}\right)d = \left(-\frac{9}{7}\right) \cdot 5$$ Multiply each side by the reciprocal of $-\frac{7}{9}$, $-\frac{9}{7}$.

$$\left(-\frac{9}{7}\right) \cdot \left(-\frac{7}{9}\right)d = \left(-\frac{9}{7}\right) \cdot \frac{5}{1}$$ Write 5 as $\frac{5}{1}$.

$$\left(-\frac{\overset{1}{\cancel{9}}}{\underset{}{7}}\right) \cdot \left(-\frac{\overset{1}{\cancel{7}}}{\underset{1}{\cancel{9}}}\right)d = \left(-\frac{9}{7}\right) \cdot \frac{5}{1}$$ Divide by common factors.

$$d = -\frac{45}{7} \text{ or } -6\frac{3}{7}$$ Simplify.

Check $$-\frac{7}{9}d = 5$$ Write the original equation.

$$-\frac{7}{9}\left(-\frac{45}{7}\right) \overset{?}{=} 5$$ Replace d with $-\frac{45}{7}$.

$$\frac{315}{63} \overset{?}{=} 5$$ Simplify.

$$5 = 5 \checkmark$$ This sentence is true.

Got It? Do these problems to find out.

e. $\frac{1}{2}x = 8$

f. $-\frac{3}{4}x = 9$

g. $-\frac{7}{8}x = -\frac{21}{64}$

<aside>
Fractions as Coefficients

The expression $\frac{3}{4}x$ can be read as $\frac{3}{4}$ of x, $\frac{3}{4}$ multiplied by x, $3x$ divided by 4, or $\frac{x}{4}$ multiplied by 3.
</aside>

 Show your work.

e. _____

f. _____

g. _____

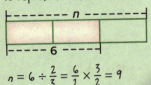

Bar Diagrams

A bar diagram can be used to represent this situation.

$n = 6 \div \frac{2}{3} = \frac{6}{1} \times \frac{3}{2} = 9$

 Example

5. Valerie needs $\frac{2}{3}$ yard of fabric to make each hat for the school play. Write and solve an equation to find how many hats she can make with 6 yards of fabric.

Write and solve a multiplication equation. Let n represent the number of hats.

$$\frac{2}{3}n = 6 \qquad \text{Write the equation.}$$

$$\left(\frac{3}{2}\right) \cdot \frac{2}{3}n = \left(\frac{3}{2}\right) \cdot 6 \qquad \text{Multiply each side by } \frac{3}{2}.$$

$$n = 9 \qquad \text{Simplify.}$$

Valerie can make 9 hats.

Guided Practice

 Check ✓

Solve each equation. Check your solution. (Examples 1, 3, and 4)

1. $1.6k = 3.2$

2. $-2.5b = 20.5$

3. $-\frac{1}{2} = -\frac{5}{18}h$

 Show your work.

Write and solve an equation. (Examples 2 and 5)

4. The average growth of human hair is 0.5 inch per month. Find how long it takes a human to grow 3 inches of hair.

Equation: _____ Solution: _____

5. Three fourths of the fruit in a refrigerator are apples. There are 24 apples in the refrigerator. How many pieces of fruit are in the refrigerator?

Equation: _____ Solution: _____

6. ⓔ **Building on the Essential Question** What is the process for solving a multiplication equation with a rational coefficient? _____

_____

_____

_____

_____

Rate Yourself!

Are you ready to move on? Shade the section that applies.

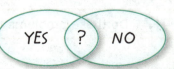

YES   ?   NO

For more help, go online to access a Personal Tutor. Tutor

Independent Practice

Go online for Step-by-Step Solutions

Solve each equation. Check your solution. (Examples 1, 3, and 4)

1. $1.2x = 6$

 Show your work.

2. $14.4 = -2.4b$

3 $-3.6h = -10.8$

4. $\frac{2}{5}t = \frac{12}{25}$

5. $-3\frac{1}{3} = -\frac{1}{2}g$

6. $-\frac{7}{9}m = \frac{11}{6}$

7 **Financial Literacy** Dillon deposited $\frac{3}{4}$ of his paycheck into the bank. The deposit slip shows how much he deposited. Write and solve an equation to find the amount of his paycheck. (Example 2)

Equation: _____   Solution: _____

DEPOSIT		CHECKS	4 6 5 0
Name: *Dillon Gates*			
Date: *9/22*			
Great Savings Bank			
Transaction # •54334589D•3221•8755P		DEPOSIT	$ 4 6 5 0

8. Twenty-four students brought their permission slips to attend the class field trip to the local art museum. If this represented eight tenths of the class, how many students are in the class? Use a bar diagram to solve arithmetically. Then use an equation to solve algebraically. (Example 5)

Equation: _____   Solution: _____

9. **CCGPS** **Justify Conclusions** Seventy-five percent, or 15, of the students in Emily's homeroom class are going on a field trip. Two thirds, or 12, of the students in Santiago's homeroom class are going on the field trip. Which class has more students? Justify your answer. _____

_____

_____

_____

10. **Reason Abstractly** Nora and Ryan are making stuffed animals for a toy drive. The table shows the fabric purchases they made. Who purchased the more expensive fabric? Explain your reasoning. _____

_____

_____

_____

Purchaser	Amount Purchased (yd)	Amount Paid ($)
Nora	$\frac{2}{3}$	4
Ryan	0.8	6

 H.O.T. Problems Higher Order Thinking

11. **CCGPS** **Reason Inductively** Complete the statement: If $8 = \frac{m}{4}$, then

$m - 12 = $ ■. Explain. _____

_____

12. **CCGPS** **Which One Doesn't Belong?** Identify the pair of numbers that does not belong with the other three. Explain. _____

_____

$$\frac{9}{6}, \frac{6}{9}$$ $$4, \frac{1}{4}$$ $$\frac{3}{5}, 5$$ $$\frac{2}{7}, \frac{7}{2}$$

13. **CCGPS** **Persevere with Problems** The formula for the area of a trapezoid is $A = \frac{1}{2}h(b_1 + b_2)$, where b_1 and b_2 are both bases and h is the height. Find the value of h in terms of A, b_1, and b_2. Justify your answer.

_____

_____

_____

 Georgia Test Practice

14. Audrey drove 200 miles in 3.5 hours. Which equation can you use to find the rate r at which Audrey was traveling?

Ⓐ $200 = 3.5r$

Ⓑ $200 \cdot 3.5 = r$

Ⓒ $\frac{r}{3.5} = 200$

Ⓓ $200r = 3.5$

Extra Practice

Solve each equation. Check your solution.

15. $0.4d = 2.8$

 Homework Help →

$0.4d = 2.8$

$\dfrac{0.4d}{0.4} = \dfrac{2.8d}{0.4}$

$d = 7$

16. $-5w = -24.5$

17. $-22.8 = 6n$

18. $\dfrac{7}{8}k = \dfrac{5}{6}$

$\dfrac{7}{8}k = \dfrac{5}{6}$

$\left(\dfrac{8}{7}\right) \cdot \dfrac{7}{8}k = \left(\dfrac{8}{7}\right) \cdot \dfrac{5}{6}$

$k = \dfrac{40}{42}$ or $\dfrac{20}{21}$

19. $-6\dfrac{1}{4} = \dfrac{3}{5}c$

20. $-\dfrac{4}{7}v = -8\dfrac{2}{3}$

21. The Mammoth Cave Discovery Tour includes an elevation change of 140 feet. This is $\dfrac{7}{15}$ of the elevation change on the Wild Cave Tour. What is the elevation change on the Wild Cave Tour? Use a bar diagram to solve arithmetically. Then use an equation to solve algebraically.

Equation: _____   Solution: _____

22. **CCGPS** **Model with Mathematics** Refer to the graphic novel frame below. Write and solve an equation to find how many movies they have time to show.

Equation: _____   Solution: _____

Georgia Test Practice

23. A high-speed train travels 100 miles in $\frac{2}{3}$ hour. Which speed represents the rate of the train?

Ⓐ 50 mph   Ⓒ 100 mph

Ⓑ 75 mph   Ⓓ 150 mph

24. Short Response Nithia earns $6.25 per hour at work. She wants to earn $100 for a class camping trip. Use the equation $6.25h = 100$ to find h, the number of hours she will have to work to earn the money. _____

25. The table shows the results of a survey.

Music Preference	
Type	**Fraction of Students**
Pop	$\frac{5}{8}$
Jazz	$\frac{1}{8}$
Rap	$\frac{1}{4}$

Suppose 420 students are surveyed. Which equation can be used to find the number of students s who prefer rap?

Ⓕ $\frac{1}{4}s = 420$ Ⓗ $s + \frac{1}{4} = 420$

Ⓖ $s = \frac{1}{4} \cdot 420$ Ⓘ $420 + s = \frac{1}{4}$

Common Core Review

Use the order of operations to evaluate each expression. MCC6.EE.2c

26. $6 \times 4 - 2 =$ _____

27. $70 - 5 \times 4 =$ _____

28. $18 \div 2 - 7 =$ _____

29. Write *add*, *divide*, *multiply*, and *subtract* in the correct order to complete the following sentence. MCC6.EE.2c

When using the order of operations to evaluate an expression,

always _____ and _____ before you _____

and _____.

Write and evaluate an expression for each situation. MCC6.EE.1

30. Used paperback books are $0.25, and hardback books are $0.50. If you buy 3 paperback books and 5 hardback books, how much money do you spend?

Expression: _____   Solution: _____

31. Suppose you order 2 pizzas, 2 garlic breads, and 1 order of BBQ wings. How much change would you receive from $30?

Expression: _____   Solution: _____

Item	Cost
14" pizza	$8
garlic bread	$2
BBQ wings	$4

Inquiry **HOW can a bar diagram or algebra tiles help you solve a real-world problem?**

CCGPS **Content Standards** 7.EE.4, 7.EE.4a

Mathematical Practices 1, 2, 3, 4

Sports Latoya plays basketball and tennis. She has two basketballs and three tennis balls that weigh a total of 48 ounces. Each tennis ball weighs 2 ounces. What is the weight of a basketball?

What do you know? _____

_____

What do you need to find? _____

_____

Investigation 1

You can use a bar diagram to represent the situation.

Step 1 Draw a bar diagram that represents the two basketballs and three tennis balls.

←------------------------ 48 oz ------------------------→

basketball		tennis	tennis	
⊢------?------⊣	------?-------⊢	2 oz ⊣	2 oz ⊢	[ ]

Step 2 Write an equation from the bar diagram. Let *x* represent the weight of a basketball.

$$2x + 6 = 48$$

Step 3 Use the *work backward* strategy to find the weight of a basketball. Since $2x + 6 = 48$, $2x = 48 - 6$ or 42.

So, *x* equals $42 \div 2$ or [ ].

Check $2 \cdot$ [ ] $+ 6 = 48$ ✔

The weight of one basketball is [ ] ounces.

Investigation 2

Tools

You can use algebra tiles to represent the equation $4x - 2 = 10$.

Step 1   Model the equation.

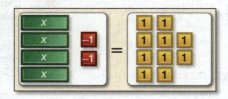

$4x - 2 = 10$

Step 2   Add ☐ 1-tiles to each side of the mat to form zero pairs on the left side.

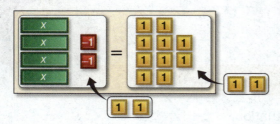

$4x - 2 + 2 = 10 + 2$

Step 3   Remove both zero pairs from the left side so that the variable is by itself.

$4x = 12$

Step 4   Divide the remaining tiles into ☐ equal groups.

$$\frac{4x}{4} = \frac{12}{4}$$

So, $x = $ ☐ .

Check $4 \cdot$ ☐ $- 2 = 10$ ✔

280   **Chapter 4** Equations and Inequalities

Work with a partner to solve the following problem.

1. **CCGPS** **Reason Abstractly** Ryan is saving money to buy a skateboard that costs $85. He has already saved $40. He plans to save the same amount each week for three weeks. Draw a bar diagram. Then write an equation. How much should Ryan save each week?

Work with a partner to solve each equation. Use algebra tiles. Show your work using drawings.

2. $2x + 1 = 5$ $x = $ _____

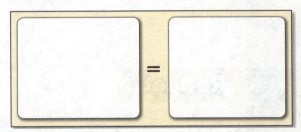

3. $3x + 2 = 11$ $x = $ _____

4. $4x + 3 = -5$ $x = $ _____

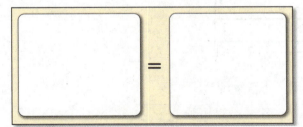

5. $2x - 1 = 7$ $x = $ _____

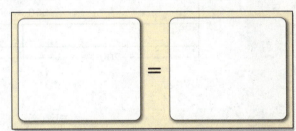

6. $5x - 2 = -7$ $x = $ _____

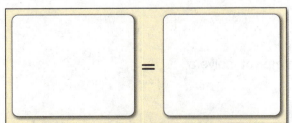

7. $3x - 4 = 5$ $x = $ _____

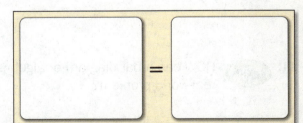

Analyze

8. **CCGPS** **Reason Inductively** Work with a partner. Read the steps to solve an equation using algebra tiles. Then circle each correct equation.

Steps to Solve	Choices of Equation		
• Add 3 1-tiles to each side of the mat. • Divide tiles into 2 equal groups.	$2x + 3 = 15$	$3x + 2 = 15$	$2x - 3 = 15$
• Add 4 1-tiles to each side of the mat. • Divide tiles into 3 equal groups.	$3x - 4 = 11$	$3x + 4 = 11$	$4x - 3 = 11$
• Remove 7 1-tiles from each side of the mat. • Divide tiles into 3 equal groups.	$7x + 3 = 10$	$3x + 7 = 10$	$3x - 7 = 10$
• Add 2 −1-tiles to each side of the mat. • Remove 2 zero pairs from the left side of the mat. • Divide tiles into 5 equal groups.	$5x - 2 = -8$	$5x + 2 = -8$	$2x + 5 = -8$

9. **CCGPS** **Construct an Argument** What did you observe while choosing the correct equations in the table above?

_____

_____

Reflect

10. **CCGPS** **Model with Mathematics** Write a real-world problem and an equation that the bar diagram below could represent. Then solve your problem.

```
|------------------ 540 ------------------|
[          |      |      ]
|------200------+--?--+--?--|
```

_____

_____

_____

_____

11. **Inquiry** HOW can a bar diagram or algebra tiles help you solve a real-world problem?

_____

_____

_____

Solve Two-Step Equations

What You'll Learn

Scan the lesson. Predict two things you will learn about solving two-step equations.

- _____
  _____

- _____
  _____

 Essential Question

WHAT does it mean to say two quantities are equal?

 Vocabulary

two-step equation

 Common Core GPS

Content Standards
MCC7.EE.4, MCC7.EE.4a

Mathematical Practices
1, 2, 3, 4

 ## Real-World Link

Balloons A company charges $2 for each balloon in an arrangement and a $3 delivery fee. You have $9 to spend. The equation $2x + 3 = 9$, where x is the number of balloons, represents the situation. Work backward to solve for x.

Start with the amount of money you have to spend. ☐ → Subtract the $3 delivery fee. ☐ → Since each balloon is $2, divide by two. ☐

So, you can purchase ☐ balloons.

Check your work by substituting your solution into the equation.

$$2\left(\boxed{}\right) + 3 \stackrel{?}{=} 9.$$

$$\boxed{} + 3 \stackrel{?}{=} 9$$

$$\boxed{} = 9$$

1. How many balloons could you have purchased if there was a $1 delivery charge?

_____

Start with the amount of money you have to spend. ☐ → Subtract the $1 delivery fee. ☐ → Since each balloon is $2, divide by two. ☐

Solve Two-Step Equations

Recall that the *order of operations* ensures that numerical expressions, such as 2 · 5 + 3, have only one value. To reverse the operations, undo them in reverse order.

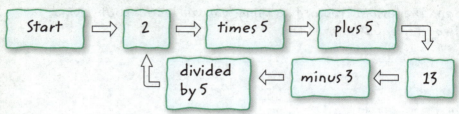

A **two-step equation**, such as 2x + 3 = 9, has two different operations, multiplication and addition. To solve a two-step equation, undo the operations in reverse order of the order of operations.

> **Step 1**   Undo the addition or subtraction first.

> **Step 2**   Undo the multiplication or division.

This equation is written as $px + q = r$, where p, q, and r are rational numbers.

Examples

Tutor

1. **Solve 2x + 3 = 9. Check your solution.**

2x + 3 =	9		Write the equation.
− 3 =	− 3		Undo the addition first by subtracting 3 from each side.
2x =	6		
$\frac{2x}{2}$ =	$\frac{6}{2}$		Next, undo the multiplication by dividing each side by 2.
x =	3		Simplify.

Check $2x + 3 = 9$ Write the original equation.

$2(3) + 3 \stackrel{?}{=} 9$ Replace x with 3.

$9 = 9$ ✔   The sentence is true.

The solution is 3.

STOP and Reflect

What are the two operations you would perform to solve $3x - 4 = 8$? Write your answer below.

2. Solve $3x + 2 = 23$. Check your solution.

$3x + 2 = 23$ Write the equation.

$\underline{\quad -2 = -2\quad}$ Undo the addition first by subtracting 2 from each side.

$3x \qquad = 21$

$\dfrac{3x}{3} = \dfrac{21}{3}$ Division Property of Equality

$x = 7$ Simplify.

Check $3x + 2 = 23$ Write the original equation.

$3(7) + 2 \stackrel{?}{=} 23$ Replace x with 7.

$23 = 23$ ✔   The sentence is true.

The solution is 7.

. . . .

3. Solve $-2y - 7 = 3$. Check your solution.

$-2y - 7 = \quad 3$ Write the equation.

$\underline{\quad +7 = +7\quad}$ Undo the subtraction first by adding 7 to each side.

$-2y \qquad = 10$

$\dfrac{-2y}{-2} = \dfrac{10}{-2}$ Division Property of Equality

$y = -5$ Simplify.

The solution is -5.   Check the solution.

. . . .

4. Solve $4 + \frac{1}{5}r = -1$. Check your solution.

$4 + \frac{1}{5}r = -1$ Write the equation.

$\underline{-4 \qquad = -4\quad}$ Undo the addition first by subtracting 4 from each side.

$\frac{1}{5}r = -5$

$5 \cdot \frac{1}{5}r = 5 \cdot (-5)$ Multiplication Property of Equality

$r = -25$ Simplify.

The solution is -25.   Check the solution.

Got It? Do these problems to find out.

Solve each equation. Check your solution.

a. $2x + 4 = 10$ **b.** $3x + 5 = 14$ **c.** $5 = 2 + 3x$

d. $4x + 5 = 13$ **e.** $-5s + 8 = -2$ **f.** $-2 + \frac{2}{3}w = 10$

Equations

Remember, solutions of the new equation are also solutions of the original equation.

Show your work.

a. _____

b. _____

c. _____

d. _____

e. _____

f. _____

Example

5. Toya had her birthday party at the movies. It cost $27 for pizza and $8.50 per friend for the movie tickets. How many friends did Toya have at her party if she spent $78?

Words	Cost of pizza	plus	Cost of 1 friend	times	number of friends	equals $78.
Variable		Let n represent the number of friends.				
Equation	27	+	8.50	$\cdot$	n	= 78

$$27 + 8.50n = 78 \quad \text{Write the equation.}$$
$$\underline{-27 \qquad\quad = -27} \quad \text{Subtract 27 from each side.}$$
$$8.50n = 51$$
$$\frac{8.50n}{8.50} = \frac{51}{8.50} \quad \text{Division Property of Equality}$$
$$n = 6 \quad \text{Simplify.}$$

Toya can have 6 friends at her party.

Solve Arithmetically

You can use a bar diagram to solve an equation arithmetically.

$78	
pizza	**tickets**
$27	$8.50n

Subtract 27 from 78. Then divide by 8.5.
$78 - 27 = 51; 51 \div 8.5 = 6$

Guided Practice

Solve each equation. Check your solution. (Examples 1–4)

1. $13 = 1 + 4s$

2. $-3y - 5 = 10$

3. $-7 = 1 + \frac{2}{3}n$

 Show your work.

4. Syreeta wants to buy some CDs that each cost $14, and a DVD that costs $23. She has $65. Write and solve an equation to find how many CDs she can buy. (Example 5)

Equation: _____

Solution: _____

5. **Building on the Essential Question** When solving an equation, explain why it is important to perform identical operations on each side of the equals sign.

_____

_____

Rate Yourself!

How well do you understand solving two-step equations? Circle the image that applies.

Clear   Somewhat Clear   Not So Clear

For more help, go online to access a Personal Tutor.

 FOLDABLES Time to update your Foldable!

Name _____ My Homework _____

Solve each equation. Check your solution. (Examples 1–4)

1. $3x + 1 = 10$

 Show your work.

2. $-3 + 8n = -5$

3. $4h - 6 = 22$

4. $-8s + 1 = 33$

5. $-4w - 4 = 8$

6. $5 + \frac{1}{7}b = -2$

7. **CCGPS** **Reason Abstractly** Cristiano is saving money to buy a bike that costs $189. He has saved $99 so far. He plans on saving $10 each week. In how many weeks will he have enough money to buy the bike? Use a bar diagram to solve arithmetically. Then use an equation to solve algebraically. (Example 5)

 Show your work.

Solve each equation. Check your solution.

8. $2r - 3.1 = 1.7$

9. $4t + 3.5 = 12.5$

10. $8m - 5.5 = 10.1$

11 Temperature is usually measured on the Fahrenheit scale (°F) or the Celsius scale (°C). Use the formula $F = 1.8C + 32$ to convert from one scale to the other.

a. Convert the temperature for Alaska's record low in July to Celsius. Round to the nearest degree.

b. Hawaii's record low temperature is −11°C. Find the difference in degrees Fahrenheit between Hawaii's record low temperature and the record low temperature for Alaska in January.

Alaska Record Low Temperatures (°F) by Month	
January	−80
April	−50
July	16
October	−48

12. **CCGPS** **Model with Mathematics** Refer to the graphic novel frame below. Jamar figured that they will spend $39 for popcorn. Each movie cost $19. Write and solve an equation to find how many movies they can purchase.

_____

_____

Replay it online!

I think we'll need $39 for popcorn.

Mmmm... popcorn.

Help us figure how many movies we can buy. Refer to the beginning of the chapter.

H.O.T. Problems Higher Order Thinking

13. **CCGPS** **Reason Inductively** Refer to Exercise 11. Is there a temperature in the table at which the number of degrees Celsius is the same as the number of degrees Fahrenheit? If so, find it. If not, explain why not.

_____

_____

14. **CCGPS** **Persevere with Problems** Suppose your school is selling magazine subscriptions. Each subscription costs $20. The company pays the school half of the total sales in dollars. The school must also pay a one-time fee of $18. What is the fewest number of subscriptions that can be sold to earn a profit of $200?

_____

_____

Georgia Test Practice

15. What operations would you perform, and in what order would you perform them, to solve $1 + 5n = 20$?

Ⓐ add 1, multiply by 5

Ⓑ subtract 1, divide by 5

Ⓒ multiply by 5, add 1

Ⓓ divide by 5, subtract 1

Extra Practice

Solve each equation. Check your solution.

16. $5x + 4 = 19$ *3*

$$5x + 4 = 19$$
$$ - 4 = -4$$
$$\frac{5x}{5} = \frac{15}{5}$$
$$x = 3$$

17. $6m + 1 = -23$

18. $5 + 4d = 37$

19. $-7y + 3 = -25$

20. $25 + \frac{11}{12}b = 47$

21. $15 - \frac{1}{2}b = -3$

22. It costs $7.50 to enter a petting zoo. Each cup of food to feed the animals is $2.50. If you have $12.50, how many cups can you buy? Use a bar diagram to solve arithmetically. Then use an equation to solve algebraically.

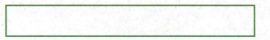

Show your work.

23. CCGPS **Multiple Representations** The perimeter of a rectangle is 48 centimeters. Its length is 16 centimeters. What is the width *w*?

a. Draw a bar diagram that represents this situation.

b. Write and solve an equation that represents this situation.

_____

c. How does solving the equation arithmetically compare to solving an equation algebraically?

_____

_____

Georgia Test Practice

24. A rental car company charges $30 a day plus $0.05 a mile. This is represented by the equation below, where m is the number of miles and c is the total cost of the rental.

$$c = 30 + 0.05m$$

If the Boggs family paid $49.75 for their car rental, how many miles did they travel?

Ⓐ 95 miles   Ⓒ 295 miles

Ⓑ 195 miles   Ⓓ 395 miles

25. Short Response The Rodriguez family is on a vacation. They started with $1,875. They have spent $140 each day and have $895 left for the rest of their vacation. Use the equation below to find d, the number of days they have been on their vacation so far.

$$1,875 - 140d = 895$$

How many days have they vacationed?

_____

Common Core Review

Use the Distributive Property to rewrite each expression. MCC6.EE.3

26. $2(x + 7) =$

27. $6(10 + n) =$

28. $5(k - 4) =$

Factor each expression. MCC6.NS.4

29. $5x + 5 \cdot 7 =$ _____

30. $4n + 4 \cdot 2 =$ _____

31. $10t + 10 \cdot 3 =$ _____

32. $7v + 7 \cdot 8 =$ _____

33. $2m + 2 \cdot 6 =$ _____

34. $25d + 25 \cdot 4 =$ _____

Inquiry **HOW** are equations in *p(x + q) = r* form different from *px + q = r* equations?

CCGPS Content Standards
MCC7.EE.4,
MCC7.EE.4a
Mathematical Practices
1, 3, 4

Money Mark has two summer jobs. He babysits and helps with the gardening. He works at each job three days a week and earns a total of $240. The table shows his earnings each day. How much does he earn each day babysitting?

Job	Daily Earnings ($)
Babysitting	x
Gardening	30

What do you know? _____

_____

What do you need to find? _____

_____

Investigation 1

Step 1 Draw a bar diagram that represents the situation.

```
|----------------[        ]----------------|
| $x + $30   |   $x + $30   |   $x + $30   |
|--- earnings ---|--- earnings ---|--- earnings ---|
|   each day     |   each day     |   each day     |
```

Step 2 Write an equation from the bar diagram.

3($x + $30) = [   ]

From the diagram, you can see that one third of Mark's total earnings is equal to $x + $30. So, $x + $30 = $\frac{\$240}{3}$ or [   ].

Mark earns [   ] − $30 or [   ] each day babysitting.

Exercise Vijay and his brother bought two hamburgers and two lemonades. The hamburgers cost $6 each. They spent a total of $16. How much did each lemonade cost?

Investigation 2

Tools

Use algebra tiles to model the situation described above.

Step 1 Model $2(x + 6) = 16$ using algebra tiles. Use ☐ groups of $x + 6$ tiles.

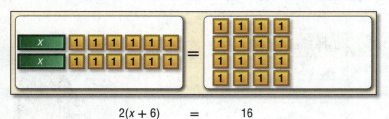

$2(x + 6)$ = 16

Step 2 Divide the tiles into ☐ equal groups on each side of the mat.

Remove ☐ group from each side.

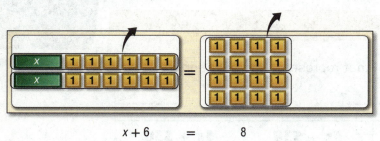

$x + 6$ = 8

Step 3 Remove the same number of 1-tiles from each side.

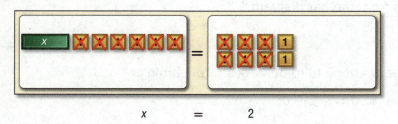

x = 2

So, $x = $ ☐. Each lemonade costs ☐.

Collaborate

Work with a partner to solve the following problems. Use a bar diagram for Exercises 1 and 2. Use algebra tiles for Exercises 3-6.

1. $3(x + 5) = 21$ $x =$ _____

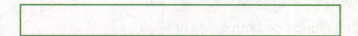

2. $2(x - 3) = 10$ $x =$ _____

3. $4(x + 1) = 8$ $x =$ _____

4. $3(x + 2) = -12$ $x =$ _____

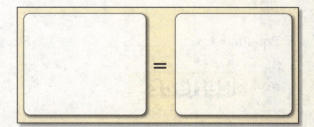

5. $2(x - 1) = 6$ $x =$ _____

6. $3(x - 4) = -3$ $x =$ _____

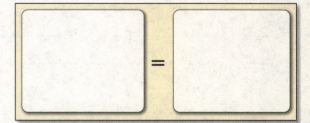

Work with a partner to solve each problem.

7. Refer to Investigation 1. If Mark worked four days a week and made $360, how much did he earn babysitting each day?

_____

8. Refer to Investigation 2. If Vijay and his brother spent a total of $15, how much did each lemonade cost?

_____

9. **CCGPS** **Reason Inductively** After modeling an equation using algebra tiles, Angelina used the steps shown below to solve the equation. Write two different equations in $p(x + q) = r$ form that Angelina could have solved.

> **Step 1** Divide the tiles into three equal groups on both sides of the mat.

> **Step 2** Remove two groups from each side.

> **Step 3** Add four 1-tiles to each side.

Equation 1: _____   Equation 2: _____

 Reflect

10. **CCGPS** **Model with Mathematics** Write a real-world problem that can be represented by the equation $4(x + 15) = 140$. Then solve the problem.

_____

_____

_____

_____

11. **Inquiry** HOW are equations in $p(x + q) = r$ form different from $px + q = r$ equations?

_____

_____

_____

More Two-Step Equations

What You'll Learn

Scan the lesson. List two real-world scenarios for which you would solve a two-step equation.

- _____
  _____

- _____

 Essential Question

WHAT does it mean to say two quantities are equal?

CCGPS **Common Core GPS**

Content Standards
MCC7.EE.4, MCC7.EE.4a
Mathematical Practices
1, 2, 3, 4

 Real-World Link

Museums A new exhibit about dinosaurs is being constructed. The exhibit is a rectangle that is 36 feet long. It has a perimeter of 114 feet. Follow the steps to write an equation that can be used to find the width of the museum exhibit.

Step 1 Draw a diagram to help visualize the exhibit.

Label the length and width. Let *w* represent the width.

w

36 ft

Step 2 Write an expression that represents the sum of the length and width of the exhibit. _____

Step 3 Write an expression that represents twice the sum of the length and width. _____

Step 4 Write an equation that represents the perimeter of the exhibit. _____

Solve Two-Step Equations

An equation like $2(w + 36) = 114$ is in the form $p(x + q) = r$. It contains two factors, p and $(x + q)$, and is considered a two-step equation. Solve these equations using the properties of equality.

Examples

1. Solve $3(x + 5) = 45$.

Method 1 Solve arithmetically.

45		
$x + 5$	$x + 5$	$x + 5$

?

Draw a bar diagram. From the diagram, you can see that $x + 5 = 45 \div 3$ or 15. So, $x = 15 - 5$ or 10.

Method 2 Solve algebraically.

$3(x + 5) = 45$ Write the equation.

$\dfrac{3(x + 5)}{3} = \dfrac{45}{3}$ Division Property of Equality

$x + 5 = 15$ Simplify.

$\underline{-5 = -5}$ Subtraction Property of Equality

$x = 10$ Simplify.

2. Solve $5(n - 2) = -30$.

$5(n - 2) = -30$ Write the equation.

$\dfrac{5(n - 2)}{5} = \dfrac{-30}{5}$ Division Property of Equality

$n - 2 = -6$ Simplify.

$\underline{+2 = +2}$ Addition Property of Equality

$n = -4$ Simplify. Check the solution.

Check Your Work

Remember to plug your solution back into the original equation to see if it makes a true statement.

Got It? Do these problems to find out.

a. $2(x + 4) = 20$ **b.** $3(b - 6) = 12$ **c.** $-7(6 + d) = 49$

a. _____

b. _____

c. _____

Equations with Rational Coefficients

Sometimes the factor p, in $p(x + q)$, will be a fraction or decimal.

Examples

3. Solve $\frac{2}{3}(n + 6) = 10$. **Check your solution.**

$\frac{2}{3}(n + 6) = 10$	Write the equation.
$\frac{3}{2} \cdot \frac{2}{3}(n + 6) = \frac{3}{2} \cdot 10$	Multiplication Property of Equality
$(n + 6) = \frac{3}{2} \cdot \left(\frac{\overset{5}{10}}{1}\right)$	$\frac{2}{3} \cdot \frac{3}{2} = 1$; write 10 as $\frac{10}{1}$.
$n + 6 = 15$	Simplify.
$\underline{-6 = -6}$	Subtraction Property of Equality
$n = 9$	Simplify.

Check	$\frac{2}{3}(n + 6) = 10$	Write the original equation.
	$\frac{2}{3}(9 + 6) \overset{?}{=} 10$	Replace n with 9. Is this sentence true?
	$10 = 10$ ✓	The sentence is true.

- -

4. Solve $0.2(c - 3) = -10$. **Check your solution.**

$0.2(c - 3) = -10$	Write the equation.
$\frac{0.2(c - 3)}{0.2} = -\frac{10}{0.2}$	Division Property of Equality
$c - 3 = -50$	Simplify.
$\underline{+3 = +3}$	Addition Property of Equality
$c = -47$	Simplify.

Check	$0.2(c - 3) = -10$	Write the original equation.
	$0.2(-47 - 3) \overset{?}{=} -10$	Replace c with -47. Is this sentence true?
	$-10 = -10$ ✓	The sentence is true.

Got It? Do these problems to find out.

d. $\frac{1}{4}(d - 3) = -15$ **e.** $0.75(6 + d) = 12$ **f.** $(t + 3)\frac{5}{9} = 40$

Reciprocals
The product of a number and its reciprocal is 1.

Show your work.

d. _____

e. _____

f. _____

Example

5. Jamal and two cousins received the same amount of money to go to a movie. Each boy spent $15. Afterward, the boys had $30 altogether. Write and solve an equation to find the amount of money each boy received.

Let m represent the amount of money each boy received.

$3(m - 15) = 30$ Write the equation.

$\dfrac{3(m - 15)}{3} = \dfrac{30}{3}$ Division Property of Equality

$m - 15 = 10$ Simplify.

$\underline{+\ 15 = +\ 15}$ Addition Property of Equality

$m = 25$ Simplify.

So, each boy received $25.

Guided Practice

 Check

Solve each equation. Check your solution. (Examples 1–4)

1. $2(p + 7) = 18$

2. $(4 + g)(-11) = 121$

3. $(v + 5)\left(-\dfrac{1}{9}\right) = 6$

4. $0.8(m - 5) = 10$

5. Mr. Singh had three sheets of stickers. He gave 20 stickers from each sheet to his students and has 12 total stickers left. Write and solve an equation to find how many stickers were originally on each sheet. (Example 5)

Equation: _____

Solution: _____

6. **Building on the Essential Question** What is the difference between $px + q = r$ and $p(x + q) = r$?

_____

_____

_____

Rate Yourself!

Are you ready to move on? Shade the section that applies.

I have a few questions.

I'm ready to move on.

I have a lot of questions.

For more help, go online to access a Personal Tutor.   Tutor

FOLDABLES Time to update your Foldable!

Independent Practice

Go online for Step-by-Step Solutions

Solve each equation. Check your solution. (Examples 1–4)

1. $8(s + 3) = 72$

2. $-7(z - 6) = -70$

3. $(t + 8)(-2) = 12$

4. $\frac{8}{11}(n - 10) = 64$

5. $-0.6(r + 0.2) = 1.8$

6. $\left(w - \frac{4}{9}\right)\left(-\frac{2}{3}\right) = -\frac{4}{5}$

7. The length of each side of an equilateral triangle is increased by 5 inches, so the perimeter is now 60 inches. Write and solve an equation to find the original length of each side of the equilateral triangle. (Example 5)

Equation: _____   Solution: _____

8. **CCGPS** **Multiple Representations** Miguel and three of his friends went to the movies. They originally had a total of $40. Each boy had the same amount of money and spent $7.50 on a ticket. How much money did each boy have left after buying his ticket?

a. Model Draw a bar diagram that represents the situation.

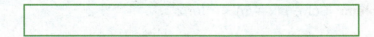

b. Algebra Write and solve an equation that represents the situation.

_____

c. Words Explain how you solved your equation.

_____

_____

d. Words Compare the arithmetic solution and the algebraic solution.

_____

_____

9. Mrs. Sorenstam bought one ruler, one compass, and one mechanical pencil at the prices shown in the table for each of her 12 students.

Item	Price ($)
compass	1.49
mechanical pencil	0.59
ruler	0.49

a. Suppose Mrs. Sorenstam had 36 cents left after buying the school supplies. Write an equation to find the amount of money Mrs. Sorenstam initially had to spend on each student.

_____

b. Describe a two-step process you could use to solve your equation. Then solve the equation.

_____
_____

 H.O.T. Problems Higher Order Thinking

10. **CCGPS** **Model with Mathematics** Write a real-world situation that can be represented by the equation $2(n + 20) = 110$.

_____
_____
_____

11. **CCGPS** **Find the Error** Marisol is solving the equation $6(x + 3) = 21$. Find her mistake and correct it.

_____
_____
_____
_____

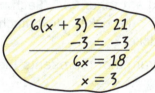

$$6(x + 3) = 21$$
$$\underline{-3 = -3}$$
$$6x = 18$$
$$x = 3$$

12. **CCGPS** **Persevere with Problems** Solve $p(x + q) = r$ for x.

_____
_____

 Georgia Test Practice

13. Each week, Payat spends a portion of his allowance to download music. The table shows the cumulative amount that he spent on music downloads during a three-week period.

At the end of Week 3, Payat had $9 left. Which equation can be used to find the amount of Payat's weekly allowance a?

Payat's Downloads	
Week	**Total Spent ($)**
1	12
2	24
3	36

Ⓐ $3(a - 12) = 9$ Ⓒ $3(a + 12) = 9$

Ⓑ $9(a + 12) = 3$ Ⓓ $9(a - 12) = 3$

Extra Practice

Solve each equation. Check your solution.

14. $0.25(3 + a) = 0.5$

$0.25(3+a) = 0.5$

$\dfrac{0.25(3+a)}{0.25} = \dfrac{0.5}{0.25}$

$3 + a = 2$

$a = -1$

15. $12(x - 20) = -48$

16. $-28 = 7(n + 3)$

17. $(t + 9)20 = 140$

18. $\dfrac{5}{9}(8 + c) = -20$

19. $(d - 3)\dfrac{2}{5} = 30$

20. **CCGPS** **Reason Abstractly** Anne bought a necklace for each of her three sisters. She paid $7 for each necklace. Suppose she had $9 left. Write and solve an equation to find how much money Anne had initially to spend on each sister.

Equation: _____

Solution: _____

Solve each equation. Check your solution.

21. $1\dfrac{3}{5}(t - 6) = -0.4$ _____

22. $\left(x + 5\dfrac{1}{2}\right)0.75 = \dfrac{5}{8}$ _____

23. Mr. Gomez bought fruit to make fruit salad. He bought $2\dfrac{1}{2}$ pounds of apples and spent $4.50 on apples and oranges. Write and solve an equation to determine the number of pounds of oranges Mr. Gomez bought.

_____

Fruit	Price per Pound ($)
apples	1.20
bananas	0.50
grapes	1.50
oranges	1.20

24. Which equation has a solution of −4?

- Ⓐ $5(n + 2) = 10$
- Ⓑ $\frac{1}{5}(n + 2) = 10$
- Ⓒ $-5(n + 2) = 10$
- Ⓓ $-\frac{1}{5}(n + 2) = 10$

25. Short Response What is the reciprocal of b?

_____

26. Which pair of operations should you use to solve $p(x - q) = r$ for x?

- Ⓕ Multiply by p. Subtract q.
- Ⓖ Multiply by p. Add q.
- Ⓗ Divide by p. Subtract q.
- Ⓘ Divide by p. Add q.

Common Core Review

Solve each equation. Then graph each solution on the number line below. MCC6.EE.6

27. $x + 3 = 5$

28. $x - 2 = -6$

29. $4x = 12$

30. $-6x = -24$

31. $\frac{x}{2} = -1$

32. $\frac{x}{-3} = 1$

Write the number or numbers from the set {−3, −2, −1, 0, 1, 2, 3} that make each statement true. MCC6.EE.5

33. $4m = 12$ _____

34. $y - 1 = 1$ _____

35. $v > 0$ _____

36. $r \leq 0$ _____

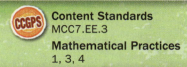
Content Standards
MCC7.EE.3
Mathematical Practices
1, 3, 4

Case #1 Yard Work

Mike earned extra money by doing yard work for his neighbor. Then he spent $5.50 at the convenience store and four times that amount at the bookstore. Now he has $7.75 left.

How much money did Mike have before he went to the convenience store and the bookstore?

Understand *What are the facts?*

You know Mike has $7.75 left. You need to find the amount before his purchases.

Plan *What is your strategy to solve this problem?*

Start with the end result and work backward.

Solve *How can you apply the strategy?*

He has $7.75 left.
Undo the four times $5.50 spent at the bookstore. $7.75
Since $5.50 × 4 is $22, add $7.75 and $22.   + $22.00
                                                               $29.75
Undo the $5.50 spent at the convenience store.   + $5.50

Add $5.50 and ⬚. $35.25

So, Mike's starting amount was ⬚.

Check *Does the answer make sense?*

Assume Mike started with $35.25. He spent $5.50 and $22. He had

$35 − $5.50 − $22 or ⬚ left. So, $35.25 is correct. ✓

Analyze the Strategy

 Construct an Argument Describe how to solve a problem by working

backward. _____

_____

_____

Case #2 Money

Marisa spent $8 on a movie ticket. Then she spent $5 on popcorn and one half of what was left on a drink. She had $2 left.

How much did she have initially?

Understand

Read the problem. What are you being asked to find?

I need to find _____.

Underline key words and values. What information do you know?

I know Marisa has ☐ left and that she spent ☐, ☐, and

_____.

Is there any information that you do *not* need to know?

I do not need to know _____.

Plan

Choose a problem-solving strategy.

I will use the _____ strategy.

Solve

Use your problem-solving strategy to solve the problem.
Marisa has $2 left.

Undo the half-of-what-was-left   _____
amount. Multiply by 2.

Undo the spent $5. Add $5.   _____

Undo the spent $8. Add $8.   _____

So, Marisa had ☐ initially.

Check

Use information from the problem to check your answer.

Marisa's initial amount: _____

Amount after spending $8:   _____

Amount after spending $5:   _____

Amount after spending half of what was left: _____

Collaborate Work with a small group to solve the following cases. Show your work on a separate piece of paper.

Case #3 Waterfalls

Angel Falls in Venezuela is 3,212 feet high. It is 87 feet higher than 2.5 times the height of the Empire State Building.

Find the height of the Empire State Building.

Case #4 Number Theory

A number is multiplied by −3. Then 6 is subtracted from the product. After adding −7, the result is −25.

What is the number?

Case #5 Time

Timothy's morning schedule is shown.

At what time does Timothy wake up if he arrives at school at 9:00 A.M.?

Timothy's Schedule	
Activity	**Time**
Wake up	◾
Get ready for school — 45 min	◾
Walk to school — 25 min	9:00 A.M.

Circle a strategy below to solve the problem.

- Determine a reasonabale answer.
- Look for a pattern.
- Make a table.
- Draw a diagram.

Case #6 Money

Antonio has saved $27 in cash to spend at the arcade.

If he has 10 bills, how many of each kind of bill does he have?

Mid-Chapter Check

Vocabulary Check

1. Define *equation*. Give an example of two equivalent equations. (Lesson 1)

_____

_____

2. Fill in the blank with the correct term. (Lesson 2)

A _____ is the numerical factor of a multiplication expression like $3x$.

Skills Check and Problem Solving

Solve each equation. Check your solution. (Lessons 1–5)

3. $21 + m = 33$

4. $a - 5 = -12$

5. $5f = -75$

6. $15 = \dfrac{b}{15}$

7. $19 = 4p + 5$

8. $3(n - 7) = -30$

9. Cameron has 11 adult Fantail goldfish. This is 7 fewer Fantail goldfish than his friend Julia has. Write and solve a subtraction equation to determine the number of Fantail goldfish g that Julia has. (Lesson 1)

Equation: _____   Solution: _____

10. Georgia Test Practice Michelann drove 44 miles per hour and covered a distance of 154 miles. Which equation accurately describes this situation if h represents the number of hours Michelann drove? (Lesson 2)

Ⓐ $154 = 44 + h$ Ⓒ $154 = 44 \div h$

Ⓑ $44h = 154$ Ⓓ $h - 44 = 154$

Inquiry **HOW is an inequality like an equation? How is it different?**

CCGPS Content Standards
MCC7.EE.4,
MCC7.EE.4b
Mathematical Practices
1, 2, 3, 4

School Dance Mr. Numkena volunteered to drive Hinto and his friends to the school dance. The car can carry up to 5 people, including the driver. How many friends can ride in the car with Hinto?

What do you know? _____

_____

What do you need to find? _____

_____

Investigation 1

The real-world situation described above can be represented by the inequality $x + 2 \leq 5$. Let x represent the friends that can ride with Hinto.

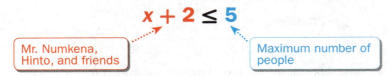

$$x + 2 \leq 5$$

Mr. Numkena, Hinto, and friends

Maximum number of people

You can use a balance to model and solve the inequality $x + 2 \leq 5$.

Step 1 On one side of a balance, place a paper bag and ☐ cubes to model $x + 2$.

Step 2 On the other side of a balance, place ☐ cubes.

Add one cube to the bag at a time. Then complete the table.

Number of Friends, x	$x + 2$	Less than or equal to 5?
1	3	yes
2		
3		
4		

$x + 2$ $\leq$ 5

So, up to ☐ friends can ride with Hinto to the school dance.

An *inequality* is a mathematical sentence that compares quantities. The table shows two examples of inequalities.

Words	Symbols
x is less than two	x < 2
x is greater than or equal to four	x ≥ 4

To solve an inequality means to find values for the variable that make the sentence true. You can use bar diagrams to solve inequalities.

Investigation 2

Money An airline charges for checked luggage that weighs more than 50 pounds. Mia's suitcase currently weighs 35 pounds and she still needs to pack her shoes. Find the maximum amount her shoes can weigh so Mia will not be charged a fee.

Step 1 In the bar diagram, write the maximum weight Mia's luggage can be without a fee. Label the weight of Mia's luggage without her shoes.

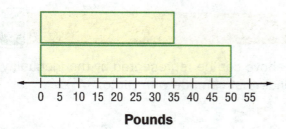

Pounds

Step 2 In the bar diagram, write an *x* beside the bar that represents the weight of Mia's luggage.

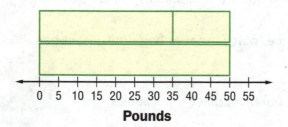

Pounds

The weight of Mia's suitcase plus the weight of her shoes must be less than or equal to the maximum luggage weight.

This can be written as $35 + x \leq 50$.

Using the bar diagram, Mia's shoes cannot weigh more than 50 – 35 or _____ pounds.

Collaborate

Work with a partner to solve the following problems.

CCGPS **Reason Inductively** For Exercises 1–3, assume the paper bag is weightless. Write the inequality represented by each balance. Then write the different possible numbers of cubes in the paper bag if the sides of each balance remain unlevel.

1.

Show your work.

Inequality: _____

Number of Cubes: _____

2.

Inequality: _____

Number of Cubes: _____

3.

Inequality: _____

Number of Cubes: _____

4. **CCGPS** **Reason Abstractly** At an amusement park, roller coaster riders are required to be at least 48 inches tall. Last year, Myron was 42 inches tall. Complete the bar diagram to determine the number of inches x Myron needed to grow this year to be able to ride the roller coaster. Then write an inequality to represent the situation.

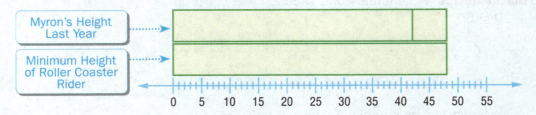

So, Myron needed to grow at least _____ inches.

Inequality: _____

Analyze

Work with a partner to circle the correct inequality for each situation.
The first one is done for you.

Real-World Situation	Inequalities
Yolanda wants to score at least 84% on the next history test.	$x \le 84$ ⬭$x \ge 84$⬭
5. To see a certain movie, you must be at least 13 years old.	$n \le 13$ $n \ge 13$
6. Kai has $4.99 left on a music download gift card. She has a download costing $1.99 in her online shopping cart. How much money does Kai have left to spend?	$x + 1.99 \le 4.99$ $x + 1.99 > 4.99$
7. In some states, teens must be at least 16 years old to obtain a driver's license.	$x < 16$ $x > 16$ $x \le 16$ $x \ge 16$
8. The Walter family budgets a maximum amount of $125 per week for groceries. Mr. Walter already spent $40. How much more can the Walter family spend on groceries?	$x + 40 < 125$ $x + 40 > 125$ $x + 40 \le 125$ $x + 40 \ge 125$
9. Miles pays $30 for a ticket to an amusement park. He cannot spend more than $50. How much more money can Miles spend at the amusement park?	$x + 30 < 50$ $x + 30 > 50$ $x + 30 \le 50$ $x + 30 \ge 50$

Reflect

10. **CCGPS** **Model with Mathematics** Write a real-world situation that could be represented by $x + 20 \ge 50$.

_____

_____

11. **Inquiry** HOW is an inequality like an equation? How is it different?

_____

_____

_____

Solve Inequalities by Addition or Subtraction

What You'll Learn

Scan the lesson. List two headings you would use to make an outline of the lesson.

- _____
- _____

Essential Question

WHAT does it mean to say two quantities are equal?

Vocabulary

Subtraction Property of Inequality
Addition Property of Inequality
inequality

Common Core GPS

Content Standards
MCC7.EE.4, MCC7.EE.4b
Mathematical Practices
1, 2, 3, 4

Real-World Link

Mail A first class stamp can be used for letters and packages weighing thirteen ounces or less. Fisher is mailing pictures to his grandmother, and only has a first class stamp. His envelope weighs 2 ounces. Follow the steps to determine how much the pictures can weigh so that Fisher can use the stamp.

Step 1 Let x represent the weight of the pictures. Write and solve an equation to find the maximum weight of the pictures.

weight of the envelope	weight of the pictures	maximum weight of the package

$$\boxed{} \quad + \quad x \quad = \quad \boxed{}$$

Solve for x.

So, the maximum weight of the pictures is $\boxed{}$ ounces.

Step 2 Replace the equals sign in your equation with the less than or equal to symbol, $\leq$.

$$2 + x \;\boxed{}\; 13$$

Refer to Step 2. Name three possible values of x that will result in a true sentence.

_____

Solve Inequalities

Work Zone

Words You can solve inequalities by using the **Addition Property of Inequalities** and the **Subtraction Property of Inequalities**. When you add or subtract the same number from each side of an inequality, the inequality remains true.

Symbols For all numbers a, b, and c,

1. if $a > b$, then $a + c > b + c$ and $a - c > b - c$.

2. if $a < b$, then $a + c < b + c$ and $a - c < b - c$.

Examples

$$
\begin{array}{rr}
2 < & 4 \\
+\,3 & +\,3 \\
\hline
5 < & 7
\end{array}
\qquad
\begin{array}{rr}
6 > & 3 \\
-\,4 & -\,4 \\
\hline
2 > & -1
\end{array}
$$

An **inequality** is a mathematical sentence that compares quantities. Solving an inequality means finding values for the variable that make the inequality true.

The table below gives some examples of the words you might use when describing different inequalities.

	Inequalities			
Words	• is less than • is fewer than	• is greater than • is more than • exceeds	• is less than or equal to • is no more than • is at most	• is greater than or equal to • is no less than • is at least
Symbols	$<$	$>$	$\leq$	$\geq$

Examples

Tutor

1. **Solve $x + 3 > 10$.**

$$
\begin{array}{ll}
x + 3 > 10 & \text{Write the inequality.} \\
\underline{-3 \quad -3} & \text{Subtract 3 from each side.} \\
x > 7 & \text{Simplify.}
\end{array}
$$

Therefore, the solution is $x > 7$.

You can check this solution by substituting a number greater than 7 into the original inequality. Try using 8.

Check

$$
\begin{array}{ll}
x + 3 > 10 & \text{Write the inequality.} \\
8 + 3 \overset{?}{>} 10 & \text{Replace } x \text{ with 8. Is this sentence true?} \\
11 > 10 & \text{This is a true statement. } ✔
\end{array}
$$

2. Solve $-6 \geq n - 5$.

$-6 \geq n - 5$ Write the inequality.

$+5 \quad\quad +5$ Add 5 to each side.

$-1 \geq n$ Simplify.

The solution is $-1 \geq n$ or $n \leq -1$.

You can check this solution by substituting -1 or a number less than -1 into the original inequality.

Got It? Do these problems to find out.

Solve each inequality.

a. $a - 3 < 8$ **b.** $0.4 + y \geq 7$

a. _____

b. _____

Example

3. Solve $a + \dfrac{1}{2} < 2$. **Graph the solution set on a number line.**

$a + \dfrac{1}{2} < 2$ Write the inequality.

$-\dfrac{1}{2} \quad -\dfrac{1}{2}$ Subtract $\dfrac{1}{2}$ from each side.

$a < 1\dfrac{1}{2}$ Simplify.

The solution is $a < 1\dfrac{1}{2}$.   Check your solution.

Graph the solution.

> Place an open dot at $1\dfrac{1}{2}$. Draw a line and an arrow to the left.

Open and Closed Dots

When graphing inequalities, an open dot is used when the value should not be included in the solution, as with $>$ and $<$ inequalities. A closed dot indicates the value is included in the solution, as with $\leq$ and $\geq$ inequalities.

Got It? Do these problems to find out.

Solve each inequality. Graph the solution set on the number line provided.

c. $h + 4 > 4$ **d.** $x - 6 \leq 4$

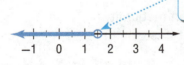

c. _____

d. _____

Write Inequalities

Inequalities can be used to represent real-world situations. You will want to first identify a variable to represent the unknown value.

 **Example**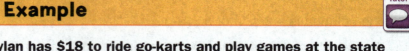

4. Dylan has $18 to ride go-karts and play games at the state fair. Suppose the go-karts cost $5.50. Write and solve an inequality to find the most he can spend on games.

Words	Cost of go-kart	plus	cost of games	must be less than or equal to	total amount.

Symbols   Let x = the cost of the games.

Inequality	5.5	+	x	≤	18

$5.5 + x \leq 18$ Write the inequality. (5.50 = 5.5)

$\underline{-5.5 \qquad -5.5}$ Subtract 5.5 from each side.

$x \leq 12.5$ Simplify.

So, the most Dylan can spend on games is $12.50.

Guided Practice

Solve each inequality. Graph the solution set on a number line. (Examples 1–3)

1. $6 + h \geq 12$ _____

2. $14 + t > 5$ _____

3. An elevator can hold 2,800 pounds or less. Write and solve an inequality that describes how much more weight the elevator can hold if it is currently holding 2,375 pounds. Interpret the solution. (Example 4)

_____
_____

4. **?** **Building on the Essential Question** Explain when you would use addition and when you would use subtraction to solve an inequality. _____

_____
_____

Rate Yourself!

Are you ready to move on? Shade the section that applies.

YES   ?   NO

For more help, go online to access a Personal Tutor.

Independent Practice

Go online for Step-by-Step Solutions

Solve each inequality. (Examples 1 and 2)

1. $h - 16 \leq -24$ _____

2. $y + 6 \geq -13$ _____

3. $-3 < n - 8$ _____

Show your work.

4. $3 \leq m + 1.4$ _____

5. $x + 0.7 > -0.3$ _____

6. $w - 8 \geq 5.6$ _____

Solve each inequality. Graph the solution set on a number line. (Example 3)

7. $m + 5 \geq -1$ _____

8. $-11 > t + 7$ _____

CCGPS **Reason Abstractly** **Write an inequality and solve each problem. For Exercises 11 and 12, interpret the solution.** (Example 4)

9 Four more than a number is more than 13.

Inequality: _____

Solution: _____

10. The sum of a number and 19 is at least 8.2.

Inequality: _____

Solution: _____

11. The high soccer team can have no more than 26 players. Write and solve an inequality to determine how many more players can make the team if the coach has already chosen 17 players.

Inequality: _____   Solution: _____

Interpretation: _____

12. Lalo has 1,500 minutes per month on his cell phone plan. How many more minutes can he use if he has already talked for 785 minutes?

Inequality: _____   Solution: _____

Interpretation: _____

13. Refer to the diagram below.

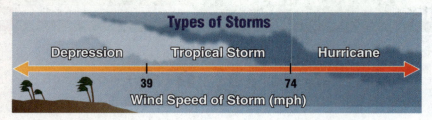

Types of Storms

Depression   Tropical Storm   Hurricane

39   74

Wind Speed of Storm (mph)

a. A hurricane has winds that are at least 74 miles per hour. Suppose a tropical storm has winds that are 42 miles per hour. Write and solve an inequality to find how much the winds must increase before the storm becomes a hurricane.

Inequality: _____   Solution: _____

b. A *major storm* has wind speeds that are at least 110 miles per hour. Write and solve an inequality that describes how much greater these wind speeds are than the slowest hurricane.

Inequality: _____   Solution: _____

 H.O.T. Problems Higher Order Thinking

14. **CCGPS** **Reason Inductively** Compare and contrast the solutions of
$a - 3 = 15$ and $a - 3 \geq 15$. _____
_____
_____

15. **CCGPS** **Model with Mathematics** Write an addition inequality for the solution set graphed below.

_____

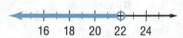

16 18 20 22 24

16. **CCGPS** **Persevere with Problems** Solve $x + b > c$ for x.

_____
_____

✏️ **Georgia Test Practice**

17. Which graph represents the solution of inequality $x + 3 > 2$?

Ⓐ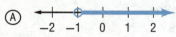
−2 −1 0 1 2

Ⓒ
3 4 5 6 7

Ⓑ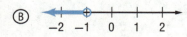
−2 −1 0 1 2

Ⓓ
3 4 5 6 7

Extra Practice

Solve each inequality.

18. $10 < b - 8$ $18 < b$

 Homework Help →

$$10 < b - 8$$
$$\underline{+\,8 \quad\quad +\,8}$$
$$18 < b$$

19. $1.2 + m \leq 5.5$ _____

20. $c - 1\frac{1}{4} > -2\frac{1}{2}$ _____

CCGPS **Model with Mathematics** Solve each inequality. Graph the solution set on a number line.

21. $-21 < a - 16$ _____

22. $t - 6.2 < 4$ _____

Write an inequality and solve each problem.

23. Eight less than a number is less than 10.

Inequality: _____

Solution: _____

24. The difference between a number and $21\frac{1}{2}$ is no more than $14\frac{1}{4}$.

Inequality: _____

Solution: _____

25. There were a total of 125 cars at a car dealership. A salesperson sold 68 of the cars in one month. Write and solve an inequality that describes how many more cars, at most, the salesman has left to sell. Interpret the solution.

Inequality: _____   Solution: _____

Interpretation: _____

Copy and Solve Solve each inequality. Graph the solution set on a number line. Show your work on a separate sheet of paper.

26. $n - \frac{1}{5} \leq \frac{3}{10}$

27. $6 > x + 3\frac{1}{3}$

28. $c + 1\frac{1}{4} < 5$

29. $9 \leq m - 2\frac{1}{5}$

30. $\frac{3}{4} + d > 4\frac{1}{2}$

31. $-\frac{7}{8} \leq n + 3\frac{5}{16}$

32. Which inequality represents a temperature that is equal to or less than 42°?

Ⓐ $t \geq 42$

Ⓑ $t > 42$

Ⓒ $t \leq 42$

Ⓓ $t < 42$

33. Which inequality represents the graph below?

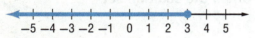

Ⓕ $x > 3$

Ⓖ $x \geq 3$

Ⓗ $x < 3$

Ⓘ $x \leq 3$

34. Arlo has $25 to spend on a T-shirt and shorts for gym class. The shorts cost $14. Use the inequality $14 + t \leq 25$, where t represents the cost of the T-shirt. What is the most Arlo can spend on the T-shirt?

Ⓐ $9

Ⓑ $10.99

Ⓒ $11

Ⓓ $11.50

35. Short Response Write and solve an inequality for the following sentence: Jan has saved $50 in her savings account and needs to save at least $268 for camp. What is the least amount that she needs to save? _____

Solve each equation. Then graph each solution on the number line below. MCC6.EE.6

36. $x + 2 = 1$

37. $x - 1 = -5$

38. $2x = 10$

39. $-2x = 4$

40. $\frac{x}{2} = 1$

41. $\frac{x}{-2} = 3$

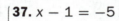

Write the number or numbers from the set {−3, −2, −1, 0, 1, 2, 3} that make each sentence true. MCC6.EE.5

42. $6x = -12$ _____

43. $r \leq 3$ _____

Solve Inequalities by Multiplication or Division

What You'll Learn

Scan the lesson. Predict two things you will learn about solving inequalities by multiplication or division.

- _____
  _____

- _____
  _____

Essential Question

WHAT does it mean to say two quantities are equal?

Vocabulary

Multiplication Property of Inequality
Division Property of Inequality

Common Core GPS

Content Standards
MCC7.EE.4, MCC7.EE.4b
Mathematical Practices
1, 2, 3, 4, 7

Real-World Link

Science An astronaut in a space suit weighs about 300 pounds on Earth, but only 50 pounds on the Moon.

weight on Earth   weight on Moon
300 lb   >   50 lb

1. If the astronaut and space suit each weighed half as much, would the inequality still be true?

$$\frac{300}{2} > \frac{50}{2}$$ Divide each side by 2.

$$\boxed{} > \boxed{}$$

Is the inequality still true? Circle yes or no.

Yes   No

2. Is the weight of one astronaut greater on Pluto or Earth? Would the weight of 5 astronauts be greater on Pluto or on Earth? Explain by using an inequality.

_____
_____

Location	Weight of Astronaut (lb)
Earth	300
Moon	50
Pluto	67
Jupiter	796

3. Is the weight of one astronaut greater on Jupiter or on Earth? Would the weight of 5 astronauts be greater on Jupiter or on Earth? Explain by using an inequality.

_____

Multiplication and Division Properties of Inequality, Positive Number

Work Zone

STOP and Reflect

What does the inequality $c > 0$ mean? Explain below.

Words   The **Multiplication Property of Inequality** and the **Division Property of Inequality** state that an inequality remains true when you multiply or divide each side of an inequality by a positive number.

Symbols   For all numbers a, b, and c, where $c > 0$,

1. if $a > b$, then $ac > bc$ and $\frac{a}{c} > \frac{b}{c}$.
2. if $a < b$, then $ac < bc$ and $\frac{a}{c} < \frac{b}{c}$.

These properties are also true for $a \geq b$ and $a \leq b$.

You can solve inequalities by using the Multiplication Property of Inequality and the Division Property of Inequality.

Examples

Tutor

1. **Solve $8x \leq 40$.**

$$8x \leq 40 \qquad \text{Write the inequality.}$$
$$\frac{8x}{8} \leq \frac{40}{8} \qquad \text{Divide each side by 8.}$$
$$x \leq 5 \qquad \text{Simplify.}$$

The solution is $x \leq 5$. You can check this solution by substituting 5 or a number less than 5 into the inequality.

- -

2. **Solve $\frac{d}{2} > 7$.**

$$\frac{d}{2} > 7 \qquad \text{Write the inequality.}$$
$$2\left(\frac{d}{2}\right) > 2(7) \qquad \text{Multiply each side by 2.}$$
$$d > 14 \qquad \text{Simplify.}$$

The solution is $d > 14$. You can check this solution by substituting a number greater than 14 into the inequality.

Show your work.

Got It?   Do these problems to find out.

a. $4x < 40$

b. $6 \geq \frac{x}{7}$

a. _____

b. _____

Multiplication and Division Properties of Inequality, Negative Number

Key Concept

Words   When you multiply or divide each side of an inequality by a negative number, the inequality symbol must be reversed for the inequality to remain true.

Symbols   For all numbers a, b, and c, where $c < 0$,

1. if $a > b$, then $ac < bc$ and $\dfrac{a}{c} < \dfrac{b}{c}$.

2. if $a < b$, then $ac > bc$ and $\dfrac{a}{c} > \dfrac{b}{c}$.

Examples

$$7 > 1$$
$$-2(7) < -2(1) \quad \text{Reverse the symbols.}$$
$$-14 < -2$$

$$-4 < 16$$
$$\dfrac{-4}{-4} > \dfrac{16}{-4}$$
$$1 > -4$$

These properties are also true for $a \geq b$ and $a \leq b$.

STOP and Reflect

What does the inequality $c < 0$ mean? Expain below.

Examples

3. Solve $-2g < 10$. Graph the solution set on a number line.

$$-2g < 10 \qquad \text{Write the inequality.}$$
$$\dfrac{-2g}{-2} > \dfrac{10}{-2} \qquad \text{Divide each side by } -2 \text{ and reverse the symbol.}$$
$$g > -5 \qquad \text{Simplify.}$$

```
  ←─┼───┼───⊕───┼───┼──→
   -7  -6  -5  -4  -3
```

4. Solve $\dfrac{x}{-3} \leq 4$. Graph the solution set on a number line.

$$\dfrac{x}{-3} \leq 4 \qquad \text{Write the inequality.}$$
$$-3\left(\dfrac{x}{-3}\right) \geq -3(4) \qquad \text{Multiply each side by } -3 \text{ and reverse the symbol.}$$
$$x \geq -12 \qquad \text{Simplify.}$$

```
  ←─┼───┼───●───┼───┼───→
   -16  -14  -12  -10  -8  -6
```

Got It?   Do these problems to find out.

c. $\dfrac{k}{-2} < 9$

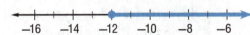

c. _____

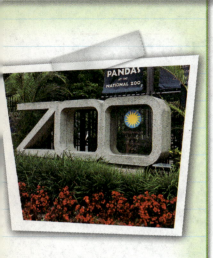

Example

Tutor

5. Ling earns $8 per hour working at the zoo. Write and solve an inequality that can be used to find how many hours she must work in a week to earn at least $120. Interpret the solution.

Words	Amount earned times per hour	number of hours	is at least	amount earned each week.
Variable	Let x represent the number of hours.			
Inequality	8 •	x	$\geq$	120

$8x \geq 120$ Write the inequality.

$\dfrac{8x}{8} \geq \dfrac{120}{8}$ Divide each side by 8.

$x \geq 15$ Simplify.

So, Ling must work at least 15 hours.

Guided Practice

Check ✓

Solve each inequality. Graph the solution set on a number line. (Examples 1–4)

1. $-3n \leq -22$ _____

2. $\dfrac{t}{-4} < -11$ _____

← —————————————→ | ← —————————————→

3. At a baseball game you can get a single hot dog for $2. You have $10 to spend. Write and solve an inequality to find the number of hot dogs you can buy. Interpret the solution. (Example 5) _____

_____

4. ⓔ **Building on the Essential Question** Explain when you should not reverse the inequality symbol when solving an inequality. _____

_____

_____

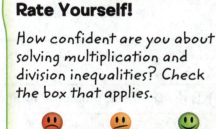
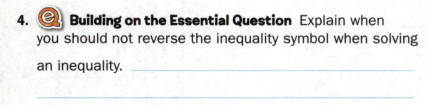

Name _____ My Homework _____

Solve each inequality. (Examples 1 and 2)

1. $6y < 18$ _____

2. $-3s \geq 33$ _____

3 $60 \leq \dfrac{m}{3}$ _____

 Show your work.

4. $\dfrac{t}{-2} < 6$ _____

5. $\dfrac{m}{-14} \leq -4$ _____

6. $-56 \leq -8x$ _____

7. $12n \leq 54$ _____

8. $\dfrac{h}{9} > \dfrac{1}{4}$ _____

9. $\dfrac{w}{-5} \geq 9$ _____

Solve each inequality. Graph the solution set on a number line. (Examples 3 and 4)

10. $4x \geq 36$ _____

11 $20 < 5t$ _____

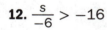

12. $\dfrac{s}{-6} > -16$ _____

13. $\dfrac{x}{-4} \geq 8$ _____

14. A pool charges \$4 each visit, or you can buy a membership. Write and solve an inequality to find how many times a person should use the pool so that a membership is less expensive than paying each time. Interpret the solution. (Example 5)

Inequality: _____   Solution: _____

Interpretation: _____

_____

CITY POOL MEMBERSHIP
3 months for \$100

15. **CCGPS** **Reason Inductively** Cross out the inequality that does not belong in the organizer shown at the right. Then explain your reasoning.

_____

_____

_____

| $-2x > 12$ | $-2 < x + 4$ |
| $\frac{x}{2} < -3$ | $-7 > x - 1$ |

Write an inequality for each sentence. Then solve the inequality.

16. Sixteen is less than eight times a number.

Inequality: _____

Solution: _____

17. The product of a number and five is at the most 30.

Inequality: _____

Solution: _____

H.O.T. Problems   Higher Order Thinking

18. **CCGPS** **Identify Structure** Write two different inequalities that have the solution $y > 6$. One inequality should be solved using multiplication properties, and the other should be solved using division properties.

_____

_____

19. **CCGPS** **Persevere with Problems** You score 15, 16, 17, 14, and 19 points out of 20 possible points on five tests. What must you score on the sixth test to have an average of at least 16 points?

_____

_____

Georgia Test Practice

20. Which inequality represents _twice a number is less than ten_?

Ⓐ $(5 + 2)n < 0$

Ⓑ $10n < -5$

Ⓒ $10 < 2n$

Ⓓ $2n < 10$

Extra Practice

Solve each inequality.

21. $-10n > -20$ $n < 2$

Homework Help
$$-10n > -20$$
$$\frac{-10n}{-10} < \frac{-20}{-10}$$
$$n < 2$$

22. $-7y < 35$

23. $15 < 3r$

24. $12p \geq -72$

25. $\dfrac{t}{-7} > 10$

26. $-8 < \dfrac{y}{5}$

Solve each inequality. Graph the solution set on a number line.

27. $-3w < -39$

28. $\dfrac{h}{5} \leq -12$

29. $10 \leq \dfrac{t}{-2}$

30. $15 < 4x$

31. **CCGPS** **Reason Abstractly** Each game at a carnival costs $0.50, or you can pay $15 and play an unlimited amount of games. Write and solve an inequality to find how many times you should play a game so that the unlimited game play is less expensive than paying each time. Interpret the solution.

Inequality: _____   Solution: _____

Interpretation: _____

Write an inequality for each sentence. Then solve the inequality.

32. The product of a number and 4 is at least -12.

Inequality: _____

Solution: _____

33. Five times a number is less than -45.

Inequality: _____

Solution: _____

34. Which sentence represents the inequality shown below?

$$\frac{x}{5} \le 8$$

- Ⓐ The difference of a number and 5 is at most 8.
- Ⓑ The quotient of a number and 5 is at most 8.
- Ⓒ The quotient of a number and 5 is 8.
- Ⓓ The quotient of a number and 5 is at least 8.

35. Karl's scores on the first five science tests are shown in the table.

Test	1	2	3	4	5
Score	85	84	90	95	88

Which inequality represents the lowest score Karl can receive in order to have an average score of more than 88?

- Ⓕ $s > 86$
- Ⓗ $s < 86$
- Ⓖ $s \ge 86$
- Ⓘ $s \le 86$

Solve each equation. Check your solution. MCC6.EE.6

36. $5k + 6 = 16$

37. $-14 = 2x - 8$

38. $-4n + 3 = 13$

39. $25 = 7m + 4$

40. $10.5 + h = 22.5$

41. $14n - 32 = 22$

42. Mrs. Lewis paid a total of $27.50 for 3 large cheese pizzas, including a $5 delivery fee. Write and solve an equation to find the amount Mrs. Lewis paid for each pizza p. MCC6.EE.7

Equation: _____   Solution: _____

Solve Two-Step Inequalities

What You'll Learn

Scan the lesson. Predict two things you will learn about solving two-step inequalities.

- _____
- _____

Essential Question

WHAT does it mean to say two quantities are equal?

Vocabulary

Vocab abc

two-step inequality

Common Core GPS

CCGPS

Content Standards
MCC7.EE.4, MCC7.EE.4b

Mathematical Practices
1, 2, 3, 4, 5

Real-World Link

Newspapers Kaitlyn is placing an ad in the local newspaper for a pottery class. The cost of placing an ad is shown in the table.

Service	Cost ($)
10-day ad with 3 lines	38.00
each additional line	9.00

1. Complete the equation to find the total cost c of an ad with 4 or more lines. Use x as the variable.

   | cost of a 10-day add with only 3 lines | cost of each additional line | total cost |

   ☐ + ☐x = ☐

2. How much will it cost to place the ad if it is 5 lines long?

   _____

3. Suppose Kaitlyn can spend only $50 on the ad. Does she have enough money to place the ad? (Circle) yes or no.

   yes   no

   If the answer is no, how much more money will Kaitlyn

   need? Explain. _____

   _____

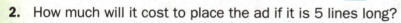

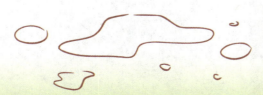

Solve a Two-Step Inequality

A **two-step inequality** is an inequality that contains two operations. To solve a two-step inequality, use inverse operations to undo each operation in reverse order of the order of operations.

Examples

1. Solve $3x + 4 \geq 16$. Graph the solution set on a number line.

$$3x + 4 \geq 16 \qquad \text{Write the inequality.}$$
$$\underline{-4 \quad -4} \qquad \text{Subtract 4 from each side.}$$
$$3x \qquad \geq 12 \qquad \text{Simplify.}$$
$$\frac{3x}{3} \geq \frac{12}{3} \qquad \text{Divide each side by 3.}$$
$$x \geq 4 \qquad \text{Simplify.}$$

Graph the solution set.

Draw a closed dot at 4 with an arrow to the right.

2. Solve $5 + 4x < 33$. Graph the solution set on a number line.

$$5 + 4x < 33 \qquad \text{Write the inequality.}$$
$$\underline{-5 \qquad -5} \qquad \text{Subtract 5 from each side.}$$
$$4x < 28 \qquad \text{Simplify.}$$
$$\frac{4x}{4} < \frac{28}{4} \qquad \text{Divide each side by 4.}$$
$$x < 7 \qquad \text{Simplify.}$$

Graph the solution set.

Draw an open dot at 7 with an arrow to the left.

 Show your work.

Got It? Do this problem to find out.

a. Solve $2x + 8 > 24$. Graph the solution on the number line provided.

a. _____

Examples

3. Solve **7 − 2x > 11. Graph the solution set on a number line.**

$7 - 2x > 11$	Write the inequality.
$\underline{-7 \qquad -7}$	Subtract 7 from each side.
$-2x > 4$	Simplify.
$\dfrac{-2x}{-2} < \dfrac{4}{-2}$	Divide each side by −2. Reverse inequality symbol.
$x < -2$	Simplify. Check your solution.

Graph the solution set.

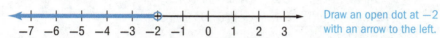

Draw an open dot at −2 with an arrow to the left.

You can check the solution by substituting a number less than −2 into the original inequality. Try using −3.

Check	$7 - 2x > 11$	Write the inequality.
	$7 - 2(-3) \stackrel{?}{>} 11$	Replace x with −3. Is the sentence true?
	$13 > 11$	This is a true statement. ✔

4. Solve $\dfrac{x}{2} - 5 < -8$. **Graph the solution set on a number line.**

$\dfrac{x}{2} - 5 < -8$	Write the inequality.
$\underline{+5 \qquad +5}$	Add 5 to each side.
$\dfrac{x}{2} < -3$	Simplify.
$\dfrac{x}{2}(2) < -3(2)$	Multiply each side by 2.
$x < -6$	Simplify. Check your solution.

Graph the solution set.

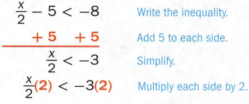

Draw an open dot at −6 with an arrow to the left.

Got It? Do these problems to find out.

Solve each inequality. Graph the solution set on the number line provided.

b. $\dfrac{x}{2} + 9 \geq 5$

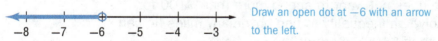

c. $8 - \dfrac{x}{3} \leq 7$

b. _____

c. _____

Solving Inequalities

Remember that if multiplying or dividing by a negative number when solving inequalities, reverse the direction of the inequality symbol.

Show your work.

5. Halfway through the bowling league season, Stewart has 34 strikes. He averages 2 strikes per game. Write and solve an inequality to find how many more games it will take for Stewart to have at least 61 strikes, the league record. Interpret the solution.

The number of strikes plus two strikes per game is at least 61. Let g represent the number of games he needs to bowl.

$$34 + 2g \geq 61 \qquad \text{Write the inequality.}$$
$$\underline{-34 \qquad\qquad -34} \qquad \text{Subtract 34 from each side.}$$
$$2g \geq 27 \qquad \text{Simplify.}$$
$$\frac{2g}{2} \geq \frac{27}{2} \qquad \text{Divide each side by 2.}$$
$$g \geq 13.5 \qquad \text{Simplify.}$$

Stewart should have at least 61 strikes after 14 more games.

Guided Practice

 Check ✓

Solve each inequality. Graph the solution set on a number line. (Examples 1–4)

1. $5x - 7 \geq 43 =$ _____

2. $11 \leq 7 + \frac{x}{5}$ _____

3. **Financial Literacy** A rental car company charges $45 plus $0.20 per mile to rent a car. Mr. Lawrence does not want to spend more than $100 for his rental car. Write and solve an inequality to find how many miles he can drive and not spend more than $100. Interpret the solution. (Example 5)

_____

_____

4. **Building on the Essential Question** Compare $2x + 8 > 18$ and $2x + 8 \leq 18$.

_____

_____

_____

_____

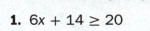

Independent Practice

Go online for Step-by-Step Solutions

Solve each inequality. Graph the solution set on a number line. (Examples 1–4)

1. $6x + 14 \geq 20$ _____

Show your work.

2. $4x - 13 < 11$ _____

3 $-20 > -2x + 4$ _____

4. $\frac{x}{13} + 3 \geq 4$ _____

5 Tyler needs at least \$205 for a new video game system. He has already saved \$30. He earns \$7 an hour at his job. Write and solve an inequality to find how many hours he will need to work to buy the system. Interpret the solution. (Example 5)

Inequality: _____ Solution: _____

Interpretation: _____

New Game System ONLY \$205

Reason Abstractly Write and solve an inequality for each sentence.

6. Three times a number increased by four is less than −62.

_____

7. The quotient of a number and −5 increased by one is at most 7.

_____

8. The quotient of a number and 3 minus two is at least −12.

_____

9. The product of −2 and a number minus six is greater than −18.

_____

Write a two-step inequality that could be represented by each number line.

10.

11 12 13 14 15 16

_____

11.

4 5 6 7 8 9

_____

12.

93 94 95 96 97 98

_____

13.

48 49 50 51 52 53

_____

 H.O.T. Problems Higher Order Thinking

14. CCGPS **Model with Mathematics** Write a real-world example that could be solved by using the inequality $4x + 8 \geq 32$. Then solve the inequality.

_____

_____

_____

_____

15. CCGPS **Persevere with Problems** In five games, you score 16, 12, 15, 13, and 17 points. How many points must you score in the sixth game to have an average of at least 15 points?

_____

16. CCGPS **Use Math Tools** Solve $-x + 6 > -(2x + 4)$. Then graph the solution set on the number line.

Solution: _____

Georgia Test Practice

17. Which inequality represents *six less than three times a number is at least fifteen?*

- Ⓐ $3n - 6 \leq 15$
- Ⓑ $3n - 6 \geq 15$
- Ⓒ $3n - 6 < 15$
- Ⓓ $3n - 6 > 15$

Extra Practice

Solve each inequality. Graph the solution set on a number line.

18. $4x - 15 \le 5$ $x \le 5$

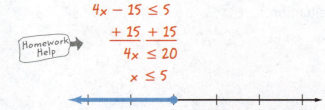

$$4x - 15 \le 5$$
$$\underline{+ 15 \quad + 15}$$
$$4x \le 20$$
$$x \le 5$$

Homework Help ➡

19. $-73 \ge 15 + 11x$ _____

20. $\dfrac{x}{5} - 2 > 1$ _____

21. $9 \le \dfrac{x}{14} + 6$ _____

22. Catie is starting a babysitting business. She spent $26 to make signs to advertise. She charges an initial fee of $5 and then $3 for each hour of service. Write and solve an inequality to find the number of hours she will have to babysit to make a profit. Interpret the solution.

Inequality: _____   Solution: _____

Interpretation: _____

23. **CCGPS** **Reason Abstractly** As a salesperson, Audrey earns $75 per week plus $5 per sale. This week, she wants her pay to be at least $125. Write and solve an inequality for the number of sales Audrey needs to make. Interpret the solution.

Inequality: _____   Solution: _____

Interpretation: _____

24. Elijah and his sister went to the movies. They had $34 altogether and spent $9.50 per ticket. Elijah and his sister bought the same snacks. Write and solve an inequality for the amount that each person spent on snacks. Interpret the solution.

Inequality: _____   Solution: _____

Interpretation: _____

25. You want to purchase a necklace for $325.75, including tax. You have already saved $115 and can set aside $22 a week. Which inequality can be used to find the number of weeks it will take to save at least $325?

Ⓐ $22w + 115 \geq 325.75$

Ⓑ $22w + 115 \leq 325.75$

Ⓒ $22 + 115w \leq 325.75$

Ⓓ $22w + 115 < 325.75$

26. Short Response Dante has 60 baseball cards. This is at least six more than three times as many cards as Anna. Write and solve an inequality to represent the situation. _____

27. Which of the following inequalities has the solution set shown below?

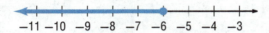

Ⓕ $-2x - 5 < 7$ Ⓖ $-2x - 5 > 7$ Ⓗ $-2x - 5 \leq 7$ Ⓘ $-2x - 5 \geq 7$

CCGPS Common Core Review

Solve and graph each inequality. MCC7.EE.4b

28. $n + 1 > -2$

Solution: _____

29. $-2y > 12$

Solution: _____

30. $\dfrac{t}{-1} > -2$

Solution: _____

Solve each equation. Check your solution. MCC7.EE.4a

31. $5y + 6 = 46$

32. $-4k - 1 = 47$

33. $5 = 8m + 1$

34. Michael's dad is 30 years of age. He is 2 years more than four times Michael's age m. Write and solve a two-step equation to determine Michael's age. MCC6.EE.7

Equation: _____ Solution: _____

Veterinary Technician

If you love being around animals, enjoy working with your hands, and are good at analyzing problems, a challenging career in veterinary medicine might be a perfect fit for you. Veterinary technicians help veterinarians by helping to diagnose and treat medical conditions. They may work in private clinics, animal hospitals, zoos, aquariums, or wildlife rehabilitation centers.

College & Career READINESS

Explore college and careers at ccr.mcgraw-hill.com

Is This the Career for You?

Are you interested in a career as a veterinary technician? Take some of the following courses in high school.

- ◆ Algebra
- ◆ Animal Science
- ◆ Biology
- ◆ Chemistry
- ◆ Veterinary Assisting

Find out how math relates to a career in Veterinary Medicine.

Vet Techs Don't Monkey Around

For each problem, use the information in the tables to write an equation. Then solve the equation.

1. The minimum tail length of an emperor tamarin is 1.6 inches greater than that of a golden lion tamarin. What is the minimum tail length of a golden lion tamarin?

   _____

2. The minimum body length of a golden lion tamarin is 5.3 inches less than the maximum body length. What is the maximum body

   length? _____

3. Tamarins live an average of 15 years. This is 13 years less than the years that one tamarin in captivity lived. How long did the tamarin in

   captivity live? _____

4. The maximum weight of a golden lion tamarin is about 1.97 times the maximum weight of an emperor tamarin. What is the maximum weight of an emperor tamarin? Round to the nearest tenth.

   _____

5. For an emperor tamarin, the maximum total length, including the body and tail, is 27 inches. What is the maximum body length of an emperor tamarin?

   _____

Golden Lion Tamarin Monkeys

Measure	Minimum	Maximum
Body length	7.9 in.	ℓ
Tail length	t	15.7 in.
Weight	12.7 oz	28 oz

Emperor Tamarin Monkeys

Measure	Minimum	Maximum
Body length	9.2 in.	b
Tail length	14 in.	15.7 in.
Weight	10.7 oz	w

Career Project

It's time to update your career portfolio! Go to the Occupational Outlook Handbook online and research a career as a veterinary technician. Include brief descriptions of the work environment, education and training requirements, and the job outlook.

_____

_____

_____

_____

Do you think you would enjoy a career as a veterinary technician? Why or why not?

- _____
- _____
- _____
- _____
- _____

Vocabulary Check

Unscramble each of the clue words.

TOW-SETP

⬜⬜⬜ — ⬜⬜⬜⬜
 7

PYORERPT

⬜⬜⬜⬜⬜⬜⬜⬜
         8

DODTIINA

⬜⬜⬜⬜⬜⬜⬜⬜
   6

NIIOSDIV

⬜⬜⬜⬜⬜⬜⬜⬜

LABVIERA

⬜⬜⬜⬜⬜⬜⬜
       5

AILEYQUITN

⬜⬜⬜⬜⬜⬜⬜⬜⬜⬜
   2

BISTAUTORNC

⬜⬜⬜⬜⬜⬜⬜⬜⬜⬜⬜
  3

NUATIEQO

⬜⬜⬜⬜⬜⬜⬜⬜
 1

TIULINTICPOLMA

⬜⬜⬜⬜⬜⬜⬜⬜⬜⬜⬜⬜⬜⬜
               4

Use the numbered letters to find another vocabulary term from this chapter.

⬜⬜⬜⬜⬜⬜⬜⬜
1 2 3 4 5 6 7 8

Use Your FOLDABLES

Use your Foldable to help review the chapter.

Tape here

Solve Two-Step Equations

Solve

Solve

Got it?

Match each phrase with the correct term.

1. The value of a variable that makes an equation true

2. The numerical factor in a multiplication expression

3. Equations that have the same solution

4. A sentence stating that two quantities are equal

a. equivalent equations

b. equation

c. Addition Property of Equality

d. coefficient

e. formula

f. solution

Problem Solving

1. **STEM** A giraffe is 3.5 meters taller than a camel. If a giraffe is 5.5 meters tall, how tall is a camel? (Lesson 1) _____

_____

2. **Financial Literacy** Martina borrowed $98 from her father. She plans to repay her father at $14 per week. Write and solve an equation to find the number of weeks w required to pay back her father. (Lesson 2)

_____

_____

3. A blimp travels 300 miles in 7.5 hours. Assume the blimp travels at a constant speed. Write and solve an equation to find the speed of the blimp. Use the formula $d = rt$. (Lesson 3) _____

_____

_____

4. Joel and two friends went to the movies. They each bought a medium popcorn. Altogether, they spent $45. Write and solve an equation to determine how much each boy spent on a movie ticket? (Lesson 5)

Popcorn Prices	
Size	**Cost ($)**
small	4.50
medium	5.50
large	6.75

_____

_____

5. **CCGPS** **Reason Abstractly** Ben is training for football and is lifting 120 pounds on the bench press. He can lift a maximum of 180 pounds. Write and solve an inequality to determine how much additional weight Ben can lift. (Lesson 6) _____

_____

6. Jessie wants to spend less than $18.75 on new socks. Each pack costs $6. Write and solve an inequality to find the maximum number of packs she can buy. (Lesson 7) _____

_____

7. **Financial Literacy** Mr. Walker works as a salesperson at an electronics store. He earns $600 a week, plus $50 for every computer he sells. Write and solve an inequality to determine the number of computers Mr. Walker must sell in order to earn at least $1,250 for the week.

Interpret the solution. (Lesson 8) _____

_____

Reflect

 Answering the Essential Question

Use what you learned about equations and inequalities to complete the
graphic organizer.

When do you use an equals sign?

 Essential Question

**WHAT does it mean to say two
quantities are equal?**

When do you use an inequality symbol?

 Answer the Essential Question. WHAT does it mean to say two
quantities are equal?

_____

_____

COLLABORATIVE PROJECT

 Become a Travel Expert Without proper planning, a family vacation could end up costing a fortune! In this project you will:

- **Collaborate** with your classmates as you research the cost of a family vacation.

- **Share** the results of your research in a creative way.

- **@ Reflect** on how you use mathematics to describe change and model real-world situations.

By the end of this project, you will be ready to plan a family vacation without breaking the bank.

Collaborate

Go Online Work with your group to research and complete each activity. You will use your results in the Share section on the following page.

1. Research the cost for a family of four to fly round trip to a destination of your choosing. Record the cost of a flight that is nonstop and one that has at least one extra stop. Make sure to include the cost of the tax.

2. Research two different rental cars that would be available at a local company. Compare the miles per gallon (mpg) that each car averages on the highway. How much gas would you use for each car if you were going to be traveling 450 miles on your trip?

3. If you are traveling out of the country you will need to know the current exchange rates. Record the exchange rate for three different countries. How much is $100 worth in those countries?

4. Choose a vacation spot that is a city in the United States. Find a popular restaurant for tourists in your city and look up their menu online. Calculate the cost for a dinner that feeds four people. Don't forget the tip.

5. Different states have different sales tax rates. Choose three different states. Research the sales tax rate for each of those states. Then, determine the total cost of buying jeans that cost $50 plus the sales tax.

With your group, decide on a way to share what you have learned about the cost of a family vacation. Some suggestions are listed below, but you can also think of other creative ways to present your information. Remember to show how you used mathematics in your project!

- Use your creative writing skills to write journal entries or blogs. Your writing should describe how you were able to save money while traveling on your vacations.
- Act as a travel agent to put together one domestic and one international travel package for a family of four. Create a digital brochure to explain each package.

Check out the note on the right to connect this project with other subjects.

 **connect** with **Language Arts**

Financial Literacy *Imagine that you are the director of tourism for your state. Write a script for a commercial that is trying to encourage tourists to visit. Your script should include:*

- *unique activities found in your state*
- *ways of traveling in your state*

 **Reflect**

6. **Answer the Essential Question** How can you use mathematics to describe change and model real-world situations?

   a. How did you use what you learned about ratios and proportional reasoning to describe change and model the real-world situations in this project?

   _____

   _____

   _____

   _____

   b. How did you use what you learned about percents to describe change and model the real-world situations in this project?

   _____

   _____

   _____

   _____

COLLABORATIVE PROJECT

Watch ▶

Explore the Ocean Depths For this project, imagine that your dream job is to become an oceanographer. In this project you will:

- **Collaborate** with your classmates as you research information about the ocean.
- **Share** the results of your research in a creative way.
- **ⓔ Reflect** on how mathematical ideas can be represented.

Collaborate

ⓤ Go Online Work with your group to research and complete each activity. You will use your results in the Share section on the following page.

1. About $\frac{2}{3}$ of Earth is covered by ocean. Research the five oceans of the world and create a table that shows about what fraction each ocean is of that $\frac{2}{3}$.

2. What is the greatest ocean depth? Find out and then display it on a vertical number line along with other facts about what you can find at different ocean depths.

3. Coral reefs are the home of many ocean creatures. Look up some facts about the state of coral reefs in the world today and display them in a creative way.

4. Choose three different types of whales that live in the ocean. Compare things like their size, the amount of food they eat, or the climate in which they live. Organize the information in a table or graph.

5. Research one of the larger icebergs in the Arctic Ocean. Sketch an image of the iceberg next to a vertical number line that shows the approximate top and bottom of the iceberg. Remember, about $\frac{7}{8}$ of an iceberg is under water.

Share

With your group, decide on a way to share what you have learned about ocean depths. Some suggestions are listed below, but you could also think of other creative ways to present your information. Remember to show how you used mathematics in your project!

- Use presentation software to organize what you have learned in this project. Share your presentation with the class.
- Imagine you need to apply for funds to go on a deep sea exploration. Write a persuasive letter or speech that highlights the importance of studying ocean depths.

Check out the note on the right to connect this project with other subjects.

connect with **Science**

Environmental Literacy Research an animal that lives in the ocean that is on the endangered species list. Give a presentation to your class that answers the following questions:

- What are some of the causes for the animals being on the endangered species list?
- What efforts are currently being made to protect the animal you chose?

Reflect

6. **ⓔ Answer the Essential Question** How can mathematical ideas be represented?

   a. How were mathematical ideas involving integers represented in the information you discovered about oceans?

   _____

   _____

   _____

   _____

   b. How were mathematical ideas involving rational numbers represented in the information you discovered about oceans?

   _____

   _____

   _____

   _____

COLLABORATIVE PROJECT

Watch ▶

Stand Up and Be Counted The U.S. Census is used to determine the number of U.S. House of Representative members that each state is assigned. In this project you will:

- **Collaborate** with your classmates as you research Census data and the U.S. House of Representatives.

- **Share** the results of your research in a creative way.

- **ℯ Reflect** on how you can communicate mathematical ideas effectively.

👥 Collaborate

⏻ Go Online Work with your group to research and complete each activity. You will use your results in the Share section on the following page.

1. Explore the official U.S. Census web site to find the 2010 state populations. There will be interactive maps that display this information. Write down a few facts you find interesting.

2. Create a table that displays the population and the number of U.S. Representatives for your state and three other states. Then create a line plot for the number of U.S. Representatives.

3. Write an equation that uses any state's population x and its number of U.S. Representative members y to describes the number of people per U.S. Representative z.

4. Use your equation from Exercise 3 to determine the approximate number of people per U.S. Representative for the four states you chose. Interpret the results.

5. Look at the 2000 and 2010 census. How did the population of your state and states in your region change? Did the population change affect the number of U.S. Representatives assigned?

6. States can be categorized by population size and density. Write at least two inequalities that compare the states using these categories.

 **Share**

With your group, decide on a way to share what you have learned about the U.S. House of Representatives and state populations. Some suggestions are listed below, but you can also think of other creative ways to present your information. Remember to show how you used mathematics to complete each of the activities in this project!

- Act as a Census representative and create a presentation to encourage people to participate in the census and explain why it is important.
- Write a letter or email to your Representative about what you learned in this project and how it can be used to improve your community.

Check out the note on the right to connect this project with other subjects.

 **with Social Studies**

Civic Literacy Research the Electoral College. Some questions to consider are:

- Why was it established?
- What is the relationship between the United States House of Representatives and the Electoral College?

 Reflect

7. **Answer the Essential Question** How can you communicate mathematical ideas effectively?

   a. How did you use what you learned about expressions to help you communicate mathematical ideas effectively in this project?

   _____

   _____

   _____

   b. How did you use what you learned about equations and inequalities to help you communicate mathematical ideas effectively in this project?

   _____

   _____

   _____

COLLABORATIVE PROJECT

Watch ▶

Turn Over a New Leaf The flatness of leaves serves an important purpose. In this project you will:

- **Collaborate** with your classmates as you research the primary function of leaves.

- **Share** the results of your research in a creative way.

- **ⓔ Reflect** on how you use different measurements to solve real-life problems.

Collaborate

⏻ Go Online Work with your group to research and complete each activity. You will use your results in the Share section on the following page.

1. Suppose you have a cube that is 10 centimeters on each side. Find the volume, surface area, and surface area to volume ratio.

2. Start with the cube from Activity 1 and imagine slicing it horizontally into ten equal sections. Arrange the sections in a 5-by-2-by-1 prism. Find the volume, surface area, and surface area to volume ratio.

3. Compare and contrast the volume, surface area, and surface area to volume ratio from Exercises 1 and 2.

4. Trace the outline of a leaf onto centimeter grid paper. Estimate the volume of the leaf. (Assume the height of your leaf is 0.1 centimeter.) Estimate the surface area. (You can ignore the edge of the leaf.) Find the surface area to volume ratio.

5. Do research to find the primary function of a leaf. Explain how the surface area to volume ratio of a leaf aids in its function.

6. Find examples from nature or man-made objects that have a small surface area to volume ratio. Explain the benefits.

Share

With your group, decide on a way to share what you have learned about the surface area to volume ratio of leaves. Some suggestions are listed below, but you could also think of other creative ways to present your information. Remember to show how you used mathematics to complete each of the activities in this project!

- Create a digital presentation that compares two types of leaves. Use what you learned about surface area to volume ratios in your presentation.
- Imagine you discovered a new type of leaf. Create an annotated diagram of your leaf. The annotations should include the type of information you learned in this project.

Check out the note on the right to connect this project with other subjects.

 **with Science**

Environmental Literacy Write a paragraph detailing facts about the leaves you researched. Some questions to consider are:

- What are the names of the trees that dropped these leaves?
- Are these types of trees common in your state?

Reflect

6. **Answer the Essential Question** How can you use different measurements to solve real-life problems?

   a. How did what you learned about geometric figures help you use different measurements to solve real-life problems in this project?

   _____

   _____

   _____

   b. How did what you learned about measuring figures to help you use different measurements to solve real-life problems in this project?

   _____

   _____

COLLABORATIVE PROJECT

Watch ▶

Math Genes A Punnett Square is a graphical way to predict the genetic traits of offspring. In this project you will:

- **Collaborate** with your classmates as you research genetics and the Punnet Square.
- **Share** the results of your research in a creative way.
- **Reflect** on why learning mathematics is important.

Complete the activities below and discover the fun you can have with genetics.

Collaborate

Go Online Work with your group to research and complete each activity. You will use your results in the Share section on the following page.

1. Use the Internet to research Punnett Squares and their role in genetics. Write a paragraph describing your findings.

2. Create sample genes for pet traits. Then create a Punnett Square using those traits. Describe what each outcome represents. Include a graph with your explanation.

3. Refer to Exercise 2. How many different genetic outcomes are possible according to your Punnett Square? What is the probability of each outcome occurring?

4. Create three word problems that involve using probability and the Punnett Squares to help answer the questions.

5. Collect two or more genetic-related information samples about students in your class. For example, you can collect data on attached/unattached earlobes. Analyze the data and make a prediction about the genetics of the entire school. Draw an appropriate graph of your results.

Share

With your group, decide on a way to share what you have learned about genetics and Punnett Squares. Some suggestions are listed below, but you can also think of other creative ways to your present your information. Remember to show how you used mathematics to complete each of the activities in this project.

- Create a digital presentation of the facts you learned about genetics.
- Act as a genetic scientist. Write a journal entry that explains your current research on predicting traits passed down from generations.

Check out the note on the right to connect this project with other subjects.

 **with Health**

Health Literacy Select a health condition or disease and research how genetics may play a part in the disease. Write 1–2 paragraphs explaining how genetics may influence someone's risk of getting the disease and steps that can be taken to reduce the risk factors.

Reflect

6. **Answer the Essential Question** Why is learning mathematics important?

a. How did what you learned about probability help you to understand why learning mathematics is important?

_____

_____

_____

b. How did what you learned about statistics help you to understand why learning mathematics is important?

_____

_____

_____

Glossary/Glosario

Go online for the eGlossary.

The eGlossary contains words and definitions in the following 13 languages:

Arabic	Cantonese	Hmong	Spanish	Urdu
Bengali	English	Korean	Tagalog	Vietnamese
Brazilian Portuguese	Haitian Creole	Russian		

English	Español

Aa

absolute value   The distance the number is from zero on a number line.

valor absoluto   Distancia a la que se encuentra un número de cero en la recta numérica.

acute angle   An angle with a measure greater than 0° and less than 90°.

ángulo agudo   Ángulo que mide más de 0° y menos de 90°.

acute triangle   A triangle having three acute angles.

triángulo acutángulo   Triángulo con tres ángulos agudos.

Addition Property of Equality   If you add the same number to each side of an equation, the two sides remain equal.

propiedad de adición de la igualdad   Si sumas el mismo número a ambos lados de una ecuación, los dos lados permanecen iguales.

Addition Property of Inequality   If you add the same number to each side of an inequality, the inequality remains true.

propiedad de desigualdad en la suma   Si se suma el mismo número a cada lado de una desigualdad, la desigualdad sigue siendo verdadera.

Additive Identity Property   The sum of any number and zero is the number.

propiedad de identidad de la suma   La suma de cualquier número y cero es el mismo número.

additive inverse   Two integers that are opposites. The sum of an integer and its additive inverse is zero.

inverso aditivo   Dos enteros opuestos.

adjacent angles   Angles that have the same vertex, share a common side, and do not overlap.

ángulos adyacentes   Ángulos que comparten el mismo vértice y un común lado, pero no se sobreponen.

algebra   A branch of mathematics that involves expressions with variables.

álgebra   Rama de las matemáticas que trata de las expresiones con variables.

algebraic expression   A combination of variables, numbers, and at least one operation.

expresión algebraica   Combinación de variables, números y por lo menos una operación.

connectED.mcgraw-hill.com

alternate exterior angles   Angles that are on opposite sides of the transversal and outside the parallel lines.

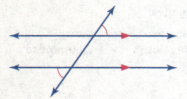

ángulos alternos externos   Ángulos en lados opuestos de la trasversal y afuera de las rectas paralelas.

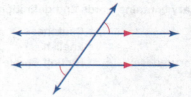

alternate interior angles   Angles that are on opposite sides of the transversal and inside the parallel lines.

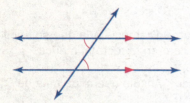

ángulos alternos internos   Ángulos en lados opuestos de la trasversal y dentro de las rectas paralelas.

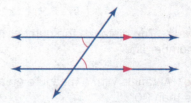

angle   Two rays with a common endpoint form an angle. The rays and vertex are used to name the angle.

$\angle ABC$, $\angle CBA$, or $\angle B$

ángulo   Dos rayos con un extremo común forman un ángulo. Los rayos y el vértice se usan para nombrar el ángulo.

$\angle ABC$, $\angle CBA$ o $\angle B$

arithmetic sequence   A sequence in which the difference between any two consecutive terms is the same.

sucesión aritmética   Sucesión en la cual la diferencia entre dos términos consecutivos es constante.

Associative Property   The way in which numbers are grouped does not change their sum or product.

propiedad asociativa   La forma en que se agrupan números al sumarlos o multiplicarlos no altera su suma o producto.

Bb

bar notation   In repeating decimals, the line or bar placed over the digits that repeat. For example, 2. $\overline{63}$ indicates that the digits 63 repeat.

notación de barra   Línea o barra que se coloca sobre los dígitos que se repiten en decimales periódicos. Por ejemplo, 2. $\overline{63}$ indica que los dígitos 63 se repiten.

base   In a power, the number used as a factor. In 10^3, the base is 10. That is, $10^3 = 10 \times 10 \times 10$.

base   En una potencia, el número usado como factor. En 10^3, la base es 10. Es decir, $10^3 = 10 \times 10 \times 10$.

base   One of the two parallel congruent faces of a prism.

base   Una de las dos caras paralelas congruentes de un prisma.

biased sample   A sample drawn in such a way that one or more parts of the population are favored over others.

box plot   A method of visually displaying a distribution of data values by using the median, quartiles, and extremes of the data set. A box shows the middle 50% of the data.

muestra sesgada   Muestra en que se favorece una o más partes de una población.

diagrama de caja   Un método de mostrar visualmente una distribución de valores usando la mediana, cuartiles y extremos del conjunto de datos. Una caja muestra el 50% del medio de los datos.

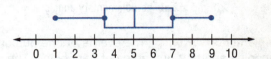

Cc

center   The point from which all points on circle are the same distance.

circle   The set of all points in a plane that are the same distance from a given point called the center.

circle graph   A graph that shows data as parts of a whole. In a circle graph, the percents add up to 100.

centro   El punto desde el cual todos los puntos en una circunferencia están a la misma distancia.

círculo   Conjunto de todos los puntos de un plano que están a la misma distancia de un punto dado denominado "centro".

gráfica circular   Gráfica que muestra los datos como partes de un todo. En una gráfica circular los porcentajes suman 100.

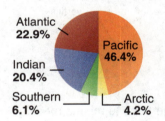

Area of Oceans

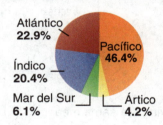

Área de superficie de los océanos

circumference   The distance around a circle.

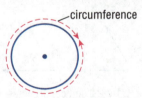

circunferencia   Distancia en torno a un círculo.

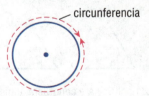

coefficient   The numerical factor of a term that contains a variable.

common denominator   A common multiple of the denominators of two or more fractions. 24 is a common denominator for $\frac{1}{3}$, $\frac{5}{8}$, and $\frac{3}{4}$ because 24 is the LCM of 3, 8, and 4.

Commutative Property   The order in which two numbers are added or multiplied does not change their sum or product.

coeficiente   El factor numérico de un término que contiene una variable.

común denominador   El múltiplo común de los denominadores de dos o más fracciones. 24 es un denominador común para $\frac{1}{3}$, $\frac{5}{8}$ y $\frac{3}{4}$ porque 24 es el mcm de 3, 8 y 4.

propiedad conmutativa   El orden en que se suman o multiplican dos números no altera el resultado.

complementary angles   Two angles are complementary if the sum of their measures is 90°.

∠1 and ∠2 are complementary angles.

complementary events   The events of one outcome happening and that outcome not happening. The sum of the probabilities of an event and its complement is 1 or 100%. In symbols, $P(A) + P(not\ A) = 1$.

complex fraction   A fraction $\frac{A}{B}$ where A or B are fractions and B does not equal zero.

composite figure   A figure that is made up of two or more three-dimensional figures.

compound event   An event consisting of two or more simple events.

cone   A three-dimensional figure with one circular base connected by a curved surface to a single vertex.

congruent   Having the same measure.

congruent angles   Angles that have the same measure.

∠1 and ∠2 are congruent angles.

congruent figures   Figures that have the same size and same shape and corresponding sides and angles with equal measure.

congruent segments   Sides with the same length.

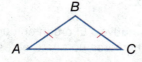

Side $\overline{AB}$ is congruent to side $\overline{BC}$.

ángulos complementarios   Dos ángulos son complementarios si la suma de sus medidas es 90°.

∠1 y ∠2 son complementarios.

eventos complementarios   Los eventos de un resultado que ocurre y ese resultado que no ocurre. La suma de las probabilidades de un evento y su complemento es 1 ó 100. En símbolos $P(A) + P(no\ A) = 1$.

fracción compleja   Una fracción $\frac{A}{B}$ en la cual A o B son fracciones y B no es igual a cero.

figura compuesta   Figura formada por dos o más figuras tridimensionales.

evento compuesto   Un evento que consiste en dos o más eventos simples.

cono   Una figura tridimensional con una base circular conectada por una superficie curva para un solo vértice.

congruente   Que tiene la misma medida.

ángulos congruentes   Ángulos que tienen la misma medida.

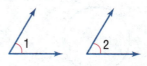

∠1 y ∠2 son congruentes.

figuras congruentes   Figuras que tienen el mismo tamaño y la misma forma y los lados y los ángulos correspondientes tienen igual medida.

segmentos congruentes   Lados con la misma longitud.

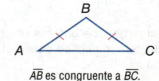

$\overline{AB}$ es congruente a $\overline{BC}$.

constant   A term that does not contain a variable.

constant of proportionality   A constant ratio or unit rate of two variable quantities. It is also called the constant of variation.

constant of variation   The constant ratio in a direct variation. It is also called the constant of proportionality.

constant rate of change   The rate of change in a linear relationship.

continuous data   Data that take on any real number value. It can be determined by considering what numbers are reasonable as part of the domain.

convenience sample   A sample which consists of members of a population that are easily accessed.

coordinate plane   A plane in which a horizontal number line and a vertical number line intersect at their zero points. Also called a coordinate grid.

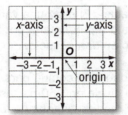

coplanar   Lines or points that lie in the same plane.

corresponding angles   Angles in the same position on parallel lines in relation to a transversal.

corresponding sides   The sides of similar figures that are in the same relative postion.

counterexample   A specific case which proves a statement false.

cross product   The product of the numerator of one ratio and the denominator of the other ratio. The cross products of any proportion are equal.

cross section   The cross section of a solid and a plane.

constante   Término que no contiene ninguna variable.

constante de proporcionalidad   Una razón constante o tasa por unidad de dos cantidades variables. También se llama constante de variación.

constante de variación   Una razón constante o tasa por unidad de dos cantidades variables. También se llama constante de proporcionalidad.

razón constante de cambio   Tasa de cambio en una relación lineal.

datos continuos   Datos que asumen cualquier valor numérico real. Se pueden determinar al considerar qué números son razonables como parte del dominio.

muestra de conveniencia   Muestra que incluye miembros de una población fácilmente accesibles.

plano de coordenadas   Plano en el cual se han trazado dos rectas numéricas, una horizontal y una vertical, que se intersecan en sus puntos cero. También conocido como sistema de coordenadas.

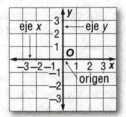

coplanar   Líneas o puntos situados en el mismo plano.

ángulos correspondientes   Ángulos que están en la misma posición sobre rectas paralelas en relación con la transversal.

lados correspondientes   Lados de figuras semejantes que estan en la misma posición.

contraejemplo   Caso específico que demuestra la falsedad de un enunciado.

producto cruzado   Producto del numerador de una razón por el denominador de la otra razón. Los productos cruzados de cualquier proporción son iguales.

sección transversal   Intersección de un sólido con un plano.

cube root   One of three equal factors of a number. If $a^3 = b$, then a is the cube root of b. The cube root of 125 is 5 since $5^3 = 125$.

cubed   The product in which a number is a factor three times. Two cubed is 8 because $2 \times 2 \times 2 = 8$.

cylinder   A three-dimensional figure with two parallel congruent circular bases connected by a curved surface.

raíz cúbica   Uno de tres factores iguales de un número. Si $a^3 = b$, entonces a es la raíz cúbica de b. La raíz cúbica de 125 es 5, dado que $5^3 = 125$.

al cubo   El producto de un número por sí mismo, tres veces. Dos al cubo es 8 porque $2 \times 2 \times 2 = 8$.

cilindro   Una figura tridimensional con dos paralelas congruentes circulares bases conectados por una superficie curva.

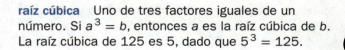

decagon   A polygon having ten sides.

decágono   Un polígono con diez lados.

defining a variable   Choosing a variable and a quantity for the variable to represent in an expression or equation.

degrees   The most common unit of measure for angles. If a circle were divided into 360 equal-sized parts, each part would have an angle measure of 1 degree.

dependent events   Two or more events in which the outcome of one event affects the outcome of the other event(s).

dependent variable   The variable in a relation with a value that depends on the value of the independent variable.

derived unit   A unit that is derived from a measurement system base unit, such as length, mass, or time.

diagonal   A line segment that connects two nonconsecutive vertices.

diameter   The distance across a circle through its center.

definir una variable   El elegir una variable y una cantidad que esté representada por la variable en una expresión o en una ecuacion.

grados   La unidad más común para medir ángulos. Si un círculo se divide en 360 partes iguales, cada parte tiene una medida angular de 1 grado.

eventos dependientes   Dos o más eventos en que el resultado de un evento afecta el resultado de otro u otros eventos.

variable dependiente   La variable en una relación cuyo valor depende del valor de la variable independiente.

unidad derivada   Unidad que se deriva de una unidad básica de un sistema de medidas, como la longitud, la masa o el tiempo.

diagonal   Segmento de recta que une dos vértices no consecutivos de un polígono.

diámetro   Segmento que pasa por el centro de un círculo y lo divide en dos partes iguales.

diameter

diámetro

dimensional analysis   The process of including units of measurement when you compute.

análisis dimensional   Proceso que incluye las unidades de medida al hacer cálculos.

direct variation   The relationship between two variable quantities that have a constant ratio.

variación directa   Relación entre las cantidades de dos variables que tienen una tasa constante.

discount   The amount by which the regular price of an item is reduced.

descuento   Cantidad que se le rebaja al precio regular de un artículo.

discrete data   When solutions of a function are only integer values. It can be determined by considering what numbers are reasonable as part of the domain.

datos discretos   Cuando las soluciones de una función son solo valores enteros. Se pueden determinar considerando qué números son razonables como parte del dominio.

disjoint events   Events that cannot happen at the same time.

eventos disjuntos   Eventos que no pueden ocurrir al mismo tiempo.

Distributive Property   To multiply a sum by a number, multiply each addend of the sum by the number outside the parentheses. For any numbers a, b, and c, $a(b + c) = ab + ac$ and $a(b - c) = ab - ac$.
Example: $2(5 + 3) = (2 \times 5) + (2 \times 3)$ and $2(5 - 3) = (2 \times 5) - (2 \times 3)$

propiedad distributiva   Para multiplicar una suma por un número, multiplíquese cada sumando de la suma por el número que está fuera del paréntesis. Sean cuales fuere los números a, b, y c, $a(b + c) = ab + ac$ y $a(b - c) = ab - ac$.
Ejemplo: $2(5 + 3) = (2 \cdot 5) + (2 \cdot 3)$ y $2(5 - 3) = (2 \cdot 5) - (2 \cdot 3)$

Division Property of Equality   If you divide each side of an equation by the same nonzero number, the two sides remain equal.

propiedad de igualdad de la división   Si divides ambos lados de una ecuación entre el mismo número no nulo, los lados permanecen iguales.

Division Property of Inequality   When you divide each side of an inequality by a negative number, the inequality symbol must be reversed for the inequality to remain true.

propiedad de desigualdad en la división   Cuando se divide cada lado de una desigualdad entre un número negativo, el símbolo de desigualdad debe invertirse para que la desigualdad siga siendo verdadera.

domain   The set of input values for a function.

dominio   El conjunto de valores de entrada de una función.

double box plot   Two box plots graphed on the same number line.

doble diagrama de caja   Dos diagramas de caja sobre la misma recta numérica.

double dot plot   A method of visually displaying a distribution of two sets of data values where each value is shown as a dot above a number line.

doble diagrama de puntos   Un método de mostrar visualmente una distribución de dos conjuntos de valores donde cada valor se muestra como un punto arriba de una recta numérica.

Ee

edge   The line segment where two faces of a polyhedron intersect.

borde   El segmento de línea donde se cruzan dos caras de un poliedro.

enlargement   An image larger than the original.

ampliación   Imagen más grande que la original.

equation   A mathematical sentence that contains an equals sign, =, stating that two quantities are equal.

ecuación   Enunciado matemático que contiene el signo de igualdad = indicando que dos cantidades son iguales.

equiangular   In a polygon, all of the angles are congruent.

equilateral   In a polygon, all of the sides are congruent.

equilateral triangle   A triangle having three congruent sides.

equivalent equations   Two or more equations with the same solution.

equivalent expressions   Expressions that have the same value.

equivalent ratios   Two ratios that have the same value.

evaluate   To find the value of an expression.

experimental probability   An estimated probability based on the relative frequency of positive outcomes occurring during an experiment. It is based on what *actually* occurred during such an experiment.

exponent   In a power, the number that tells how many times the base is used as a factor. In 5^3, the exponent is 3. That is, $5^3 = 5 \times 5 \times 5$.

exponential form   Numbers written with exponents.

equiangular   En un polígono, todos los ángulos son congruentes.

equilátero   En un polígono, todos los lados son congruentes.

triángulo equilátero   Triángulo con tres lados congruentes.

ecuaciones equivalentes   Dos o más ecuaciones con la misma solución.

expresiones equivalentes   Expresiones que tienen el mismo valor.

razones equivalentes   Dos razones que tienen el mismo valor.

evaluar   Calcular el valor de una expresión.

probabilidad experimental   Probabilidad estimada que se basa en la frecuencia relativa de los resultados positivos que ocurren durante un experimento. Se basa en lo que *en realidad* ocurre durante dicho experimento.

exponente   En una potencia, el número que indica las veces que la base se usa como factor. En 5^3, el exponente es 3. Es decir, $5^3 = 5 \times 5 \times 5$.

forma exponencial   Números escritos usando exponentes.

Ff

face   A flat surface of a polyhedron.

factor   To write a number as a product of its factors.

factored form   An expression expressed as the product of its factors.

factors   Two or more numbers that are multiplied together to form a product.

cara   Una superficie plana de un poliedro.

factorizar   Escribir un número como el producto de sus factores.

forma factorizada   Una expresión expresada como el producto de sus factores.

factores   Dos o más números que se multiplican entre sí para formar un producto.

fair game   A game where each player has an equally likely chance of winning.

juego justo   Juego donde cada jugador tiene igual posibilidad de ganar.

first quartile   For a data set with median M, the first quartile is the median of the data values less than M.

primer cuartil   Para un conjunto de datos con la mediana M, el primer cuartil es la mediana de los valores menores que M.

formula   An equation that shows the relationship among certain quantities.

fórmula   Ecuación que muestra la relación entre ciertas cantidades.

function   A relationship which assigns exactly one output value for each input value.

función   Relación que asigna exactamente un valor de salida a cada valor de entrada.

function rule   The operation performed on the input of a function.

regla de función   Operación que se efectúa en el valor de entrada.

function table   A table used to organize the input numbers, output numbers, and the function rule.

tabla de funciones   Tabla que organiza las entradas, la regla y las salidas de una función.

Fundamental Counting Principle   Uses multiplication of the number of ways each event in an experiment can occur to find the number of possible outcomes in a sample space.

Principio Fundamental de Contar   Este principio usa la multiplicación del número de veces que puede ocurrir cada evento en un experimento para calcular el número de posibles resultados en un espacio muestral.

---

gram   A unit of mass in the metric system equivalent to 0.001 kilogram. The amount of matter an object can hold.

gramo   Unidad de masa en el sistema métrico que equivale a 0.001 de kilogramo. La cantidad de materia que puede contener un objeto.

graph   The process of placing a point on a number line or on a coordinate plane at its proper location.

graficar   Proceso de dibujar o trazar un punto en una recta numérica o en un plano de coordenadas en su ubicación correcta.

gratuity   Also known as a tip. It is a small amount of money in return for a service.

gratificación   También conocida como propina. Es una cantidad pequeña de dinero en retribución por un servicio.

---

heptagon   A polygon having seven sides.

heptágono   Polígono con siete lados.

hexagon   A polygon having six sides.

hexágono   Polígono con seis lados.

histogram A type of bar graph used to display numerical data that have been organized into equal intervals.

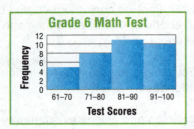

Grade 6 Math Test

Frequency / Test Scores

histograma Tipo de gráfica de barras que se usa para exhibir datos que se han organizado en intervalos iguales.

Examen de matemáticas de 6º grado

Frecuencia / Calificaciones

Ii

Identity Property of Zero The sum of an addend and zero is the addend. Example: $5 + 0 = 5$

propiedad de identidad del cero La suma de un sumando y cero es igual al sumando. Ejemplo: $5 + 0 = 5$

independent events Two or more events in which the outcome of one event does not affect the outcome of the other event(s).

eventos independientes Dos o más eventos en los cuales el resultado de uno de ellos no afecta el resultado de los otros eventos.

independent variable The variable in a function with a value that is subject to choice.

variable independiente Variable en una función cuyo valor está sujeto a elección.

indirect measurement Finding a measurement using similar figures to find the length, width, or height of objects that are too difficult to measure directly.

medición indirecta Hallar una medición usando figuras semejantes para calcular el largo, ancho o altura de objetos que son difíciles de medir directamente.

inequality An open sentence that uses $<, >, \neq, \leq,$ or $\geq$ to compare two quantities.

desigualdad Enunciado abierto que usa $<, >, \neq, \leq$ o $\geq$ para comparar dos cantidades.

integer Any number from the set $\{..., -4, -3, -2, -1, 0, 1, 2, 3, 4, ...\}$, where ... means continues without end.

entero Cualquier número del conjunto $\{..., -4, -3, -2, -1, 0, 1, 2, 3, 4, ...\}$, donde ... significa que continúa sin fin.

interquartile range A measure of variation in a set of numerical data. It is the distance between first and third quartiles of the data set.

rango intercuartil Una medida de la variación en un conjunto de datos numéricos. Es la distancia entre el primer y el tercer cuartiles del conjunto de datos.

inverse variation A relationship where the product of x and y is a constant k. As x increases in value, y decreases in value, or as y decreases in value, x increases in value.

variación inversa Relación en la cual el producto de x y y es una constante k. A medida que aumenta el valor de x, disminuye el valor de y o a medida que disminuye el valor de y, aumenta el valor de x.

irrational number A number that cannot be expressed as the ratio of two integers.

número irracional Número que no se puede expresar como el razón de dos enteros.

isosceles triangle A triangle having at least two congruent sides.

triángulo isósceles Triángulo que tiene por lo menos dos lados congruentes.

kilogram   The base unit of mass in the metric system. One kilogram equals 1,000 grams.

kilogramo   Unidad básica de masa del sistema métrico. Un kilogramo equivale a 1,000 gramos.

Ll

lateral face   In a polyhedron, a face that is not a base.

cara lateral   En un poliedro, las caras que no forman las bases.

lateral surface area   The sum of the areas of all of the lateral faces of a solid.

área de superficie lateral   Suma de las áreas de todas las caras de un sólido.

least common denominator (LCD)   The least common multiple of the denominators of two or more fractions. You can use the LCD to compare fractions.

mínimo común denominador (mcd)   El menor de los múltiplos de los denominadores de dos o más fracciones. Puedes usar el mínimo común denominador para comparar fracciones.

like fractions   Fractions that have the same denominators.

fracciones semejantes   Fracciones que tienen los mismos denominadores.

like terms   Terms that contain the same variables raised to the same power. Example: 5x and 6x are like terms.

términos semejante   Términos que contienen las mismas variables elevadas a la misma potencia. Ejemplo: 5x y 6x son *términos semejante*.

line graph   A type of statistical graph using lines to show how values change over a period of time.

gráfica lineal   Tipo de gráfica estadística que usa segmentos de recta para mostrar cómo cambian los valores durante un período de tiempo.

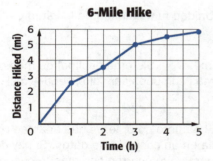

6-Mile Hike

Caminata de 6 millas

linear expression   An algebraic expression in which the variable is raised to the first power.

expresión lineal   Expresión algebraica en la cual la variable se eleva a la primera potencia.

linear function   A function for which the graph is a straight line.

función lineal   Función cuya gráfica es una recta.

linear relationship   A relationship for which the graph is a straight line.

relación lineal   Una relación para la cual la gráfica es una línea recta.

liter   The base unit of capacity in the metric system. The amount of dry or liquid material an object can hold.

litro   Unidad básica de capacidad del sistema métrico. La cantidad de materia líquida o sólida que puede contener un objeto.

markdown   An amount by which the regular price of an item is reduced.

markup   The amount the price of an item is increased above the price the store paid for the item.

mean   The sum of the data divided by the number of items in the data set.

mean absolute deviation   A measure of variation in a set of numerical data, computed by adding the distances between each data value and the mean, then dividing by the number of data values.

measures of center   Numbers that are used to describe the center of a set of data. These measures include the mean, median, and mode.

measures of variation   A measure used to describe the distribution of data.

median   A measure of center in a set of numerical data. The median of a list of values is the value apprearing at the center of a sorted version of the list—or the mean of the two central values, if the list contains an even number of values.

meter   The base unit of length in the metric system.

metric system   A decimal system of measures. The prefixes commonly used in this system are kilo-, centi-, and milli-.

mode   The number or numbers that appear most often in a set of data. If there are two or more numbers that occur most often, all of them are modes.

monomial   A number, variable, or product of a number and one or more variables.

Multiplication Property of Equality   If you multiply each side of an equation by the same nonzero number, the two sides remain equal.

Multiplication Property of Inequality   When you multiply each side of an inequality by a negative number, the inequality symbol must be reversed for the inequality to remain true.

rebaja   Una cantidad por la cual el precio regular de un artículo se reduce.

margen de utilidad   Cantidad de aumento en el precio de un artículo por encima del precio que paga la tienda por dicho artículo.

media   La suma de los datos dividida entre el número total de artículos en el conjunto de datos.

desviación media absoluta   Una medida de variación en un conjunto de datos numéricos que se calcula sumando las distancias entre el valor de cada dato y la media, y luego dividiendo entre el número de valores.

medidas del centro   Números que se usan para describir el centro de un conjunto de datos. Estas medidas incluyen la media, la mediana y la moda.

medidas de variación   Medida usada para describir la distribución de los datos.

mediana   Una medida del centro en un conjunto de dados númericos. La mediana de una lista de valores es el valor que aparace en el centro de una versíon ordenada de la lista, o la media de dos valores centrales si la lista contiene un número par de valores.

metro   Unidad fundamental de longitud del sistema métrico.

sistema métrico   Sistema decimal de medidas. Los prefijos más comunes son kilo-, centi- y mili-.

moda   El número o números que aparece con más frecuencia en un conjunto de datos. Si hay dos o más números que ocurren con más frecuencia, todosellos son modas.

monomio   Número, variable o producto de un número y una o más variables.

propiedad de multiplicación de la igualdad
Si multiplicas ambos lados de una ecuación por el mismo número no nulo, lo lados permanecen iguales.

propiedad de desigualdad en la multiplicación
Cuando se multiplica cada lado de una desigualdad por un número negativo, el símbolo de desigualdad debe invertirse para que la desigualdad siga siendo verdadera.

Multiplicative Identity Property   The product of any number and one is the number.

Multiplicative Property of Zero   The product of any number and zero is zero.

multiplicative inverse   Two numbers with a product of 1. For example, the multiplicative inverse of $\frac{2}{3}$ is $\frac{3}{2}$.

propiedad de identidad de la multiplicación   El producto de cualquier número y uno es el mismo número.

propiedad del cero en la multiplicación   El producto de cualquier número y cero es cero.

inverso multiplicativo   Dos números cuyo producto es 1. Por ejemplo, el inverso multiplicativo de $\frac{2}{3}$ es $\frac{3}{2}$.

negative exponent   Any nonzero number to the negative *n* power. It is the multiplicative inverse of its *n*th power.

negative integer   An integer that is less than zero. Negative integers are written with a − sign.

net   A two-dimensional figure that can be used to build a three-dimensional figure.

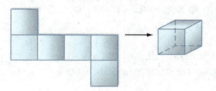

nonagon   A polygon having nine sides.

nonlinear function   A function for which the graph is *not* a straight line.

nonproportional   The relationship between two ratios with a rate or ratio that is not constant.

numerical expression   A combination of numbers and operations.

exponente negativo   Cualquier número que no sea cero a la potencia negative de *n*. Es el inverso multiplicativo de su *en*ésimo potencia.

entero negativo   Número menor que cero. Se escriben con el signo −.

red   Figura bidimensional que sirve para hacer una figura tridimensional.

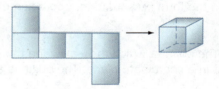

enágono   Polígono que tiene nueve lados.

nonlinear function   Función cuya gráfica *no* es una línea recta.

no proporcional   Relación entre dos razones cuya tasa o razón no es constante.

expresión numérica   Combinación de números y operaciones.

obtuse angle   Any angle that measures greater than 90° but less than 180°.

ángulo obtuso   Cualquier ángulo que mide más de 90° pero menos de 180°.

obtuse triangle   A triangle having one obtuse angle.

triángulo obtusángulo   Triángulo que tiene un ángulo obtuso.

octagon   A polygon having eight sides.

octágono   Polígono que tiene ocho lados.

opposites   Two integers are opposites if they are represented on the number line by points that are the same distance from zero, but on opposite sides of zero. The sum of two opposites is zero.

opuestos   Dos enteros son opuestos si, en la recta numérica, están representados por puntos que equidistan de cero, pero en direcciones opuestas. La suma de dos opuestos es cero.

order of operations   The rules to follow when more than one operation is used in a numerical expression.
1. Evaluate the expressions inside grouping symbols.
2. Evaluate all powers.
3. Multiply and divide in order from left to right.
4. Add and subtract in order from left to right.

orden de las operaciones   Reglas a seguir cuando se usa más de una operación en una expresión numérica.
1. Primero, evalúa las expresiones dentro de los símbolos de agrupación.
2. Evalúa todas las potencias.
3. Multiplica y divide en orden de izquierda a derecha.
4. Suma y resta en orden de izquierda a derecha.

ordered pair   A pair of numbers used to locate a point in the coordinate plane. An ordered pair is written in the form (*x*-coordinate, *y*-coordinate).

par ordenado   Par de números que se utiliza para ubicar un punto en un plano de coordenadas. Se escribe de la siguiente forma: (coordenada *x*, coordenada *y*).

origin   The point at which the *x*-axis and the *y*-axis intersect in a coordinate plane. The origin is at (0, 0).

origen   Punto en que el eje *x* y el eje *y* se intersecan en un plano de coordenadas. El origen está ubicado en (0, 0).

outcome   Any one of the possible results of an action. For example, 4 is an outcome when a number cube is rolled.

resultado   Cualquiera de los resultados posibles de una acción. Por ejemplo, 4 puede ser un resultado al lanzar un cubo numerado.

outlier   A data value that is either much *greater* or much *less* than the median.

valor atípico   Valor de los datos que es mucho *mayor* o mucho *menor* que la mediana.

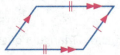

Pp

parallel lines   Lines in a plane that never intersect.

rectas paralelas   Rectas en un plano que nunca se intersecan.

parallelogram   A quadrilateral with opposite sides parallel and opposite sides congruent.

paralelogramo   Cuadrilátero cuyos lados opuestos son paralelos y congruentes.

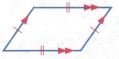

pentagon A polygon having five sides.

percent equation An equation that describes the relationship between the part, whole, and percent.

$$\text{part} = \text{percent} \cdot \text{whole}$$

percent error A ratio that compares the inaccuracy of an estimate (amount of error) to the actual amount.

percent of change A ratio that compares the change in a quantity to the original amount.

$$\text{percent of change} = \frac{\text{amount of change}}{\text{original amount}}$$

percent of decrease A negative percent of change.

percent of increase A positive percent of change.

percent proportion One ratio or fraction that compares part of a quantity to the whole quantity. The other ratio is the equivalent percent written as a fraction with a denominator of 100.

$$\frac{\text{part}}{\text{whole}} = \frac{\text{percent}}{100}$$

perfect squares Numbers with square roots that are whole numbers. 25 is a perfect square because the square root of 25 is 5.

permutation An arrangement, or listing, of objects in which order is important.

perpendicular lines Lines that meet or cross each other to form right angles.

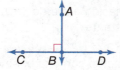

pi The ratio of the circumference of a circle to its diameter. The Greek letter π represents this number. The value of pi is 3.1415926. . . . Approximations for pi are 3.14 and $\frac{22}{7}$.

plane A two-dimensional flat surface that extends in all directions.

pentágono Polígono que tiene cinco lados.

ecuación porcentual Ecuación que describe la relación entre la parte, el todo y el por ciento.

$$\text{parte} = \text{por ciento} \cdot \text{todo}$$

porcentaje de error Una razón que compara la inexactitud de una estimación (cantidad del error) con la cantidad real.

porcentaje de cambio Razón que compara el cambio en una cantidad a la cantidad original.

$$\text{porcentaje de cambio} = \frac{\text{cantidad del cambio}}{\text{cantidad original}}$$

porcentaje de disminución Porcentaje de cambio negativo.

porcentaje de aumento Porcentaje de cambio positivo.

proporción porcentual Razón o fracción que compara parte de una cantidad a toda la cantidad. La otra razón es el porcentaje equivalente escrito como fracción con 100 de denominador.

$$\frac{\text{parte}}{\text{todo}} = \frac{\text{porcentaje}}{100}$$

cuadrados perfectos Números cuya raíz cuadrada es un número entero. 25 es un cuadrado perfecto porque la raíz cuadrada de 25 es 5.

permutación Arreglo o lista de objetos en la cual el orden es importante.

rectas perpendiculares Rectas que al encontrarse o cruzarse forman ángulos rectos.

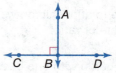

pi Relación entre la circunferencia de un círculo y su diámetro. La letra griega π representa este número. El valor de pi es 3.1415926. . . . Las aproximaciones de pi son 3.14 y $\frac{22}{7}$.

plano Superficie bidimensional que se extiende en todas direcciones.

polygon   A simple closed figure formed by three or more straight line segments.

polygono   Figura cerrada simple formada por tres o más segmentos de recta.

polyhedron   A three-dimensional figure with faces that are polygons.

poliedro   Una figura tridimensional con caras que son polígonos.

population   The entire group of items or individuals from which the samples under consideration are taken.

población   El grupo total de individuos o de artículos del cual se toman las muestras bajo estudio.

positive integer   An integer that is greater than zero. They are written with or without a + sign.

entero positivo   Entero que es mayor que cero; se escribe con o sin el signo +.

powers   Numbers expressed using exponents. The power 3^2 is read *three to the second power*, or *three squared.*

potencias   Números que se expresan usando exponentes. La potencia 3^2 se lee *tres a la segunda potencia o tres al cuadrado.*

precision   The ability of a measurement to be consistently reproduced.

precisión   Capacidad que tiene una medición de poder reproducirse consistentemente.

principal   The amount of money deposited or borrowed.

capital   Cantidad de dinero que se deposita o se toma prestada.

prism   A polyhedron with two parallel congruent faces called bases.

prisma   Un poliedro con dos caras congruentes paralelas llamadas bases.

probability   The chance that some event will happen. It is the ratio of the number of favorable outcomes to the number of possible outcomes.

probabilidad   La posibilidad de que suceda un evento. Es la razón del número de resultados favorables al número de resultados posibles.

probability model   A model used to assign probabilities to outcomes of a chance process by examining the nature of the process.

modelo de probabilidad   Un modelo usado para asignar probabilidades a resultados de un proceso aleatorio examinando la naturaleza del proceso.

properties   Statements that are true for any number or variable.

propiedades   Enunciados que son verdaderos para cualquier número o variable.

proportion   An equation stating that two ratios or rates are equivalent.

proporción   Ecuación que indica que dos razones o tasas son equivalentes.

proportional   The relationship between two ratios with a constant rate or ratio.

proporcional   Relación entre dos razones con una tasa o razón constante.

pyramid   A polyhedron with one base that is a polygon and three or more triangular faces that meet at a common vertex.

pirámide   Un poliedro con una base que es un polígono y tres o más caras triangulares que se encuentran en un vértice común.

Qq

quadrant One of the four regions into which the two perpendicular number lines of the coordinate plane separate the plane.

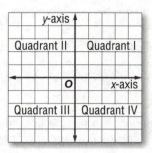

cuadrante Una de las cuatro regiones en que dos rectas numéricas perpendiculares dividen el plano de coordenadas.

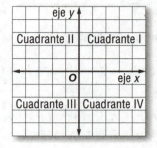

quadrilateral A closed figure having four sides and four angles.

cuadrilátero Figura cerrada que tiene cuatro lados y cuatro ángulos.

quartile A value that divides the data set into four equal parts.

cuartil Valor que divide el conjunto de datos en cuatro partes iguales.

Rr

radical sign The symbol used to indicate a nonnegative square root, $\sqrt{}$.

signo radical Símbolo que se usa para indicar una raíz cuadrada no negativa, $\sqrt{}$.

radius The distance from the center of a circle to any point on the circle.

radio Distancia desde el centro de un círculo hasta cualquiera de sus puntos.

radius

radio

random Outcomes occur at random if each outcome occurs by chance. For example, rolling a number on a number cube occurs at random.

azar Los resultados ocurren aleatoriamente si cada resultado ocurre por casualidad. Por ejemplo, sacar un número en un cubo numerado ocurre al azar.

range The set of output values for a function.

rango Conjunto de valores de salida para una función.

range The difference between the greatest and least data value.

rango La diferencia entre el número mayor y el menor en un conjunto de datos.

rate A ratio that compares two quantities with different kinds of units.

tasa Razón que compara dos cantidades que tienen distintas unidades de medida.

rate of change A rate that describes how one quantity changes in relation to another. A rate of change is usually expressed as a unit rate.

tasa de cambio Tasa que describe cómo cambia una cantidad con respecto a otra. Por lo general, se expresa como tasa unitaria.

rational numbers   The set of numbers that can be written in the form $\frac{a}{b}$, where a and b are integers and $b \neq 0$.
Examples: $1 = \frac{1}{1}, \frac{2}{9}, -2.3 = -2\frac{3}{10}$

real numbers   A set made up of rational and irrational numbers.

reciprocal   The multiplicative inverse of a number.

rectangle   A parallelogram having four right angles.

rectangular prism   A prism that has two parallel congruent bases that are rectangles.

reduction   An image smaller than the original.

regular polygon   A polygon that has all sides congruent and all angles congruent.

regular pyramid   A pyramid whose base is a regular polygon and in which the segment from the vertex to the center of the base is the altitude.

relation   Any set of ordered pairs.

relative frequency   A ratio that compares the frequency of each category to the total.

repeating decimal   The decimal form of a rational number.

rhombus   A parallelogram having four congruent sides.

right angle   An angle that measures exactly 90°.

números racionales   Conjunto de números que puede escribirse en la forma $\frac{a}{b}$ donde a y b son números enteros y $b \neq 0$.
Ejemplos: $1 = \frac{1}{1}, \frac{2}{9}, -2.3 = -2\frac{3}{10}$

números reales   Conjunto de números racionales e irracionales.

recíproco   El inverso multiplicativo de un número.

rectángulo   Paralelogramo con cuatro ángulos rectos.

prisma rectangular   Un prisma con dos bases paralelas congruentes que son rectángulos.

reducción   Imagen más pequeña que la original.

polígono regular   Polígono con todos los lados y todos los ángulos congruentes.

pirámide regular   Pirámide cuya base es un polígono regular y en la cual el segmento desde el vértice hasta el centro de la base es la altura.

relación   Cualquier conjunto de pares ordenados.

frecuencia relativa   Razón que compara la frecuencia de cada categoría al total.

decimal periódico   La forma decimal de un número racional.

rombo   Paralelogramo que tiene cuatro lados congruentes.

ángulo recto   Ángulo que mide exactamente 90°.

right triangle   A triangle having one right angle.

triángulo rectángulo   Triángulo que tiene un ángulo recto.

sales tax   An additional amount of money charged on items that people buy.

impuesto sobre las ventas   Cantidad de dinero adicional que se cobra por los artículos que se compran.

sample   A randomly selected group chosen for the purpose of collecting data.

muestra   Grupo escogido al azar o aleatoriamente que se usa con el propósito de recoger datos.

sample space   The set of all possible outcomes of a probability experiment.

espacio muestral   Conjunto de todos los resultados posibles de un experimento probabilístico.

scale   The scale that gives the ratio that compares the measurements of a drawing or model to the measurements of the real object.

escala   Razón que compara las medidas de un dibujo o modelo a las medidas del objeto real.

scale drawing   A drawing that is used to represent objects that are too large or too small to be drawn at actual size.

dibujo a escala   Dibujo que se usa para representar objetos que son demasiado grandes o demasiado pequeños como para dibujarlos de tamaño natural.

scale factor   A scale written as a ratio without units in simplest form.

factor de escala   Escala escrita como una razón sin unidades en forma simplificada.

scale model   A model used to represent objects that are too large or too small to be built at actual size.

modelo a escala   Réplica de un objeto real, el cual es demasiado grande o demasiado pequeño como para construirlo de tamaño natural.

scalene triangle   A triangle having no congruent sides.

triángulo escaleno   Triángulo sin lados congruentes.

scatter plot   In a scatter plot, two sets of related data are plotted as ordered pairs on the same graph.

diagrama de dispersión   Diagrama en que dos conjuntos de datos relacionados aparecen graficados como pares ordenados en la misma gráfica.

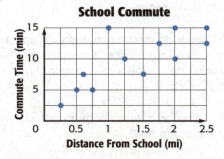

selling price   The amount the customer pays for an item.

semicircle   Half of a circle. The formula for the area of a semicircle is $A = \frac{1}{2}\pi r^2$.

sequence   An ordered list of numbers, such as 0, 1, 2, 3 or 2, 4, 6, 8.

similar figures   Figures that have the same shape but not necessarily the same size.

similar solids   Solids with the same shape. Their corresponding linear measures are proportional.

simple event   One outcome or a collection of outcomes.

simple interest   The amount paid or earned for the use of money. The formula for simple interest is $I = prt$.

simple random sample   An unbiased sample where each item or person in the population is as likely to be chosen as any other.

simplest form   An expression is in simplest form when it is replaced by an equivalent expression having no like terms or parentheses.

simplify   Write an expression in simplest form.

simulation   An experiment that is designed to model the action in a given situation.

slant height   The height of each lateral face.

slope   The rate of change between any two points on a line. It is the ratio of vertical change to horizontal change. The slope tells how steep the line is.

solution   A replacement value for the variable in an open sentence. A value for the variable that makes an equation true. Example: The *solution* of $12 = x + 7$ is 5.

square   The product of a number and itself. 36 is the square of 6.

precio de venta   Cantidad de dinero que paga un consumidor por un artículo.

semicírculo   Medio círculo La fórmula para el área de un semicírculo es $A = \frac{1}{2}\pi r^2$.

sucesión   Lista ordenada de números, como 0, 1, 2, 3 ó 2, 4, 6, 8.

figuras semejantes   Figuras que tienen la misma forma, pero no necesariamente el mismo tamaño.

sólidos semejantes   Sólidos con la misma forma. Sus medidas lineales correspondientes son proporcionales.

eventos simples   Un resultado o una colección de resultados.

interés simple   Cantidad que se paga o que se gana por el uso del dinero. La fórmula para calcular el interés simple es $I = prt$.

muestra aleatoria simple   Muestra de una población que tiene la misma probabilidad de escogerse que cualquier otra.

expresión mínima   Expresión en su forma más simple cuando es reemplazada por una expresión equivalente que no tiene términos similares ni paréntesis.

simplificar   Escribir una expresión en su forma más simple.

simulación   Un experimento diseñado para modelar la acción en una situación dada.

altura oblicua   Altura de cada cara lateral.

pendiente   Razón de cambio entre cualquier par de puntos en una recta. Es la razón del cambio vertical al cambio horizontal. La pendiente indica el grado de inclinación de la recta.

solución   Valor de reemplazo de la variable en un enunciado abierto. Valor de la variable que hace que una ecuación sea verdadera. Ejemplo: La *solución* de $12 = x + 7$ es 5.

cuadrado   Producto de un número por sí mismo. 36 es el cuadrado de 6.

square   A parallelogram having four right angles and four congruent sides.

square root   The factors multiplied to form perfect squares.

squared   The product of a number and itself. 36 is the square of 6.

standard form   Numbers written without exponents.

statistics   The study of collecting, organizing, and interpreting data.

straight angle   An angle that measures exactly 180°.

Subtraction Property of Equality   If you subtract the same number from each side of an equation, the two sides remain equal.

Subtraction Property of Inequality   If you subtract the same number from each side of an inequality, the inequality remains true.

supplementary angles   Two angles are supplementary if the sum of their measures is 180°.

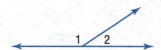

∠1 and ∠2 are supplementary angles.

surface area   The sum of the areas of all the surfaces (faces) of a three-dimensional figure.

survey   A question or set of questions designed to collect data about a specific group of people, or population.

systematic random sample   A sample where the items or people are selected according to a specific time or item interval.

cuadrado   Paralelogramo con cuatro ángulos rectos y cuatro lados congruentes.

al cuadrado   Factores multiplicados para formar cuadrados perfectos.

raíz cuadrada   El producto de un número por sí mismo. 36 es el cuadrado de 6.

forma estándar   Números escritos sin exponentes.

estadística   Estudio que consiste en recopilar, organizar e interpretar datos.

ángulo llano   Ángulo que mide exactamente 180°.

propiedad de sustracción de la igualdad   Si restas el mismo número de ambos lados de una ecuación, los dos lados permanecen iguales.

propiedad de desigualdad en la resta   Si se resta el mismo número a cada lado de una desigualdad, la desigualdad sigue siendo verdadera.

ángulos suplementarios   Dos ángulos son suplementarios si la suma de sus medidas es 180°.

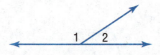

∠1 y ∠2 son suplementarios.

área de superficie   La suma de las áreas de todas las superficies (caras) de una figura tridimensional.

encuesta   Pregunta o conjunto de preguntas diseñadas para recoger datos sobre un grupo específico de personas o población.

muestra aleatoria sistemática   Muestra en que los elementos o personas se eligen según un intervalo de tiempo o elemento específico.

term   Each number in a sequence.

term   A number, a variable, or a product or quotient of numbers and variables.

terminating decimal   A repeating decimal which has a repeating digit of 0.

término   Cada número en una sucesión.

término   Número, variable, producto o cociente de números y de variables.

decimal finito   Un decimal periódico que tiene un dígito que se repite que es 0.

theoretical probability The ratio of the number of ways an event can occur to the number of possible outcomes. It is based on what *should* happen when conducting a probability experiment.

probabilidad teórica Razón del número de maneras en que puede ocurrir un evento al número de resultados posibles. Se basa en lo que *debería* pasar cuando se conduce un experimento probabilístico.

three-dimensional figure A figure with length, width, and height.

figura tridimensional Figura que tiene largo, ancho y alto.

third quartile For a data set with median *M*, the third quartile is the median of the data values greater than *M*.

tercer cuartil Para un conjunto de datos con la mediana *M*, el tercer cuartil es la mediana de los valores mayores que *M*.

tip Also known as a gratuity, it is a small amount of money in return for a service.

propina También conocida como gratificación; es una cantidad pequeña de dinero en recompensa por un servicio.

transversal The third line formed when two parallel lines are intersected.

transversal Tercera recta que se forma cuando se intersecan dos rectas paralelas.

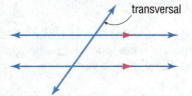

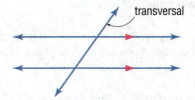

trapezoid A quadrilateral with one pair of parallel sides.

trapecio Cuadrilátero con un único par de lados paralelos.

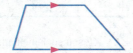

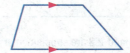

tree diagram A diagram used to show the sample space.

diagrama de árbol Diagrama que se usa para mostrar el espacio muestral.

triangle A figure with three sides and three angles.

triángulo Figura con tres lados y tres ángulos.

triangular prism A prism that has two parallel congruent bases that are triangles.

prisma triangular Un prisma que tiene dos bases congruentes paralelas que triángulos.

two-step equation An equation having two different operations.

ecuación de dos pasos Ecuación que contiene dos operaciones distintas.

two-step inequality An inequality than contains two operations.

desigualdad de dos pasos Desigualdad que contiene dos operaciones.

Uu

unbiased sample   A sample representative of the entire population.

unfair game   A game where there is not a chance of each player being equally likely to win.

uniform probability model   A probability model which assigns equal probability to all outcomes.

unit rate   A rate that is simplified so that it has a denominator of 1 unit.

unit ratio   A unit rate where the denominator is one unit.

unlike fractions   Fractions with different denominators.

muestra no sesgada   Muestra que se selecciona de modo que se representativa de la población entera.

juego injusto   Juego donde cada jugador no tiene la misma posibilidad de ganar.

modelo de probabilidad uniforme   Un modelo de probabilidad que asigna igual probabilidad a todos los resultados.

tasa unitaria   Tasa simplificada para que tenga un denominador igual a 1.

razón unitaria   Tasa unitaria en que el denominador es la unidad.

fracciones con distinto denominador   Fracciones cuyos denominadores son diferentes.

Vv

variable   A symbol, usually a letter, used to represent a number in mathematical expressions or sentences.

vertex   A vertex of an angle is the common endpoint of the rays forming the angle.

vertex   The point where three or more faces of a polyhedron intersect.

vertex   The point at the tip of a cone.

vertical angles   Opposite angles formed by the intersection of two lines. Vertical angles are congruent.

∠1 and ∠2 are vertical angles.

visual overlap   A visual demonstration that compares the centers of two distributions with their variation, or spread.

variable   Símbolo, por lo general una letra, que se usa para representar un número en expresiones o enunciados matemáticos.

vértice   El vértice de un ángulo es el extremo común de los rayos que lo forman.

vértice   El punto donde tres o más caras de un poliedro se cruzan.

vértice   El punto en la punta de un cono.

ángulos opuestos por el vértice   Ángulos opuestos formados por la intersección de dos rectas. Los ángulos opuestos por el vértice son congruentes.

∠1 y ∠2 son ángulos opuestos por el vértice.

superposición visual   Una demostración visual que compara los centros de dos distribuciones con su variación, o magnitud.

volume   The number of cubic units needed to fill the space occupied by a solid.

volumen   Número de unidades cúbicas que se requieren para llenar el espacio que ocupa un sólido.

voluntary response sample   A sample which involves only those who want to participate in the sampling.

muestra de respuesta voluntaria   Muestra que involucra sólo aquellos que quieren participar en el muestreo.

Xx

x-axis   The horizontal number line in a coordinatWe plane.

eje x   La recta numérica horizontal en el plano de coordenadas.

x-coordinate   The first number of an ordered pair. It corresponds to a number on the x-axis.

coordenada x   El primer número de un par ordenado. Corresponde a un número en el eje x.

Yy

y-axis   The vertical number line in a coordinate plane.

eje y   La recta numérica vertical en el plano de coordenadas.

y-coordinate   The second number of an ordered pair. It corresponds to a number on the y-axis.

coordenada y   El segundo número de un par ordenado. Corresponde a un número en el eje y.

Zz

zero pair   The result when one positive counter is paired with one negative counter. The value of a zero pair is 0.

par nulo   Resultado de hacer coordinar una ficha positiva con una negativa. El valor de un par nulo es 0.

Chapter 1 Integers

Chapter 1 Are You Ready?

1. 6   **3.** 24

4–9.

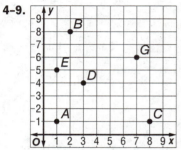

Lesson 1-1 Independent Practice

1. 9   **3.** −53

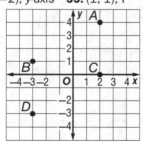

7. 10   **9** 8   **11.** −7   **13.** $299.97; |−200| + |−40| + |−60| = 200 + 40 + 60 = 300   **15.** always; It is true if A and B are both positive or if A or B is negative, and if both A and B are negative.   **17.** A

Lesson 1-1 Extra Practice

19. 12

21.

23. 11   **25.** 25   **27.** 5   **29.** C   **31.** Wednesday
33. (0, −2); y-axis   **35.** (1, 1); I

36–39.

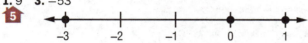

Lesson 1-2 Independent Practice

1. −38   **3.** 16   **5** 0   **7.** 9   **9.** −4   **11** green; profit of $1; white; profit of $3; black; profit of $3   **13.** Sample answer: In science, atoms may contain 2 positive charges and 2 negative charges. In business, a stock's value may fall 0.75 one day and rise 0.75 the next day.   **15.** a
17. $m + (−15)$

Lesson 1-2 Extra Practice

19. 13   **21.** −6   **23.** 15   **25.** 22   **27.** −19   **29.** −5 + (−15) + 12; The team has lost a total of 8 yards.   **31.** D
33. −8 + (−3) = −11   **35.** −8   **37.** 4   **39.** 5

Lesson 1-3 Independent Practice

1. −10   **3** −12   **5.** −30   **7.** 23   **9.** 104   **11.** 0
13 **a.** 2,415 ft   **b.** 3,124 ft   **c.** 627 ft   **d.** 8 ft   **15.** 16
17. Sample answer: −5 − 11 = −5 + (−11) = −16; Add 5 and 11 and keep the negative sign.   **19.** He did not find the additive inverse of −18. −15 − (−18) = −15 + 18 or 3. The correct answer is 3.   **21.** D

Lesson 1-3 Extra Practice

23. 35   **25.** −14   **27.** 6   **29.** 15   **31.** 11   **33.** 1   **35.** A
37. 10 − 12   **39.** 195   **41.** 12   **43.** 2

Problem-Solving Investigation   Look for a Pattern

Case 3. Add the previous 2 terms; 89, 144
Case 5. 13 toothpicks

Lesson 1-4 Independent Practice

1. −96   **3.** 36   **5** −64   **7** 5(−650); −3,250; Ethan burns 3,250 Calories each week.   **9.** 5 black T-shirts
11.

×	+	−
+	+	−
−	−	+

Sample answer: When you multiply a negative and a positive integer, the product is negative. When you multiply two negative integers the product is positive.   **13.** Sample answer: Evaluate −7 + 7 first. Since −7 + 7 = 0, and any number times 0 is 0, the value of the expression is 0.
15. D

Lesson 1-4 Extra Practice

17. 160   **19.** −64   **21.** −45   **23.** 12(−4); −48; Lily's gift card has $48 less than its starting amount.   **25.** 16
27. −12   **29.** 648   **31.** −243   **33.** Sample answer: The answer should be −24. A negative multiplied by a negative will be positive. Then, if it is multiplied by a negative it will be negative.   **35.** 8(−15); −120   **37.** A   **39.** <   **41.** >
43.

Lesson 1-5 Independent Practice

1. −10   **3** 5   **5.** −11   **7.** −2   **9.** −3   **11.** −6
13 −$60 miles per hour   **15.** 4   **17.** 16   **19.** No; Sample answer: 9 ÷ 3 ≠ 3 ÷ 9   **21.** −2   **23.** B

Lesson 1-5   Extra Practice

25. 9   **27.** 4   **29.** 9   **31.** −12   **33.** 2   **35.** −10°F; The boiling point decreases 10°F at an altitude of 5,000 ft.
37. B   **39.** 4; Sample answer: Christopher answered 6 questions incorrectly. If each question is worth the same, each incorrect answer is worth −24 ÷ 6 or −4 points. So, Nythia answered −16 ÷ (−4) or 4 questions incorrectly.
41. −9   **43.** 5   **45.** III

Chapter Review   Vocabulary Check

1. additive   **3.** integers   **5.** opposites

Chapter Review   Key Concept Check

1. not correct; |−5| + |2| = 5 + 2 or 7   **3.** not correct; −24 ÷ |−2| = −24 ÷ 2 = −12

Chapter Review   Problem Solving

1.
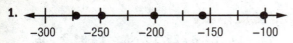
-300 -250 -200 -150 -100

3. 100°C   **5.** 4(−2); $33

Chapter 2 Rational Numbers

Chapter 2   Are You Ready?

1. $\frac{2}{3}$ **3.** $\frac{8}{11}$
4–7.
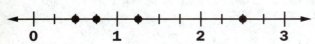
0 1 2 3

Lesson 2-1   Independent Practice

1. 0.5   **3** 0.125   **5.** −0.66   **7.** 5.875   **9.** −0.$\overline{8}$
11. −0.$\overline{72}$ **13.** −$\frac{1}{5}$ **15.** 5$\frac{24}{25}$ **17** 10$\frac{1}{2}$ **19.** Sample answer: $\frac{3}{5}$ **21.** Sample answer: $3\frac{1}{7} \approx 3.14286$ and $3\frac{10}{71} \approx 3.14085$; Since 3.1415926... is between $3\frac{1}{7}$ and $3\frac{10}{71}$, Archimedes was correct.

Lesson 2-1   Extra Practice

23. 0.8   **25.** −0.$\overline{4}$ **27.** 0.75   **29.** $\frac{17}{50}$ **31.** −$\frac{13}{1}$ **33.** −$\frac{16}{5}$
35. D   **37.** B   **39.** 0.1
41–43.
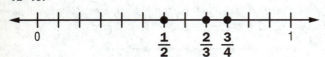
0 $\frac{1}{2}$ $\frac{2}{3}$ $\frac{3}{4}$ 1

Lesson 2-2   Independent Practice

1. >
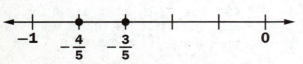
-1 $-\frac{4}{5}$ $-\frac{3}{5}$ 0

3. >   **5** first quiz   **7.** −$\frac{5}{8}$, −0.62, −0.615   **9** <
11. Yes; $69\frac{1}{8} < 69\frac{6}{8}$.   **13.** Sample answer: $\frac{63}{32}$ is closest to 2 because the difference of $\frac{63}{32}$ and 2 is the least.

Lesson 2-2   Extra Practice

15. <   **17.** <   **19.** Jim; $\frac{10}{16} > \frac{4}{15}$ **21.** −1.4, −1.25, −$1\frac{1}{25}$
23. C   **25.** D   **27.** >   **29.** >   **31.** >

Lesson 2-3   Independent Practice

1. $1\frac{4}{7}$ **3.** −$\frac{2}{3}$ **5** −$1\frac{1}{2}$ **7** $\frac{3}{14}$ **9a.** $\frac{33}{100}$ **9b.** $\frac{67}{100}$
9c. $\frac{41}{100}$ **11.** Sample answer: $\frac{11}{18}$ and $\frac{5}{18}$; $\frac{11}{18} - \frac{5}{18} = \frac{6}{18}$, which simplifies to $\frac{1}{3}$.   **13.** C

Lesson 2-3   Extra Practice

15. −$1\frac{2}{3}$ **17.** $\frac{1}{4}$ **19.** $\frac{1}{9}$ **21.** $1\frac{47}{100}$ **23.** $\frac{1}{2}$ c   **25.** D   **27.** 4
29. <   **31.** <   **33.** 28   **35.** 60

Lesson 2-4   Independent Practice

1 $\frac{13}{24}$ **3.** $1\frac{2}{5}$ **5.** $\frac{4}{9}$ **7.** −$\frac{26}{45}$ **9.** $1\frac{11}{18}$
11 Subtraction; Sample answer: To find how much time remained, subtract $\left(\frac{1}{6} + \frac{1}{4}\right)$ from $\frac{2}{3}$; $\frac{1}{4}$ h

13.

Homework	Fraction of Time	
	Pepita	**Francisco**
Math	$\frac{1}{6}$	$\frac{1}{2}$
English	$\frac{2}{3}$	$\frac{1}{8}$
Science	$\frac{1}{6}$	$\frac{3}{8}$

15. Sample answer: Let $\frac{1}{a}$ and $\frac{1}{b}$ represent the unit fractions, where a and b are not zero. Multiply the first numerator by b and the second numerator by a. Write the product over the denominator ab. Write in simplest form.   **17.** C

Lesson 2-4   Extra Practice

19. $\frac{19}{30}$ **21.** $\frac{11}{20}$ **23.** −$\frac{13}{24}$ **25.** Subtraction; Sample answer: To find how much more turkey Makalaya bought, subtract $\frac{1}{4}$ from $\frac{5}{8}$; $\frac{3}{8}$ lb   **27.** Theresa did not rename the fractions using the LCD. $\frac{5}{20} + \frac{12}{20} = \frac{17}{20}$ **29.** I   **31.** $1\frac{2}{5}$
33. $1\frac{1}{100}$ **35.** $7\frac{7}{10}$ **37.** 26   **39.** 27

Lesson 2-5   Independent Practice

1. $9\frac{5}{9}$ **3.** $8\frac{3}{5}$ **5** $7\frac{5}{12}$ **7.** $4\frac{14}{15}$ **9.** $4\frac{1}{3}$
11 Subtraction; the width is shorter than the length; $1\frac{3}{4}$ ft
13. −5   **15.** $13\frac{5}{9}$ **17.** Sample answer: A board with a

length of $3\frac{7}{8}$ ft needs to be cut from a $5\frac{1}{2}$ –foot existing board. How much wood will be left after the cut is made?; $1\frac{5}{8}$ ft   **19.** B

Lesson 2-5   Extra Practice

21. $18\frac{17}{24}$ **23.** $7\frac{5}{7}$ **25.** $5\frac{7}{8}$ **27.** Subtraction twice; the amount of flour is less than the original amount; $2\frac{2}{3}$ c
29. $7\frac{1}{8}$ yd   **31.** D   **33.** 5; 8; 40   **35.** 5; 11; 55   **37.** 14 mi; Sample answer: $6\frac{4}{5} \approx 7$ and $1\frac{3}{4} \approx 2$; $7 \times 2 = 14$

Problem-Solving Investigation   Draw a Diagram

Case 3. $\frac{3}{8}$ **Case 5.** $\frac{1}{4}$ mi

Lesson 2-6   Independent Practice

1. $\frac{3}{32}$ **3.** $-4\frac{1}{2}$ **5.** $\frac{1}{6}$ **7** $\frac{3}{8}$ **9.** -1 **11** $\frac{1}{16}$
13. $\frac{1}{3} \times \left(\frac{11}{16}\right) = \frac{11}{48}$ **15.** Sample answer: Three fourths of the students at Walnut Middle School were on the honor roll. Of that group, only $\frac{1}{8}$ of them received all As. What fraction of the students received all As?   **17.** A

Lesson 2-6   Extra Practice

19. $\frac{1}{9}$ **21.** $\frac{1}{4}$ **23.** $2\frac{1}{6}$ **25.** $\frac{3}{16}$ **27.** $-\frac{8}{27}$ **29.** broccoli: $1\frac{7}{8}$ c, pasta: $5\frac{5}{8}$ c, salad dressing: 1 c, cheese: 2 c; Multiply each amount by $1\frac{1}{2}$.   **31.** B   **33.** <   **35.** $\frac{1}{18} \div \frac{1}{3} = \frac{1}{6}$; $\frac{1}{18} \div \frac{1}{6} = \frac{1}{3}$ **37.** $6\frac{3}{4} \div 1\frac{1}{5} = 5\frac{5}{8}$; $6\frac{3}{4} \div 5\frac{5}{8} = 1\frac{1}{5}$
39. $5\frac{1}{4}$ pints

Lesson 2-7   Independent Practice

1. 12.7   **3** 128.17   **5.** 0.04   **7.** 15.75   **9.** 1.5
11. 887.21 mL   **13** 1.5 lb   **15.** 1,000 mL or 1 L
17. 0.031 m, 0.1 ft, 0.6 in., 1.2 cm   **19.** 0.7 gal, 950 mL, 0.4 L, $1\frac{1}{4}$ c   **21.** C

Lesson 2-7   Extra Practice

23. 158.76   **25.** 121.28   **27.** 41.89   **29.** 2 L   **31.** 3 gal
33. 4 mi   **35.** B   **37.** 5.7   **39.** 15,840   **41.** 1   **43.** 5   **45.** 1

Lesson 2-8   Independent Practice

1. $\frac{7}{16}$ **3** $\frac{1}{15}$ **5.** $\frac{2}{9}$ **7** 84 movies
9. $1\frac{1}{4}$

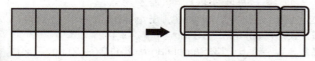

Sample answer: The model on the left shows that one half of a rectangle with ten sections is five sections. Two fifths of ten sections is four sections. The model on the right

shows the five sections divided into $1\frac{1}{4}$ groups of four sections.   **11.** $\frac{1}{6}$ of a dozen; 2 folders   **13.** $\frac{10}{3}$

Lesson 2-8   Extra Practice

15. $\frac{2}{3}$ **17.** $-7\frac{4}{5}$ **19.** 11 servings   **21.** $\frac{1}{2}$ **23.** C   **25.** $\frac{9}{20}$
27. $\frac{46}{63}$ **29.** $\frac{3}{4}$ ft   **31a.** $\frac{5}{8}$ mi   **31b.** $\frac{13}{16}$ mi

Chapter Review   Vocabulary Check

1. bar notation   **3.** common denominator   **5.** terminating

Chapter Review   Key Concept Check

1. $\frac{3}{5}$ **3.** denominator   **5.** multiply

Chapter Review   Problem Solving

1. $5.1\overline{3}$ min   **3.** $1\frac{5}{8}$ c   **5.** $\frac{7}{30}$; Sample answer: The product of $\frac{7}{20}$ and $\frac{2}{3}$ is $\frac{14}{60}$ or $\frac{7}{30}$.   **7.** 140 oz

Chapter 3 Expressions

Chapter 3   Are You Ready?

1. 16   **3.** 16   **5.** -50 **7.** 25

Lesson 3-1   Independent Practice

1. 34   **3** 3   **5.** 3   **7.** 2   **9.** -1 **11** $50 + 0.17m$; $75.50   **13.** 9.1   **15.** 37.85   **17.** Sample answer: The fee to rent a bicycle is $10 plus $5 for each hour. The expression $5x + 10$ represents the total cost for renting a bicycle for x hours.   **19.** B

Lesson 3-1   Extra Practice

21. 4   **23.** -12 **25.** 5   **27.** $8.75   **29.** G   **31.** Let $h =$ the height; $h - 8$ **33.** Let $j =$ the number of Jacob's goals; $2j$ **35.** $4(8) + 3(5)$; $47

Lesson 3-2   Independent Practice

1. 7 is added to the previous term; 28, 35, 42   **3** 8 is added to the previous term; 58, 66, 74   **5.** 0.8 is added to the previous term; 5.6, 6.4, 7.2   **7** $3n$; 36 in.
9a.

x	1	2	3	4	5
y	3	6	9	12	15

9b. $3n$

9c.

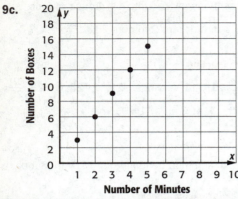

Sample answer: The number of boxes increases by 3 each minute. The points appear to fall in a straight line passing through the origin. **9d.** 135 boxes **11.** + 1, + 2, + 3, + 4, ...; 16, 22, 29 **13.** B

Lesson 3-2 Extra Practice

15. 10 is added to the previous term; 46, 56, 66 **17.** 1.5 is added to the previous term; 10.5, 12.0, 13.5 **19.** 4 is added to the previous term; 20.6, 24.6, 28.6 **21.** 25 is added to the previous term; 120, 145, 170 **23a.** Each figure is 8 less than the previous figure. **23b.** 40, 32 **25.** 33, 30, 27 **27.** D **29.** $2n + 3$ **31.** 27 **33.** 10,000 **35.** 16,807

Lesson 3-3 Independent Practice

1. Commutative (+) **3** Associative (+) **5.** false; Sample answer: $(24 \div 4) \div 2 \neq 24 \div (4 \div 2)$

7. $= (15 + 12) + 8a$ Associative (+)
    $= 27 + 8a$ Simplify.

9 $= 3x \cdot (x \cdot 7)$ Commutative (×)
    $= (3x \cdot x) \cdot 7$ Associative (×)
    $= 3x^2 \cdot 7$ Simplify.
    $= 3 \cdot 7 \cdot x^2$ Commutative (×)
    $= (3 \cdot 7) \cdot x^2$ Associative (×)
    $= 21x^2$ Simplify.

11. $[7 + (47 + 3)][5 \cdot (2 \cdot 3)]$, Associative (+); $(7 + 50)[5 \cdot (2 \cdot 3)]$, Simplify; $57[5 \cdot (2 \cdot 3)]$, Simplify; $57[(5 \cdot 2) \cdot 3]$, Associative (×); $57 \cdot 10 \cdot 3$, Simplify; $(57 \cdot 10) \cdot 3$, Associative (×); $570 \cdot 3$, Simplify; 1,710
13. Blake incorrectly multiplied both the 5 and m by 4. He should have used the Associative Property to group the 5 and 4 together, simplify, and then multiply by m. $4 \cdot (5 \cdot m) = 20m$ **15.** C

Lesson 3-3 Extra Practice

17. Commutative (×) **19.** Associative (+) **21.** 48 s; Sample answer: $12.4 + 12.6 = 25$ and $11.8 + 11.2 = 23$, $25 + 23 = 48$
23. $= (18 + 5) + 6m$ Associative (+)
    $= 23 + 6m$ Simplify.

25. $= 10 \cdot 7 \cdot y$ Commutative (×)
    $= (10 \cdot 7) \cdot y$ Associative (×)
    $= 70y$ Simplify.
27. C **29.** $2.29 + 2.50 + 2.21$ **31.** 76 **33.** 88 **35.** 1.5

Lesson 3-4 Independent Practice

1. 33 **3** -30 **5.** 4 **7.** $-12x + 24$ **9.** $30 - 6q$
11. $-15 + 3b$ **13** $27.40; 4($7.00 - $0.15) = 4 \cdot 7 - 4 \cdot 0.15$
15. 315;
$$9(30 + 5) = 9(30) + 9(5)$$
$$= 270 + 45$$
17. 672;
$$(100 + 12)6 = 100(6) + 12(6)$$
$$= 600 + 72$$
19. 488;
$$4(120 + 2) = 4(120) + 4(2)$$
$$= 480 + 8$$
21. Sample answer: $6(2a + 3b - c)$ **23.** $2a + ay + 2b + by$

Lesson 3-4 Extra Practice

25. -72 **27.** -40 **29.** $10b + 40$ **31.** \$31.96; $4($8.00 - $0.01) = 4 \cdot 8 - 4 \cdot 0.01$ **33.** $0.5xy - 0.5xz$
35. $-12mn + 24mp$ **37.** $-6a + 4b$ **39.** $8(x + 4)$; $8x + 32$ **41.** H **43.** \$448.50; $30($15.00 - $0.05) = 30 \cdot 15 - 30 \cdot 0.05$ **45.** 756 **47.** 4; x

Problem-Solving Investigation Make a Table

Case 3. 55 containers **Case 5.** 18 toothpicks

Lesson 3-5 Independent Practice

1. terms: 2, $3a$, $9a$; like terms: $3a$, $9a$; coefficients: 3, 9; constant: 2 **3.** terms: 9, $-z$, 3, $-2z$; like terms: 9 and 3, $-z$ and $-2z$; coefficients: -1, -2; constants: 9, 3 **5.** $11c$
7. $1.03t$; \$74.16 **9** $2x + 30$ **11** **a.** $7 + 5x + 4y + 2z$ **b.** \$43 **13.** $16a + 8b + 4$ **15.** Sample answer: $3x + x - 7$; coefficients: 3, 1; constant: -7 **17.** $8x^2 + 10x - 3$; $8x^2 + 10x - 3 = 8(2)^2 + 10(2) - 3 = 49$ and $8x^2 - 2x + 12x - 3 = 8(2)^2 - 2(2) + 12(2) - 3 = 49$

Lesson 3-5 Extra Practice

19. terms: 4, $5y$, $-6y$, y; like terms: $5y$, $-6y$, y; coefficients: 5, -6, 1; constant: 4 **21.** terms: $-3d$, 8, $-d$, -2; like terms: $-3d$ and $-d$, 8 and -2; coefficients: -3, -1; constants: 8, -2 **23.** $2 + 4d$ **25.** $2m - 2$
27. $7m - 20$ **29.** $20x + 9$ **31.** $38g + 36h - 38$
33. $3x - 10y$ **35.** $7(5)(4)$; \$140 **37.** b = cost of a book; $4b$ **39.** 7

Lesson 3-6 Independent Practice

1. $11x + 11$ **3** $4x - 16$ **5.** $4x + 14$
7. $(10x + 18)$ mm; 118 mm **9** $-x + 2$
11. $8.7x - 1.6$ **13.** Sample answer: $(10x + 2)$ and $(-15x + 2)$ **15.** $2x + 1$; The expression $2x + 1$ will always be odd when x is an integer because when an integer is doubled, the result is always even. Adding one to the result will give an odd number.

Lesson 3-6   Extra Practice

17. $-4x + 16$ **19.** $-2x - 2$ **21.** $-6x + 5$
23. $(24x + 9)$ yd; 177 yd   **25.** D   **27.** $(4x - 36)$ m   **29.** 56
31. 66   **33.** 23 students; Sample answer: $6 + 4 = 10$, $5 + 8 = 13, 10 + 13 = 23$

Lesson 3-7   Independent Practice

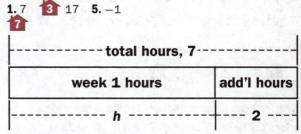 **1** $5x + 2$ **3.** $2x + 2$ **5.** $8x - 12$ **7.** $5x - 2$;
248 customers   **9** $x + 0.51$
11. Sample answer: The additive inverse of $(2x + 1)$ is
$(-2x - 1)$.
$$(5x + 3) - (2x + 1) = (5x + 3) + (-2x - 1)$$
$$= 5x + 3 + (-2x) + (-1)$$
$$= 5x + (-2x) + 3 + (-1)$$
$$= 3x + 2$$
13. $-x + 5$

Lesson 3-7   Extra Practice

15. $-10x - 11$ **17.** $3x + 13$ **19.** $7x + 5$ **21.** $2x - 11$;
5 questions   **23.** $-1\frac{1}{2}x + 1\frac{1}{2}$ **25.** $4x - 15$ **27.** $5x + 3$
29. $(12x - 4)$ ft; 32 ft   **31.** $-\frac{1}{4}$ **33.** $\frac{1}{8}$ **35.** $\frac{2}{3}$

Lesson 3-8   Independent Practice

1. 24   **3** $36k$ **5.** cannot be factored   **7** 4 units by
$(x - 2)$ units   **9.** $(x + 2)$ dollars   **11.** $5(x + 4)$ units^2
13. $4(5x + 19)$ units^2 **15.** Sample answer: $20m$ and
$12mn$ **17.** B

Lesson 3-8   Extra Practice

19. $6rs$ **21.** $20x$ **23.** $25xy$ **25.** $6(3x + 1)$ **27.** $5(2x - 7)$
29. $10(3x - 4)$ **31.** $(2x + 5)$ in.   **33.** $\frac{2}{3}(x + 9)$
35. $\frac{5}{6}(x - 36)$ **37.** $\frac{3}{8}(x + 48)$ **39.** D   **41.** $4x + 4$
43. $14b + 35$
45.

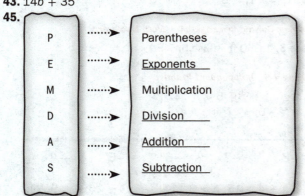

P ┈┈▶	Parentheses
E ┈┈▶	Exponents
M ┈┈▶	Multiplication
D ┈┈▶	Division
A ┈┈▶	Addition
S ┈┈▶	Subtraction

Chapter Review   Vocabulary Check

Across
3. simplest form   **7.** sequence   **11.** counter example
13. define
Down
1. equivalent   **5.** variable   **9.** term

Chapter Review   Key Concept Check

1. $1 + 3$ **3.** $2x - 4$ **5.** $3(x + 7)$

Chapter Review   Problem Solving

1. $5.75h + 8.95s$; $62   **3.** 49 points; Sample answer: $8 + 12 = 20, 13 + 7 = 20, 20 + 20 + 9 = 49$ **5.** $5(x - 5)°$

Chapter 4 Equations and Inequalities

Chapter 4   Are You Ready?

1. $p + 3$ **3.** $g + 10$ **5.** 17   **7.** 1   **9.** 35

Lesson 4-1   Independent Practice

1. 7   **3** 17   **5.** -1
7

------ total hours, 7 ------	
week 1 hours	add'l hours
------ h ------	---- 2 ----

$7 = h + 2$; 5 h   **9a.** $s - 65 = 13$; 78 mph
9b.

--------176 ft--------	
El Toro	
The Rattler	----52 ft----
-------- d --------	

$d + 52 = 176$; 124 ft   **9c.** The solution of each
equation is 170; Colossos is 170 feet tall.   **11.** $115 + 115 + 65 + x = 360$; 65   **13.** She should have
subtracted 5 from each side; -13 **15.** C

Lesson 4-1   Extra Practice

17. 18   **19.** 7   **21.** -4
23.

-------------- x points --------------	
Chicago Bull points	
Miami Heat points	13 points
--------- 79 points ---------	

$x - 13 = 79$; 92 points   **25.** 18.4   **27.** $\frac{5}{12}$ **29.**
6.4   **31.** $\frac{1}{12}$ **33.** $\frac{7}{18}$ **35.** 7   **37.** -20 **39.** 60   **41.**
-36 **43.** $3h = -3; h = -1$

Lesson 4-2   Independent Practice

1. 7   **3.** 8   **5.** 80   **7** -5 **9.** -90 **11** $205 = \frac{d}{3}$;
615 mi

13a.

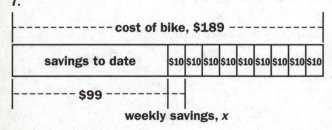

amount saved in 1 hour

13b. $5.5x = 44$ **13c.** Sample answer: Divide each side by 5.5. Then simplify. $x = 8$ **15.** True; Sample answer: Multiply each side of the equation by $\frac{1}{5}$ instead of dividing each side by 5.   **17.** D

Lesson 4-2   Extra Practice

19. 4   **21.** 70   **23.** -120 **25.** $50 = 25t$; 2 s   **27.** C
29. G   **31.** $5\frac{5}{7}$ **33.** $\frac{16}{7}$ **35.** $\frac{95}{9}$ **37.** 9   **39.** $\frac{14}{45}$ **41.** $\frac{1}{6}$

Lesson 4-3   Independent Practice

1. 5   **3** 3   **5.** $\frac{20}{3}$ or $6\frac{2}{3}$ **7** $\frac{3}{4}p = 46.50$; \$62   **9.** Emily's homeroom class; Sample answer: Write and solve the equations $0.75e = 15$ and $\frac{2}{3}s = 12$; $e = 20$ and $s = 18$; Since $20 > 18$, Emily's homeroom class has more students.   **11.** 20; Sample answer: Solve to $8 = \frac{m}{4}$, find that $m = 32$. So, replace m with 32 to find $32 - 12 = 20$.   **13.** Sample answer: Multiply each side by 2. Then divide each side by $(b_1 + b_2)$. So, $\frac{2A}{b_1 + b_2} = h$.

Lesson 4-3   Extra Practice

15. 7   **17.** -3.8 **19.** $-\frac{125}{12}$ or $-10\frac{5}{12}$
21.

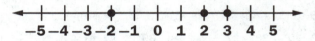

$\frac{7}{15}$ of elevation, 140 ft

total elevation, x ft

$140 = \frac{7}{15}x$; 300 ft

23. D   **25.** G   **27.** 50   **29.** multiply; divide; add; subtract
31. $30 - (2 \times 8 + 2 \times 2 + 4)$; \$6

Lesson 4-4   Independent Practice

1. 3   **3** 7   **5.** -3
7.

cost of bike, \$189

savings to date

\$99

weekly savings, x

$189 = 10x + 99$; 9 weeks
9. 2.25   **11** **a.** $-9°C$ **b.** $92.2°F$ **13.** No, none of the Fahrenheit temperatures convert to the same temperature in Celsius. Only $-40°F = -40°C$.   **15.** B

Lesson 4-4   Extra Practice

17. -4 **19.** 4   **21.** 36
23a.

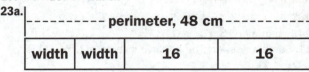

perimeter, 48 cm

| width | width | 16 | 16 |

23b. $48 = 32 + 2w$; 8 cm   **23c.** Sample answer: Using either method, you would subtract first and then divide
25. 7 days   **27.** $6 \cdot 10 + 6 \cdot n$ or $60 + 6n$ **29.** $5(x + 7)$
31. $10(t + 3)$ **33.** $2(m + 6)$

Lesson 4-5   Independent Practice

1. 6   **3** -14 **5.** -3.2 **7** $3(\ell + 5) = 60$; 15 in.
9a. $12(m - 2.57) = 0.36$ **9b.** Sample answer: I first divided each side by 12 and then added 2.57 to each side; \$2.60.   **11.** Sample answer: Marisol should have divided by six before subtracting three; $6(x + 3) = 21$, $x + 3 = 3.5$, $x = 3.5 - 3$, $x = 0.5$ **13.** A

Lesson 4-5   Extra Practice

15. 16   **17.** -2 **19.** 78   **21.** $5\frac{3}{4}$ or 5.75
23. $1.20\left(n + 2\frac{1}{2}\right) = 4.50$; 1.25 or $1\frac{1}{4}$ pounds   **25.** $\frac{1}{b}$
27. 2; See answer 31 for graph.   **29.** 3; See answer 31 for graph   **31.** -2

```
  +---+---+---+---●---+---+---●---●---+---+
 -5  -4  -3  -2  -1   0   1   2   3   4   5
```

33. 3   **35.** 1, 2, 3

Problem-Solving Investigation   Work Backward

Case 3. 1,250 ft   **Case 5.** 7:50 A.M.

Lesson 4-6   Independent Practice

1. $h \leq -8$ **3** $5 < n$ **5.** $x > -1$
7. $m \geq -6$;

```
  +-------+-------●━━━━━━━+-------+
 -8      -7      -6      -5      -4
```

9 $n + 4 > 13$; $n > 9$ **11.** $p + 17 \leq 26$; $p \leq 9$; Nine additional players or fewer can make the team.
13a. $42 + x \geq 74$; $x \geq 32$ **13b.** $74 + y \geq 110$; $y \geq 36$
15. Sample answer: $x + 3 < 25$ **17.** A

Lesson 4-6   Extra Practice

19. $m \leq 4.3$
21. $-5 < a$

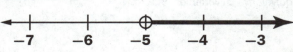

```
  ◄-------+-------+-------⊕-------+-------+-►
 -7      -6      -5      -4      -3
```

23. $n - 8 < 10$; $n < 18$ **25.** $68 + c \leq 125$; $c \leq 57$; The salesman has 57 cars or less left to sell.

27. $2\frac{2}{3} > x$ or $x < 2\frac{2}{3}$

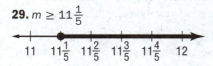

29. $m \geq 11\frac{1}{5}$

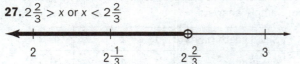

31. $n \geq -4\frac{3}{16}$

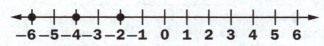

33. I **35.** $50 + x \geq 268$; \$218 **37.** -4; See answer 41 for graph. **39.** -2; See answer 41 for graph.
41. -6;

43. $\{-3, -2, -1, 0, 1, 2, 3\}$

Lesson 4-7 Independent Practice

1. $y < 3$ **3.** $180 \leq m$ **5.** $m \geq 56$ **7.** $n \leq 4.5$
9. $w \leq -45$
11. $4 < t$

13. $x \leq -32$

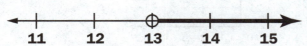

15. Sample answer: The inequalities $-2x > 12$, $\frac{x}{2} < -3$, and $-7 > x - 1$ are equal to $x < -6$. The inequality $-2 < x + 4$ is equal to $x > -6$. **17.** $4 + 5n \leq 34$; $n \leq 6$
19. at least a 15

Lesson 4-7 Extra Practice

21. $n < 2$ **23.** $5 < r$ or $r > 5$ **25.** $t < -70$
27. $w > 13$

29. $-20 \geq t$ or $t \leq -20$

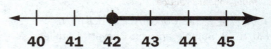

31. $0.5x > 15$; $x > 30$; A person should play more than 30 games. **33.** $5n < -45$; $n < -9$ **35.** F **37.** -3
39. 3 **41.** $3\frac{6}{7}$

Lesson 4-8 Independent Practice

1. $x \geq 1$;

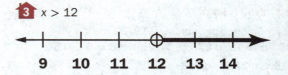

3. $x > 12$

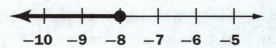

5. $30 + 7x \geq 205$; $x \geq 25$ hours; He will have to work at least 25 hours. **7.** $\frac{x}{-5} + 1 \leq 7$; $x \geq -30$
9. $-2x - 6 > -18$; $x < 6$ **11.** Sample answer: $-2x + 5 > -7$ **13.** Sample answer: $\frac{x}{2} + 5 \geq 30$ **15.** at least 17 points **17.** B

Lesson 4-8 Extra Practice

19. $x \leq -8$

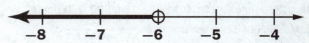

21. $x \geq 42$

[number line graph]

23. $75 + 5s \geq 125$; $s \geq 10$; Audrey needs to make at least 10 sales for her pay to be \$125. **25.** A **27.** I
29. $y < -6$

[number line graph]

31. 8 **33.** $\frac{1}{2}$

Chapter Review Key Concept Check

1. f **3.** a

Chapter Review Problem Solving

1. 2 m **3.** $300 = 7.5r$; 40 mph **5.** $x + 120 \leq 180$; Ben can lift up to 60 pounds more. **7.** $50c + 600 \geq 1{,}250$; Mr. Walker must sell at least 13 computers.

Chapter 5 Ratios and Proportional Reasoning

Chapter 5 Are You Ready?

1. $\frac{2}{15}$ **3.** $\frac{1}{51}$ **5.** No; $\frac{12}{20} = \frac{3}{5}$, $\frac{15}{30} = \frac{1}{2}$

Lesson 5-1 Independent Practice

1. 60 mi/h **3.** 3.5 m/s **5.** Sample answer: about \$0.50 per pair **7.** 510 words **9. a.** 20.04 mi/h

b. about 1.5 h   **13.** Sometimes; a ratio that compares two measurements with different units is a rate, such as $\frac{2 \text{ miles}}{10 \text{ minutes}}$.   **15.** C

Lesson 5-1   Extra Practice

17. 203.75 Calories per serving   **19.** 32 mi/gal
21. $108.75 \div 15 = \$7.25$, $\$7.25 \times 18 = \$130.50$
23. C   **25.** G   **27.** $\frac{2}{7}$ **29.** $\frac{2}{3}$

Lesson 5-2   Independent Practice

1. $1\frac{1}{2}$ **3** $\frac{4}{27}$ **5.** $\frac{2}{25}$ **7** $6 per yard   **9.** $\frac{5}{6}$ page
11. $\frac{39}{250}$ **13.** $\frac{11}{200}$ **15.** Sample answer: If one of the numbers in the ratio is a fraction, then the ratio can be a complex fraction.   **17.** $\frac{1}{2}$

Lesson 5-2   Extra Practice

19. 4   **21.** $\frac{1}{10}$ **23.** $\frac{1}{10}$ **25.** 8 costumes   **27.** $\frac{3}{125}$
29. $\frac{1}{12}$ **31.** D   **33.** C   **35.** 24   **37.** 32   **39.** 1,000

Lesson 5-3   Independent Practice

1 115 mi/h   **3** 322,000 m/h   **5.** 6.1 mi/h
7. 7,200 Mb/h   **9.** Sample answer: Convert 42 miles per hour to miles per minute.   **11.** 461.5 yd/h

Lesson 5-3   Extra Practice

13. 1,760   **15.** 66   **17.** 35.2   **19a.** 6.45 ft/s
19b. 2,280 times   **19c.** 0.11 mi   **19d.** 900,000 times
21. H   **23.** no; Since the unit rates, $\frac{\$9}{1 \text{ baseball hat}}$ and $\frac{\$8}{1 \text{ baseball hat}}$ are not the same, the rates are not equivalent.

25.

Payment	$22	÷ 2 × 5	$55
Hours	2	÷ 2 × 5	5

Lesson 5-4   Independent Practice

1

Time (days)	1	2	3	4
Water (L)	225	450	675	900

Yes; the time to water ratios are all equal to $\frac{1}{225}$.
3. The table for Desmond's Time shows a proportional relationship. The ratio between the time and the number of laps is always 73.
5 a. yes; Sample answer:

Side Length (units)	1	2	3	4
Perimeter (units)	4	8	12	16

The side length to perimeter ratio for side lengths of 1, 2, 3, and 4 units is $\frac{1}{4}$, $\frac{2}{8}$ or $\frac{1}{4}$, $\frac{3}{12}$ or $\frac{1}{4}$, $\frac{4}{16}$ or $\frac{1}{4}$. Since

these ratios are all equal to $\frac{1}{4}$, the measure of the side length of a square is proportional to the square's perimeter.
b. no; Sample answer:

Side Length (units)	1	2	3	4
Area (units²)	1	4	9	16

The side length to area ratio for side lengths of 1, 2, 3, and 4 units is $\frac{1}{1}$ or 1, $\frac{2}{4}$ or $\frac{1}{2}$, $\frac{3}{9}$ or $\frac{1}{3}$, $\frac{4}{16}$ or $\frac{1}{4}$. Since these ratios are not equal, the measure of the side length of a square is not proportional to the square's area.
7. It is not proportional because the ratio of laps to time is not consistent; $\frac{4}{1} \neq \frac{6}{2} \neq \frac{8}{3} \neq \frac{10}{4}$.   **9.** B

Lesson 5-4   Extra Practice

11.

Degrees Celsius	0	10	20	30
Degrees Fahrenheit	32	50	68	86

No; the degrees Celsius to degrees Fahrenheit ratios are not all equal.   **13a.** No; the fee to ride tickets ratios are not equal.   **13b.** no; Sample answer: The fee increase is inconsistent. The table shows an increase of $4.50 from 5 to 10 tickets, an increase of $4 from 10 to 15 tickets, and an increase of $2.50 from 15 to 20 tickets.
15.

n	30	60	120	**173**
p	90	180	360	519

17. 20   **19.** 12   **21.** 3

Problem-Solving Investigation   The Four-Step Plan

Case 3. $360   **Case 5.** Add 2 to the first term, 3 to the second, 4 to the third, and so on; 15, 21, 28.

Lesson 5-5   Independent Practice

1

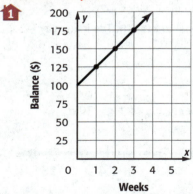

Not proportional; The graph does not pass through the origin.
3 Plant B; The graph is a straight line through the origin.
5. Proportional; Sample answer: The ordered pairs would be (0, 0), (1, 35), (2, 70). This would be a straight line through the origin.

7.

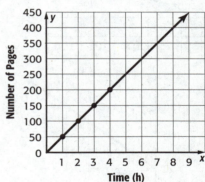

Temperature (°F) axis: 60, 65, 70, 75, 80, 85, 90, 95, 100, 105

Time axis: 1:00 PM, 3:00 PM, 5:00 PM, 7:00 PM

Time

Not proportional; The graph does not pass through the origin.

Lesson 5-5   Extra Practice

9. Not proportional; The graph does not pass through the origin.   **11.** Not proportional; The graph does not pass through the origin.   **13.** The number of heartbeats is proportional to the number of seconds because the graph is a straight line through the origin.   **15.** Samora's; The graph is a straight line through the origin.   **17.** $\frac{5}{1}$ **19.** $\frac{1}{5}$

Lesson 5-6   Independent Practice

1 40   **3.** 3.5   **5.** $\frac{2}{5} = \frac{x}{20}$; 8 ounces   **7** $c = 0.50p$; $4.00   **9.** $\frac{360}{3} = \frac{n}{7}$; 840 visitors   **11.** 256 c; Sample answer: The ratio of cups of mix to cups of water is 1:8, which means that the proportion $\frac{1}{8} = \frac{32}{x}$ is true and can be solved.   **13.** 18   **15.** B

Lesson 5-6   Extra Practice

17. 7.2   **19.** $\frac{6}{7} = \frac{c}{40}$; about 34 patients   **21.** $s = 45w$; $360   **23.** B   **25.** No, the ratios for each age and height are not equal.   **27.** Yes; the unit rate is $\frac{15}{1}$ or $15 per hour.   **29.** 500 kB/min

Lesson 5-7   Independent Practice

1 6 m per s   **3** $9 per shirt; Sample answer: The point (0, 0) represents 0 T-shirts purchased and 0 dollars spent. The point (1, 9) represents 9 dollars spent for 1 T-shirt.   **5.** 10 inches per hour
7. Sample answer:

Feet	Inches
3	18
6	36
9	54
12	72

9. C

Lesson 5-7   Extra Practice

11. $0.03 per minute   **13.** Josh; sample answer: The unit rate for Ramona is $9 per hour. The unit rate for Josh is $10 per hour.   **15.** A
17.

Input	Add 4	Output
1	1 + 4	5
2	2 + 4	6
3	3 + 4	7
4	4 + 4	8

19.

Input	Multiply by 2	Output
1	1 × 2	2
2	2 × 2	4
3	3 × 2	6
4	4 × 2	8

21.

Input	Add 6	Output
4	?	10
5	?	11
6	?	12
7	?	13

Lesson 5-8   Independent Practice

1 $\frac{50}{1}$ or 50; Adriano read 50 pages every hour.

Number of Pages axis: 0, 50, 100, 150, 200, 250, 300, 350, 400, 450

Time (h) axis: 1 2 3 4 5 6 7 8 9

3 **a.** It shows that car A travels 120 miles in 2 hours.
b. It shows that car B travels 67.5 miles in 1.5 hours.
c. the speed of each car at that point   **d.** the average speed of the car   **e.** Car A; the slope is steeper.

5. Marisol found $\frac{run}{rise}$. Her answer should be $\frac{3}{2}$.   **7.** D

Lesson 5-8   Extra Practice

9a. It costs $20 to rent a paddle boat from Water Wheels for 1 hour.   **9b.** It costs $50 to rent a paddle boat from Fun in the Sun for 2 hours.

11.

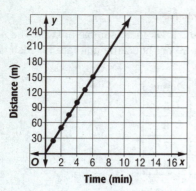

13.

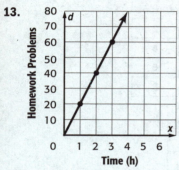

15. C   **17.** No; sample answer:
$\frac{3.50}{1} \neq \frac{4.50}{2}$ **19.** Yes; sample answer:
$\frac{7.50}{1} = \frac{15}{2} = \frac{22.5}{3} = \frac{30}{4}$

Lesson 5-9   Independent Practice

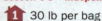 30 lb per bag

3.

Time (h)	1	2	3	4
Charge ($)	75	100	125	150

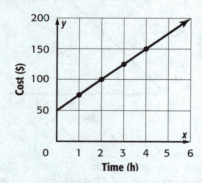

No; sample answer: $\frac{75}{1} \neq \frac{100}{2}$; Because there is no constant ratio and the line does not go through the origin, there is no direct variation.   **5** no   **7.** no   **9.** $y = \frac{7}{4}x$; 21
11. $y = \frac{1}{4}x$; −28   **13.** Sample answer: 9; $5\frac{1}{2}$; 36; 22   **15.** C

Lesson 5-9   Extra Practice

17. 7 c   **19.** yes; 0.2   **21.** C   **23.** yes; 36

25. $\frac{8}{1}$; Each ticket costs $8.

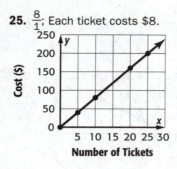

Chapter Review   Vocabulary Check

1. rate   **3.** ordered   **5.** complex   **7.** slope   **9.** proportion   **11.** Dimensional

Chapter Review   Key Concept Check

1. denominator   **3.** vertical change to horizontal change

Chapter Review   Problem Solving

1. the 16-ounce bottle   **3.** No; Sample answer: The cost for 1 month of service is $60, while the cost for 2 months is $90; $\frac{60}{1} \neq \frac{90}{2}$ **5.** 721.8 lb

Chapter 6 Percents

Chapter 6   Are You Ready?

1. 48   **3.** $70   **5.** 72.5%   **7.** 92%

Lesson 6-1   Independent Practice

1. 120.9   **3.** $147.20   **5** 17.5   **7.** 1.3   **9.** 30.1
11. $7.19 at Pirate Bay, $4.46 at Funtopia, $9.62 at Zoomland   **13.** 4   **15** 0.61   **17.** 520   **19.** 158
21. 0.14   **23.** Sample answer: It is easiest to use a fraction when the denominator of the fraction is a multiple of the number. If this is not the case, a decimal may be easier to use.

Lesson 6-1   Extra Practice

25. 45.9   **27.** 14.7   **29.** $54   **31.** 0.3   **33.** 2.25
35. $19.95   **35.** D   **37.** 91.8   **39.** 133.92   **41.** 160

Lesson 6-2   Independent Practice

1. 35
$$\frac{1}{2} \cdot 70 = 35$$
$$0.1 \cdot 70 = 7 \text{ and}$$
$$5 \cdot 7 = 35$$

3 18
$$\frac{1}{5} \cdot 90 = 18$$
$$0.1 \cdot 90 = 9 \text{ and}$$
$$2 \cdot 9 = 18$$

5. 168

$$\frac{7}{10} \cdot 240 = 168$$
$$0.1 \cdot 240 = 24 \text{ and}$$
$$7 \cdot 24 = 168$$

7. 720

$$(2 \cdot 320) + \left(\frac{1}{4} \cdot 320\right) = 720$$

9. 2

$$0.01 \cdot 500 = 5 \text{ and}$$
$$\frac{2}{5} \cdot 5 = 2$$

11 about 96 mi; $0.01 \cdot 12{,}000 = 120$ and $\frac{4}{5} \cdot 120 = 96$

13. 6

$$\frac{2}{3} \cdot 9 = 6$$

15. 24

$$\frac{1}{10} \cdot 240 = 24$$

17a. Sample answer: about 260 canned foods; $200 + 0.3 \cdot 200$ **17b.** Sample answer: about 780 canned foods; $600 + 0.3 \cdot 600$ **19.** sometimes; Sample answer: one estimate for 37% of 60 is $\frac{2}{5} \cdot 60 = 24$.

Lesson 6-2 Extra Practice

21. 135

23. 90

$$\frac{9}{10} \cdot 100 = 90$$
$$0.1 \cdot 100 = 10 \text{ and}$$
$$9 \cdot 10 = 90$$

25. 0.7

$$0.01 \cdot 70 = 0.7$$

27. about 12 muscles; $\frac{3}{10} \cdot 40 = 12$ **29a.** Sample answer: 420; $\frac{7}{10} \cdot 600 = 420$ **29b.** Greater; both the number of passes and the percent were rounded up. **29c.** Tony Romo; sample answer: 64% of 520 must be greater than 64% of 325. **31.** G **33.** 300 **35.** $\frac{1}{4}$

Lesson 6-3 Independent Practice

1. 25% **3** 75 **5.** 36 **7.** $68 **9.** 80 **11** 0.2% **13a.** about 3.41% **13b.** about 24,795.62 km **13c.** about 6,378.16 km **15.** 20% of 500, 20% of 100, 5% of 100; If the percent is the same but the base is greater, then the part is greater. If the base is the same but the percent is greater, then the part is greater.

Lesson 6-3 Extra Practice

17. 45 **19.** 20 **21.** 20% **23.** 8 pencils; $0.25 \times 8 = 2$ **25.** 120% **27.** A **29.** 60% **31.** $\frac{3}{20}$ **33.** $\frac{8}{15}$ **35.** $\frac{7}{25}$

Lesson 6-4 Independent Practice

1 50%; $75 = n \cdot 150$ **3.** 63.7; $p = 0.65 \cdot 98$ **5.** 6; $p = 0.24 \cdot 25$ **7.** 50 books **9** a. 37% b. 31% **11.** 0.3;

$p = 0.004 \cdot 82.1$ **13.** 115%; $230 = n \cdot 200$ **15.** Sample answer: If the percent is less than 100%, then the part is less than the whole; if the percent equals 100%, then the part equals the whole; if the percent is greater than 100%, then the part is greater than the whole.

Lesson 6-4 Extra Practice

17. 20% **19.** 25%; $98 = n \cdot 392$ **21.** 4.4; $1.45 = 0.33 \cdot w$ **23.** 42.5; $17 = 0.4 \cdot w$ **25.** $17 = n \cdot 27$; 63% **27.** $6.15; $0.25 \cdot 6 = 0.15$ and $6 + 0.15 = 6.15$ **29.** F **31.** < **33.** < **35.** 140; There are 140 students that participate in fall sports.

Problem-Solving Investigation   Determine Reasonable Answers

Case 3. 70 families **Case 5.** 240 students; Sample answer: $0.6 \times 400 = 240$

Lesson 6-5 Independent Practice

1. 20%; increase **3** 25%; decrease **5.** 41%; decrease **7** 28% **9.** 38%; decrease **11a.** 100% **11b.** 300% **13.** about 4.2% **15.** He did not write a ratio comparing the change to the original amount. It should have had a denominator of $52 and the percent of change would be about 140%.

Lesson 6-5 Extra Practice

17. 50%; decrease **19.** 33%; increase **21a.** about 3.8%; increase **21b.** about 2.9%; decrease **23.** 25% **25.** 6,500 comments **27.** 200% **29.** 45.93 **31.** 49,695.72 mi

Lesson 6-6 Independent Practice

1. $69.60 **3** $1,605 **5** $35.79 **7.** $334.80 **9.** $10.29 **11.** 7% **13.** $54, $64.80; The percent of gratuity is 20%. All of the other pairs have a gratuity of 15%.

Lesson 6-6 Extra Practice

15. $103.95 **17.** $7.99 **19.** $96.26 **21.** Yes; $84 was earned. $5\% \times \$70 = \$3.50$; $\$70 + \$3.50 = \$73.50$; $15\% \times \$70 = \$10.50$; $\$73.50 + \$10.50 = \$84$ **23.** B **25.** Store B; The total cost of the boots at store A is $58.19. The total cost of the boots at store B is $56.98. **27.** 57.85 **29.** $50

Lesson 6-7 Independent Practice

1. $51.20 **3** $6.35 **5** $4.50 **7a.** $28.76, $25.29, $28.87 **7b.** Funtopia **9.** $9.00 **11.** Sample answers are given.

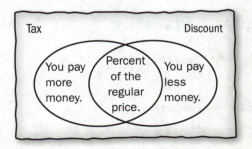

13. $25

Lesson 6-7 Extra Practice

15. $102.29 **17.** $169.15 **19.** Mr. Chang; $22.50 < $23.99 **21.** A **23.** 29%; increase **25.** 35%; decrease **27.** Carlos, 18 months; Karen, 16 months; Beng, 14 months

Lesson 6-8 Independent Practice

1. $38.40 **3.** $5.80 $1,417.50 **7.** $75.78 **9.** **a.** 5% **b.** Yes; he would have $5,208. **11.** Sample answer: If the rate is increased by 1%, then the interest earned is $60 more. If the time is increased by 1 year, then the interest earned is $36 more. **13.** C

Lesson 6-8 Extra Practice

15. $6.25 **17.** $123.75 **19.** $45.31 **21.** $14.06
23. C
25–28.

0 1 2 3 4 5 6 7 8 9 10

29. Belinda; Sample answer: Since 6 > 4, 5.6 > 5.4. So, Belinda walks a longer distance to school.

Lesson 6-9 Independent Practice

1 102.6 mi **3** 12 cm; $\frac{1}{300}$ **5.** 108 ft² **7.** 3x; about $6\frac{1}{3}$ ft or 6 feet 4 in.

Lesson 6-9 Extra Practice

9. 50 km **11.** 102.5 km **13.** $109\frac{3}{8}$ ft **15.** 3,420 ft²
17. H **19.** 5 feet **21.** 21

Chapter Review Vocabulary Check

Down
1. increase **3.** markdown **5.** selling **7.** discount
9. sales tax
Across
11. interest

Chapter Review Key Concept Check

1. 300 **3.** 18 **5.** 12

Chapter Review Problem Solving

1. 21 students; 12% = 0.12, 0.12(175) = 21 **3.** 5%
5. $18

Chapter 7 Statistics

Chapter 7 Are You Ready?

1. Rihanna **3.** 75

Lesson 7-1 Independent Practice

1. $\frac{3}{10}$, 0.3, or 30% **3** $\frac{2}{25}$, 0.08, or 8% **5** 9 students

7. About 143 students prefer humor books, and the number of students that prefer nonfiction is 88. So, there are about 55 more students who prefer humor books to nonfiction books. **9.** about 100 times **11.** D

Lesson 7-1 Extra Practice

13. 36 games **15.** about 6 free throws **17.** n = 27 · 2.38
19. D **21.** 35 **23.** 14.4 **25.** 2

Lesson 7-2 Independent Practice

1 The conclusion is valid. This is an unbiased systematic random sample. **3** This is a simple random sample. So, the sample is valid; about 205 people. **5.** Sample answer: Questions should be asked in a neutral manner. For example, the question "You really don't like Brand X, do you?" might not get the same answer as the question "Do you prefer Brand X or Brand Y?" **7.** Sometimes; Sample answer: The sample needs to represent the entire population to be valid. **9.** Sample answer: The sample will be biased because it is a convenience sample. Marisol will be asking only basketball fans.

Lesson 7-2 Extra Practice

11. This is an unbiased, simple random sample because randomly selected Californians were surveyed. So, the conclusion is valid. **13.** This is an unbiased, simple random sample. So, the conclusion is valid; 304 students. **15.** The survey results in a convenience sample; Sample answer: The school district should survey every tenth family living within the school district's boundaries. **17.** F
19. median; Sample answer: She scored better than the mean on four of the tests. She scored lower than the mode on four of the tests.

Lesson 7-3 Independent Practice

1 Graph B; Sample answer: The ratio of the area of the gas pumps in the graph on the right are not proportional to the cost of gas. **3** The median or the mode because they are much closer in value to most of the data.

5.

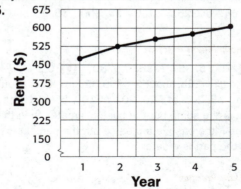

7. Sample answer: Since the graph makes it seem as if rent has been stable, a person may choose to become a tenant. **9.** C

Lesson 7-3 Extra Practice

11. Sample answer: The scale of the graph is not divided into equal intervals, so differences in heights appear less

than they actually are.   **13.** Sample answer: The mode is 100, but she only received 100 two times out of 6 tests.
15. 225 min; Sample answer: The ratios of the area of the cell phones are not proportional to the number of minutes.

Problem-Solving Investigation   Use a Graph

Case 3. Sample answer: 2017

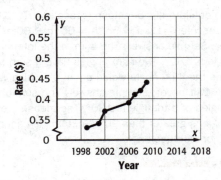

Year

Case 5. Sample answer: about $34

Lesson 7-4   Independent Practice

1 Sample answer: The times at Lucy's Steakhouse have a median of 20 minutes with an interquartile range of 20 minutes. The times at Gary's Grill have a median of 15 minutes with an interquartile range of 10 minutes. In general, a customer will wait longer at Lucy's Steakhouse.
3a. Plant A: 2.75, 0.75; Plant B: 3.1; 0.7
3b.

Plant Growth

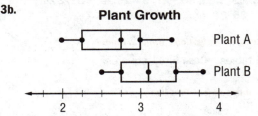

3c. Sample answer: Both populations have similar interquartile ranges. The median for Plant A is higher. So, Plant B generally showed more growth.   **5.** The data shown in the histograms are only shown in intervals. Specific values are not shown.   **7.** A

Lesson 7-4   Extra Practice

9. this season; Sample answer: Both seasons' scores have a median of 20 points, but last season's scores have an interquartile range of 15 points while this season's interquartile range is 10 points. So, the football team's performance was more consistent this season.
11. Sample answer: 2, 4, 4, 5, 8, 9, 10   **13.** 12.5 mph
15. Sample answer: There is a peak at 3 and a gap between 5 and 7.

Lesson 7-5   Independent Practice

1 box plot; shows the median
3.   **Number of Push-ups**

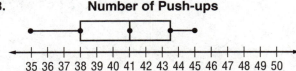

A box plot is an appropriate graph because there is a large set of data and it will show the measures of variation of the data set. This graph has a median of 41.
5a. Situation B; Sample answer: A bar graph can show the number of customers who made a purchase by each individual age.   **5b.** Yes; Sample answer: line plot; A line plot shows the frequency of data on a number line.
7. always; Sample answer: The sections of the circle graph can be taken from the bars of the graph and the percents can be found by dividing each bar's value by the total number of data values.   **9.** C

Lesson 7-5   Extra Practice

11. circle graph; compares parts to a whole
13a.

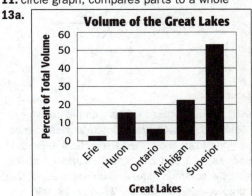

13b. Sample answer: The circle graph is most appropriate because it shows how each lake compares to the whole.
15.

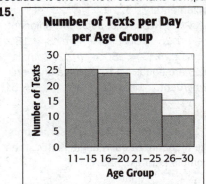

A histogram is an appropriate graph because the data is given in intervals. The graph shows people ages 26–30 text the least amount.   **17.** I   **19.** 65 men; 65 women

Chapter Review   Vocabulary Check

Across
5. population   **9.** sample
Down
1. systematic   **3.** simple   **7.** unbiased

Chapter Review   Key Concept Check

1. survey   **3.** biased sample

Chapter Review   Problem Solving

1. $\frac{3}{10}$ or 0.3 or 30%   **3.** This is a systematic random sample.   **5.** Sample answer: The median score for Class A

is about 6 points lower than the median score for Class B.
7. no; Sample answer: A circle graph compares parts of the data to the whole.

Chapter 8 Geometric Figures

Chapter 8 Are You Ready?

1. 40° **3.** 90° **5.** 6.72 yd^2

Lesson 8-1 Independent Practice

1. ∠ABC, ∠CBA, ∠B, ∠4; acute **3** ∠MNP, ∠PNM, ∠N, ∠1; obtuse **5** neither **7.** adjacent **9.** vertical **11.** 11
15. True; Sample answer:

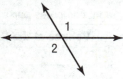

17. A

Lesson 8-1 Extra Practice

19. ∠HKI, ∠IKH, ∠K, ∠8; obtuse **21a.** Sample answer: ∠1 and ∠3; Since ∠1 and ∠3 are opposite angles formed by the intersection of two lines, they are vertical angles.
21b. Sample answer: ∠1 and ∠2; Since ∠1 and ∠2 share a common vertex, a common side, and do not overlap, they are adjacent angles. **23.** 9 **25.** B **27.** 40 **29.** 90°
31. $\overline{AB}, \overline{BA}$

Lesson 8-2 Independent Practice

1. neither **3** supplementary **5.** 20 **7** 23
9. Sample answer: ∠CGK, ∠KGJ **11a.** adjacent; adjacent; vertical **11b.** m∠1 + m∠2 = 180°; m∠2 + m∠3 = 180°
11c. m∠1 = 180° − m∠2; m∠3 = 180° − m∠2; Sample answer: m∠1 and m∠3 are equal. **11d.** Sample answer: Vertical angles are congruent. **13.** m∠E = 39°, m∠F = 51°

Lesson 8-2 Extra Practice

15. supplementary **17.** neither **19.** 16 **21.** sometimes; Sample answer: If the measure of each angle is 45°, then the two angles are complementary. **23.** D

25. 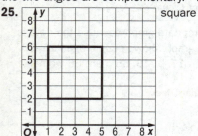 square

27. parallelogram

Lesson 8-3 Independent Practice

1 Sample answer: acute equilateral

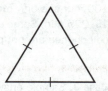

3 acute equilateral **5.** obtuse isosceles **7.** 118
9. acute isosceles **11.** a = 55; b = 65; c = 60; d = 30
13a. never; Sample answer: The sum of the interior angles of a triangle is 180°. Two right angles have a sum of 180°. This means the third angle would equal 0°, which is not possible. **13b.** never; Sample answer: The sum of the interior angles of a triangle is 180°. The measure of an obtuse angle is greater than 90°. So, triangle cannot have more than one obtuse angle.

Lesson 8-3 Extra Practice

15. acute isosceles **17.** right scalene
19. obtuse isosceles;
Sample answer:

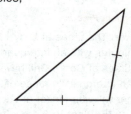

21. 90 **23.** 53° **25.** 30 **27.** B **29.** 47 **31.** 32 ft^2
33. 25 m^2 **35.** 36 in^2

Problem-Solving Investigation   Make a Model

Case 3. 15 tables   **Case 5.** 41 squares

Lesson 8-4 Independent Practice

1.   top   side   front

3.   top   side   front

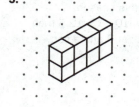

5.

7. top   side   front

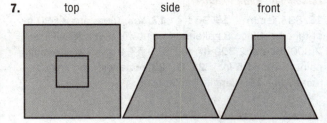

9. triangle; It is the only two-dimensional figure.   **11.** C

Lesson 8-4   Extra Practice

13. top   side   front

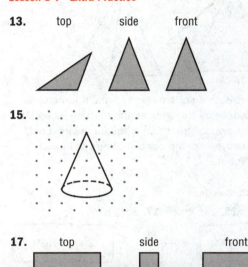

15.

17. top   side   front

19. B

Lesson 8-5   Independent Practice

1 **Figure name:** triangular pyramid
bases: *ACD*
faces: *ACD, ABD, ABC, DBC*
edges: $\overline{AB}, \overline{BC}, \overline{CD}, \overline{AD}, \overline{AC}, \overline{BD}$
vertices: *A, B, C, D*
3 rectangle   **5.** triangle   **7.** False; two planes intersect at a line, which is an infinite number of points.
9. Sometimes; a rectangular prism has 2 bases and 4 faces, but a triangular prism has 2 bases and 3 faces.
11. C

Lesson 8-5   Extra Practice

13. Figure name: rectangular prism
bases: *ABCD, EFGH, ABFE, DCGH, ADHE, BCGF*
faces: *ABCD, EFGH, ABFE, DCGH, ADHE, BCGF*
edges: $\overline{AB}, \overline{BC}, \overline{CD}, \overline{AD}, \overline{EF}, \overline{FG}, \overline{GH}, \overline{EH}, \overline{AE}, \overline{BF}, \overline{CG}, \overline{DH}$
vertices: *A, B, C, D, E, F, G, H*
15. curve   **17.** Because there are two parallel, congruent triangular bases, it is a triangular prism.   **19.** F
21. trapezoid   **23.** parallelogram

Chapter Review   Vocabulary Check
Across
11. equilateral   **15.** complementary
Down
1. adjacent   **3.** supplementary   **5.** triangle   **7.** vertical
9. acute   **13.** right

Chapter Review   Key Concept Check
1. vertex   **3.** 90°

Chapter Review   Problem Solving
1. Sample answer: vertical: ∠1 and ∠3; adjacent: ∠1 and ∠2   **3.** 40
5.   top   side   front

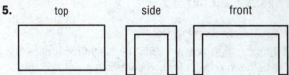

Chapter 9 Measure Figures

Chapter 9   Are You Ready?
1. 42 sq m   **3.** 76.5 sq mm

Lesson 9-1   Independent Practice
1. 2.5 mm   **3.** 34 cm   **5** $3.14 \times 13 = 40.8$ cm
7 19 people   **9a.** 30 mm   **9b.** 31.4 mm
9c. 31.4159 mm   **9d.** Sample answer: The more decimal places of the estimate of π, the more precise the circumference.   **11.** 18 in.   **13.** 257 cm   **15.** Greater than; Sample answer: Since the radius is 4 feet, the diameter is 8 feet. Since π is a little more than 3, the circumference will be a little more than 3 times 8, or 24 feet.   **17.** The circumference would double. For example, with a diameter of 4 feet, the circumference is about 12.6 feet. With a diameter of 8 feet, the circumference is about 25.1 feet.

Lesson 9-1   Extra Practice
19. 3.5 in.   **21.** 72 ft   **23.** $\frac{22}{7} \times 21 = 66$ ft   **25.** $\frac{22}{7} \times 42 = 132$ mm   **27.** 37.7 cm   **29.** Each is π, or about 3.14, units longer than the previous circle.   **31.** I
33. 315 cm^2 **35.** 2,015 mm^2 **37.** 375 in^2

Lesson 9-2   Independent Practice
1. $3.14 \times 6 \times 6 = 113.0$ cm^2 **3** $3.14 \times 5.5 \times 5.5 = 95.0$ ft^2 **5.** $3.14 \times 6.3 \times 6.3 = 124.6$ mm^2
7. 254.3 ft^2 **9.** 226.1 in^2 **11.** 163.3 yd^2 **13.** The large pizza; the medium pizza's area is 78.5 square inches and costs $0.102 per square inch. The large pizza's area is 153.86 square inches and costs $0.097 per square inch.
15. When the radius of a circle is doubled, the circumference doubles and the area is 4 times as large. In the formula for area of a circle, the radius is squared, so when the radius of a circle is doubled, the area is 2^2 or 4 times as large.   **17.** 5.9 in^2 **19.** D

Lesson 9-2   Extra Practice

21. 3.14 × 6.3 × 6.3 = 124.6 cm² **23.** 3.14 × 5.4 × 5.4 = 91.6 yd² **25.** 3.14 × 9.3 × 9.3 = 271.6 mm² **27.** 144.7 ft² **29.** 64.3 in² **31.** circle; $\frac{1}{2}$ · 100 · 100 < 3 · 50 · 50 **33.** D **35.** 210 in² **37.** 39.5 cm²

Lesson 9-3   Independent Practice

1. 64 cm² **3.** 220.5 cm² **5** 38.6 ft² **7** 119.5 ft² **9.** 77 cm² **11.** 38 ft²; 28 ft **13.** 110.8 ft²

Lesson 9-3   Extra Practice

15. 87.5 m² **17.** 180 cm² **19.** 9 cm² **21.** 240 ft² **23.** G **25.** 3.7 cm² **27.** 4.7 m

Lesson 9-4   Independent Practice

1 192 m³ **3** 108 m³ **5b.** The height must allow the water to be deep enough for someone to get wet and the length and width must allow a person to fit. So the first and last sets of dimensions would not work. **7a.** Sample answer: There is a direct relationship between the volume and the length. Since the length is doubled, the volume is also doubled. **7b.** The volume is eight times greater. **7c.** Neither; Sample answer: doubling the height will result in a volume of 4 · 4 · 10 or 160 in³; doubling the width will result in a volume of 4 · 8 · 5 or 160 in³. **9.** D

Lesson 9-4   Extra Practice

11. 236.3 cm³ **13.** 20.4 mm³ **15.** 306.52 = 19.4h; 15.8 m **17.** 166$\frac{1}{4}$ yd³ **19.** B **21.** C **23.** 25.8 m **25.** 29.2 cm

Problem-Solving Investigation   Solve a Simpler Problem

Case 3. 80 chairs **Case 5.** Sample answer: Asia, 17,251,712.4 mi²; Africa, 11,616,153.02 mi²; N. America, 9,488,441.82 mi²

Lesson 9-5   Independent Practice

1 80 ft³ **3.** 42 ft³ **5.** 14 in. **7** 10 in³ **9.** The volume is eight times greater; Sample answer: Since each dimension is two times greater, the volume is 2 × 2 × 2 or eight times greater. **11.** Sample answer: first set: area of the base, 40 ft²; height of the pyramid, 12 ft; second set: area of the base, 30 ft²; height of the pyramid, 16 ft **13.** The volumes are the same.

Lesson 9-5   Extra Practice

15. 60 in³ **17.** 195 yd³ **19.** 11 ft **21.** 22 in. **23.** 1,234.2 m³ **25.** H **27.** 1.5 ft² **29.** 28.75 ft²

Lesson 9-6   Independent Practice

1 314 cm² **3** 207 in² **5.** 180 in² **7.** S.A. = 6x² **9.** False; Sample answer: A 9 × 7 × 13 rectangular prism has a surface area of 2(9 × 13) + 2(9 × 7) + 2(13 × 7) or 542 square units. Doubling the length, the surface area is 2(18 × 13) + 2(18 × 7) + 2(13 × 7) or 902 square units. 2 × 542 ≠ 902 **11.** 1,926 cm²

Lesson 9-6   Extra Practice

13. 833.1 mm² **15.** 96 ft² **17.** Yes; there are 2,520 ft² of fencing. Since 8 gallons of paint will cover 350 · 8 or 2,800 ft² and 2,800 ft² > 2,520 ft², 8 gallons is enough paint. **19.** 64.5 in² **21.** G **23.** rectangle; rectangle; rectangle **25.** triangle; circle; oval

Lesson 9-7   Independent Practice

1 95 in² **3.** 328 in² **5.** 0.52 ft² **7** 78 in² **9.** 6.5 cm **11.**

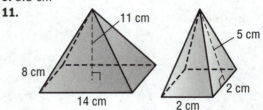

Sample answer: Both a square pyramid and a rectangular pyramid have isosceles triangles as their lateral faces. All the lateral faces are congruent on a square pyramid but, on a rectangular pyramid, the opposite pairs of lateral faces are congruent.

Lesson 9-7   Extra Practice

13. 197.1 m² **15.** 765 cm² **17.** 26.1 ft² **19.**

Area of the base ·····> $$S.A. = B + \frac{1}{2}P\ell$$ <····· Slant height

Perimeter of the base

21. H **23.** 13,890 cm² **25.** 5 m

Lesson 9-8   Independent Practice

1 2.3 m³ **3.** 2,600 ft² **5** 0.5 ft³ **7.** 10.4 m² **9.** 100 in³ **13.** C

Lesson 9-8   Extra Practice

15. 100 in³ **17.** 280.2 cm² **19.** B **21.** Sample answer: Find the volume of 2 pyramids.; 192 mm³ **23.**

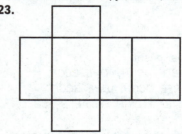

25.

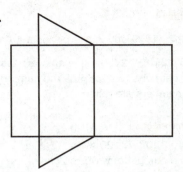

b. $\frac{6}{25}$; $\frac{13}{50}$

c.

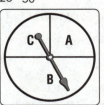

Sample answer: Section B should be one half of the spinner and sections A and C should each be one fourth of the spinner.   **7.** Yes; Sample answer:

$\frac{5 \text{ sharpened}}{10 \text{ unsharpened}} = \frac{20 \text{ sharpened}}{x \text{ unsharpened}}$. So, $x = 40$.

Chapter Review   Vocabulary Check

1. diameter   **3.** circle   **5.** circumference   **7.** semicircle
9. volume   **11.** lateral

Chapter Review   Key Concept Check

1. twice   **3.** height

Chapter Review   Problem Solving

1. 37.7 ft   **3.** 74.6 ft²; Sample answer: Find the area of the board. Then subtract the area of the circles.   **5.** 784 in³

Chapter 10 Probability

Chapter 10   Are You Ready?

1. $\frac{1}{3}$ **3.** $\frac{2}{3}$ **5.** 30   **7.** 24

Lesson 10-1   Independent Practice

1. $\frac{1}{4}$, 25%, or 0.25   **3** $\frac{1}{1}$, 100%, or 1   **5** $\frac{1}{5}$, 0.2, or 20%; Sample answer: Since 80% arrive on time, that means that 20% do not arrive on time.   **7.** Picking a black jelly bean is impossible since the probability of picking a black jelly bean is 0%.   **9a.** $\frac{1}{8}$, 0.125, 12.5%; $\frac{1}{2}$, 0.5, 50%

9b. $\frac{1}{8}$, 0.125, 12.5%   **11.** D

Lesson 10-1   Extra Practice

13. $\frac{1}{5}$, 20%, 0.2   **15.** $\frac{7}{10}$, 70%, or 0.7   **17.** $\frac{1}{2}$, 50%, or 0.5   **19.** $\frac{3}{5}$, 60%, or 0.6   **21.** The complement of selecting a girl is selecting a boy. The probability of the complement is $\frac{37}{100}$, 0.37, or 37%.   **23.** $\frac{124}{125}$, 99.2%, or 0.992; It is very likely that card 13 will *not* be chosen.   **25.** $\frac{1}{2}$, 0.5, or 50%   **27.** <   **29.** <

Lesson 10-2   Independent Practice

1 **a.** $\frac{1}{5}$; The experimental probability is close to the theoretical probability of $\frac{1}{6}$.   **b.** $\frac{9}{10}$; The experimental probability is close to the theoretical probability of $\frac{5}{6}$.

3a. 162 people   **3b.** about 134 people   **5** **a.** $\frac{1}{3}$ tosses

Lesson 10-2   Extra Practice

9. $P(\text{heads}) = \frac{\text{number of times heads occurs}}{\text{total number of coin tosses}} = \frac{9}{20}$; The experimental probability of $\frac{9}{20}$ is close to the theoretical probability of $\frac{1}{2}$.   **11.** 50 customers   **13.** B   **15.** $P(\text{not red})$ **17.** vanilla sundae, vanilla cone, chocolate sundae, chocolate cone, strawberry sundae, strawberry cone; equally likely

Lesson 10-3   Independent Practice

1. H1, H2, H3, H4, H5, T1, T2, T3, T4, T5
3 purple 10, purple 18, purple 21, purple 24, green 10, green 18, green 21, green 24, black 10, black 18, black 21, black 24, silver 10, silver 18, silver 21, silver 24

5. $\frac{1}{36}$;

1, 1	1, 2	1, 3	1, 4	1, 5	1, 6
2, 1	2, 2	2, 3	2, 4	2, 5	2, 6
3, 1	3, 2	3, 3	3, 4	3, 5	3, 6
4, 1	4, 2	4, 3	4, 4	4, 5	4, 6
5, 1	5, 2	5, 3	5, 4	5, 5	5, 6
6, 1	6, 2	6, 3	6, 4	6, 5	6, 6

7 $P(\text{Player 1}) = \frac{6}{8}$ or $\frac{3}{4}$; $P(\text{Player 2}) = \frac{2}{8}$ or $\frac{1}{4}$; RRB, RYB, RRY, RYY, BRB, BYB, BYY, BRY   **9.** The first outcome in the I bracket should be IC.

Lesson 10-3   Extra Practice

11.

Appetizer	Entree	Dessert	Sample Space
S	S	C	SSC
		A	SSA
	C	C	SCC
		A	SCA
Sa	S	C	SaSC
		A	SaSA
	C	C	SaCC
		A	SaCA

13a. 16 combinations **13b.** $\frac{1}{16}$ **13c.** 8 combinations
15. C **17.** $\frac{1}{8}$ **19.** $\frac{1}{2}$ **21.** $\frac{1}{3}$; There are 2 numbers out of 6 on a number cube that are greater than 4. $\frac{2}{6} = \frac{1}{3}$

Lesson 10-4 Independent Practice

1 Sample answer: Spin a spinner with 4 equal-size sections 50 times. **3.** Sample answer: Spin a spinner divided into 3 equal sections and roll a number cube. Repeat the simulation until all types of cookies are obtained. **5.** Sample answer: Use 3 red marbles to represent winning and 7 blue marbles to represent losing. Draw 1 marble 4 times, replacing the marble each time. **7.** Sample answer: a survey of 100 people voting on whether or not to enact a tax increase, where each person is equally likely to vote yes or no. Toss a coin 100 times. **9.** Sample answer: sometimes; The spinner must have equal-sized sections.

Lesson 10-4 Extra Practice

11. Sample answer: Use a spinner with 5 equal sections to represent the 5 discounts. Spin 4 times to represent 4 customers receiving cards. **13.** Sample answer: Toss a coin. Heads represents one color and tails represents the other. Repeat until both are selected. **15.** Sample answer: Spin a spinner with 4 equal sections. Each section represents one of the magazines. Repeat the simulation until all possible magazines are selected. **17.** F
19. 10 ways;

Number of Quarters	Number of Dimes	Number of Nickels
2	0	0
1	2	1
1	1	3
1	0	5
0	5	0
0	4	2
0	3	4
0	2	6
0	1	8
0	0	10

Problem-Solving Investigation Act It Out

Case 3. 31 **Case 5.** no; Sample answer: The experiment only produces 2 or 3 correct answers.

Lesson 10-5 Independent Practice

1 12 **3.** 84 **5.** 6 possible routes; $\frac{1}{6}$ or about 17%
7. $\frac{1}{50}$; very unlikely **9** No; the number of selections is $32 \cdot 11$ or 352, which is less than 365. **11.** 10 groups, 8 activities have 80 outcomes; the other two have 72 outcomes.

Lesson 10-5 Extra Practice

13. 48 **15.** 20 **17.** 24 **19.** 9 options; $\frac{1}{9}$ or about 11.1%; unlikely **21.** C **23.** 6 **25.** $\frac{1}{2}$ **27.** Sample answer: Assign each number of a number cube to a toy. Roll the number cube. Repeat until all numbers are rolled.

Lesson 10-6 Independent Practice

1 24 **3.** 840 **5.** 40,320 **7.** 120 ways **9** 6
11. Sample answer: The number of ways you can order 3 books on a shelf is $3 \cdot 2 \cdot 1$ or 6. **13.** C

Lesson 10-6 Extra Practice

15. 60 **17.** 120 **19.** $\frac{1}{90}$ **21.** $\frac{1}{120}$ **23.** C **25.** $\frac{29}{30}$
27.

Sweatshirt	Running Pants	Sample Space
white	black	white, black
white	gray	white, gray
red	black	red, black
red	gray	red, gray
gray	black	gray, black
gray	gray	gray, gray

Lesson 10-7 Independent Practice

1. $\frac{1}{24}$ **3** $\frac{1}{8}$ **5.** $\frac{1}{144}$ **7** $\frac{7}{95}$ **9.** $\frac{1}{19}$ **11.** $\frac{3}{8}$; dependent event; after the first piece of paper is chosen, there is one less from which to choose. **13.** Sample answer: Spinning the spinner twice represents two independent events. The probability of getting an even number is $\frac{2}{5}$ each time; $\frac{2}{5} \cdot \frac{2}{5}$ or $\frac{4}{25}$. **15** B

Lesson 10-7 Extra Practice

17. $\frac{5}{14}$ **19.** $\frac{92}{287}$ **21.** $\frac{3}{20}$ **23.** $\frac{7}{60}$ **25.** $\frac{3}{55}$ **27.** $\frac{6}{55}$
29. C **31.** $\frac{15}{77}$ **33.** 6 ways; Video 1, Video 2, Video 3; Video 1, Video 3, Video 2; Video 2, Video 1, Video 3; Video 2, Video 3, Video 1; Video 3, Video 1, Video 2; Video 3, Video 2, Video 1

Chapter Review Vocabulary Check

1. sample space **3.** theoretical

Chapter Review Key Concept Check

1. experimental probability **3.** compound event

Chapter Review Problem Solving

1. $\frac{6}{25}$ or 0.24 or 24%

3. $\frac{2}{4}$ or $\frac{1}{2}$;

First Toss	Second Toss	Sample Space
H	H	HH
	T	HT
T	H	TH
	T	TT

5. $\frac{6}{380}$ or $\frac{3}{190}$

Index

Aa

Bb

Cc

Index

Mm

Nn

Index

Unlike fractions
    adding, 107–114, 118
    subtracting, 107–114, 118

Vv

Variables, 163–166
    defining, 165

Variation
    constant of, 422–424
    direct, 421–428

Vertex
    of angles, 609
    of three-dimensional figures, 654

Vertical angles, 610

Vertical number line, 39, 49, 95, 100

Visual Overlap, 587–588

Vocabulary Check, 44, 69, 126, 153, 200, 239, 306, 337, 384, 431, 480, 533, 566, 599, 644, 663, 710, 759, 814, 843

Vocabulary Start-Up, 7, 19, 79, 87, 163, 171, 251, 261, 385, 405, 469, 507, 543, 609, 653, 673, 699, 737, 769, 833

Volume. *See also* formulas
    of composite figures, 745–748, 749–756
    of prisms, 699–706
    of pyramids, 711–712, 713–720
    surface area and, 733–736

Voluntary response sample, 552–553

Ww

Whole numbers, dividing fractions by, 358

Work Backward, 231, 303–305

Writing expressions, 165–166, 173–174

Writing inequalities, 314

Xx

x-axis, 385–388

x-coordinate, 385–388

Yy

y-axis, 385–388

y-coordinate, 385–388

Zz

Zero pair, 15, 16, 19

Name _____

$$=$$

Equation Mat **WM1**

WM2 **Centimeter Grid**

Name _____

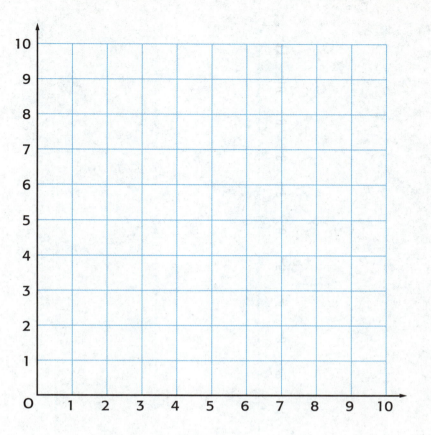

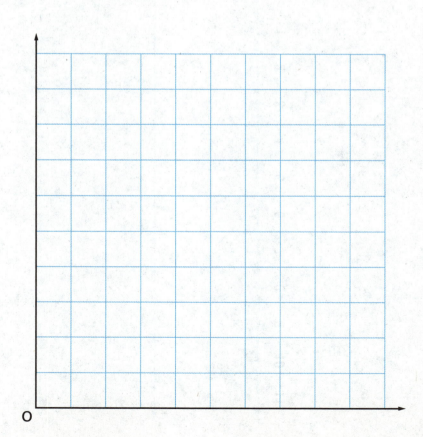

First Quadrant Grids **WM3**

Name _____

0
1
2
3
4
5
6
7
8
9

−11
−10
−9
−8
−7
−6
−5
−4
−3
−2
−1
0
1
2
3
4
5
6
7
8
9
10
11

WM4 **Number Lines**

Name _____

$$=$$

Equation Mat **WM5**

Name _____

WM6   **Centimeter Grid**

Name _____

Name _____

0 1 2 3 4 5 6 7 8 9

−11 −10 −9 −8 −7 −6 −5 −4 −3 −2 −1 0 1 2 3 4 5 6 7 8 9 10 11

What Are Foldables and How Do I Create Them?

Foldables are three-dimensional graphic organizers that help you create study guides for each chapter in your book.

Step 1 Go to the back of your book to find the Foldable for the chapter you are currently studying. Follow the cutting and assembly instructions at the top of the page.

Step 2 Go to the Key Concept Check at the end of the chapter you are currently studying. Match up the tabs and attach your Foldable to this page. Dotted tabs show where to place your Foldable. Striped tabs indicate where to tape the Foldable.

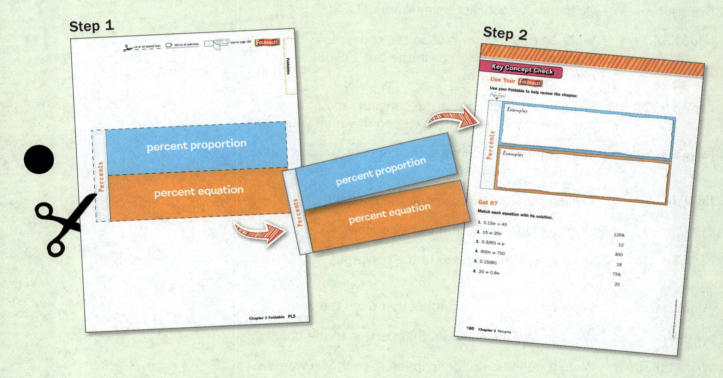

Step 1

Step 2

How Will I Know When to Use My Foldable?

When it's time to work on your Foldable, you will see a Foldables logo at the bottom of the **Rate Yourself!** box on the Guided Practice pages. This lets you know that it is time to update it with concepts from that lesson. Once you've completed your Foldable, use it to study for the chapter test.

Rate Yourself!

How well do you understand percent and proportions? Circle the image that applies.

Clear   Somewhat   No So
            Clear   Clear

For more help, go online to access a Personal Tutor.

FOLDABLES Time to update your Foldable!

How Do I Complete My Foldable?

No two Foldables in your book will look alike. However, some will ask you to fill in similar information. Below are some of the instructions you'll see as you complete your Foldable. **HAVE FUN** learning math using Foldables!

Instructions and what they mean

Best Used to...	Complete the sentence explaining when the concept should be used.
Definition	Write a definition in your own words.
Description	Describe the concept using words.
Equation	Write an equation that uses the concept. You may use one already in the text or you can make up your own.
Example	Write an example about the concept. You may use one already in the text or you can make up your own.
Formulas	Write a formula that uses the concept. You may use one already in the text.
How do I ...?	Explain the steps involved in the concept.
Models	Draw a model to illustrate the concept.
Picture	Draw a picture to illustrate the concept.
Solve Algebraically	Write and solve an equation that uses the concept.
Symbols	Write or use the symbols that pertain to the concept.
Write About It	Write a definition or description in your own words.
Words	Write the words that pertain to the concept.

Meet Foldables Author Dinah Zike

Dinah Zike is known for designing hands-on manipulatives that are used nationally and internationally by teachers and parents. Dinah is an explosion of energy and ideas. Her excitement and joy for learning inspires everyone she touches.

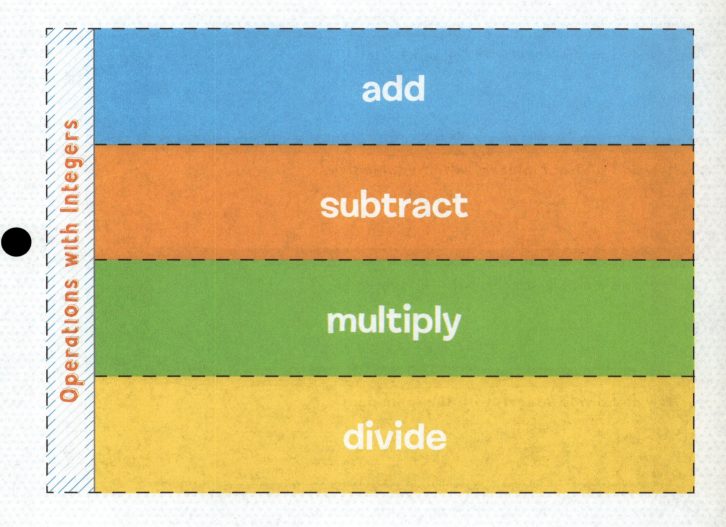

Operations with Integers

add

subtract

multiply

divide

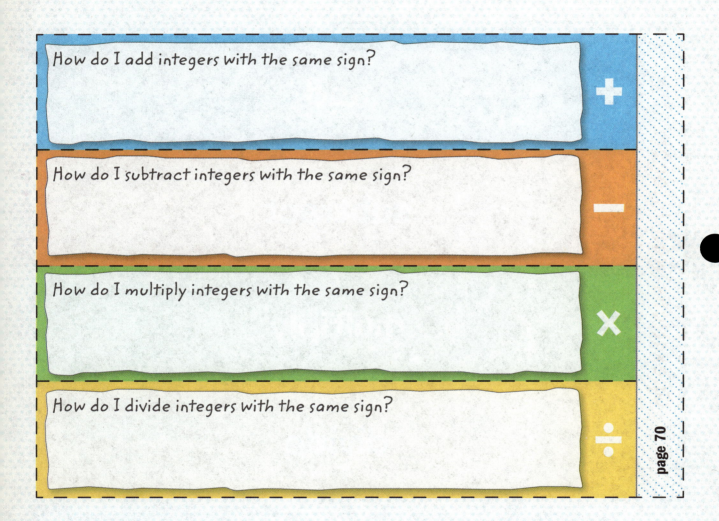

How do I add integers with the same sign?

+

How do I subtract integers with the same sign?

−

How do I multiply integers with the same sign?

✕

How do I divide integers with the same sign?

÷

page 70

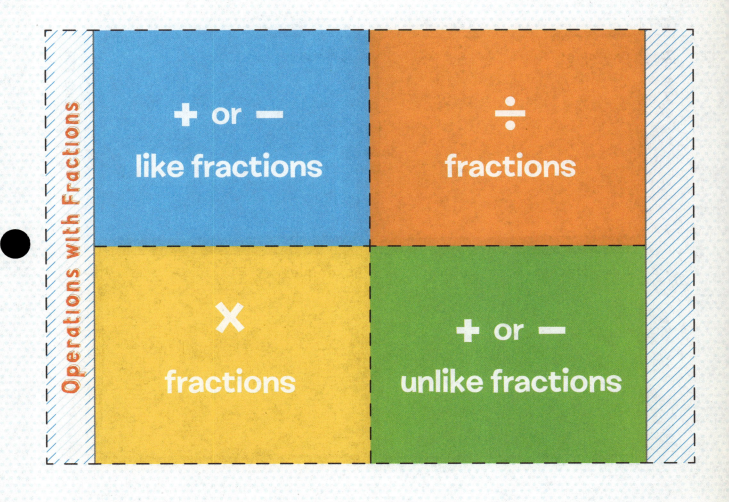

Operations with Fractions

**+ or −
like fractions**

**÷
fractions**

**✕
fractions**

**+ or −
unlike fractions**

✂ cut on all dashed lines   ⬜ fold on all solid lines   ▨ tape to page 154   **FOLDABLES**

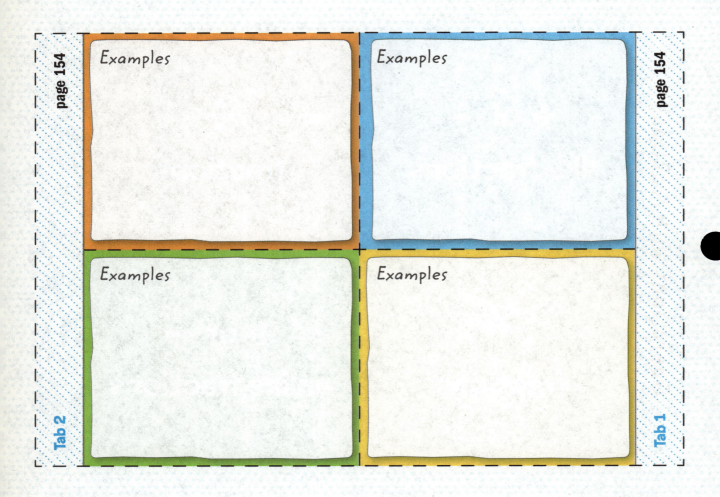

page 154

Examples

Examples

Examples

Examples

page 154

Tab 2

Tab 1

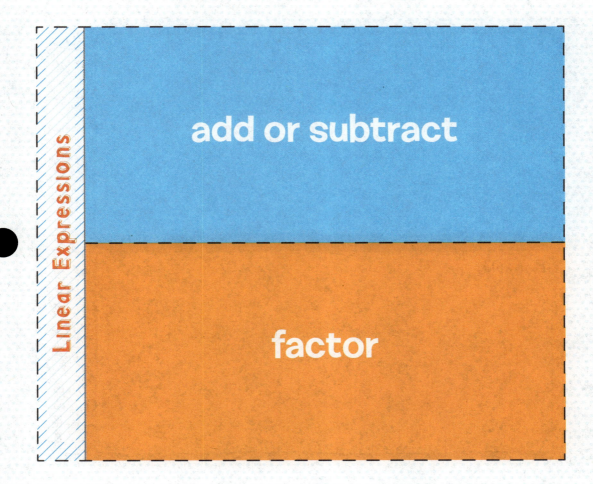

Linear Expressions

add or subtract

factor

✂ cut on all dashed lines ▱ fold on all solid lines ▨ tape to page 240

FOLDABLES®

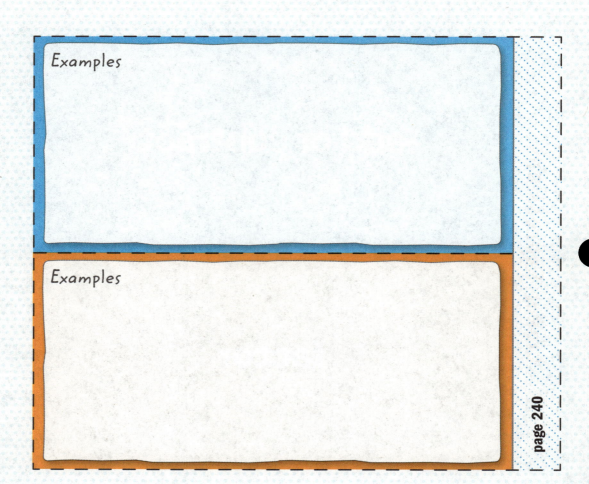

Examples

Examples

page 240

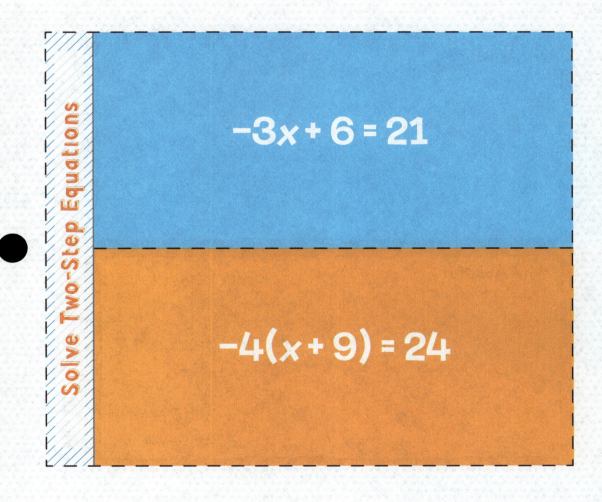

Solve Two-Step Equations

$$-3x + 6 = 21$$

$$-4(x + 9) = 24$$

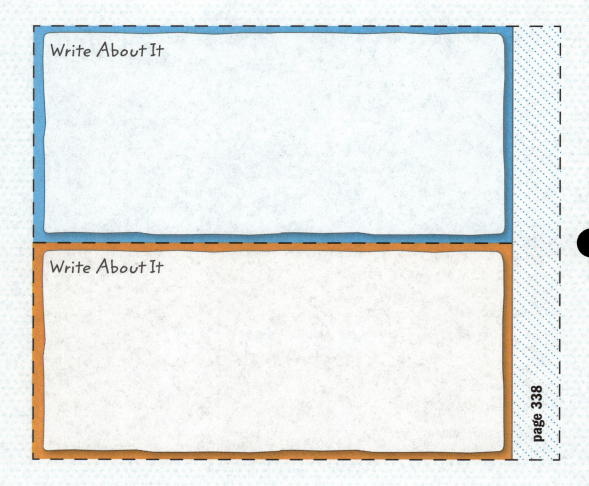

Write About It

Write About It

page 338

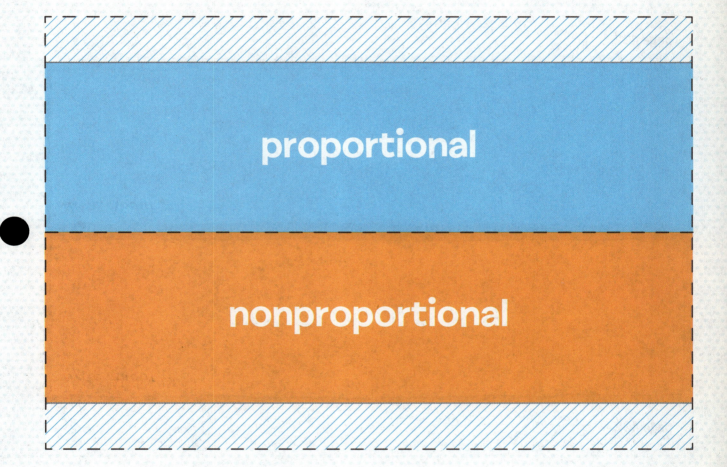

✂ - - - - - cut on all dashed lines ⬜ fold on all solid lines ▨ tape to page 432 **FOLDABLES**

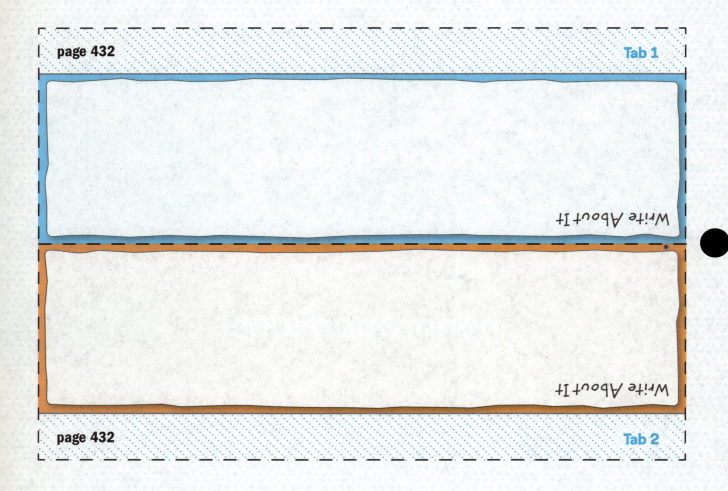

page 432   Tab 1

Write About It

Write About It

page 432   Tab 2

cut on all dashed lines | fold on all solid lines | tape to page 534

FOLDABLES

Percents

percent proportion

percent equation

cut on all dashed lines   fold on all solid lines   tape to page 534

FOLDABLES®

Definition

Definition

page 534

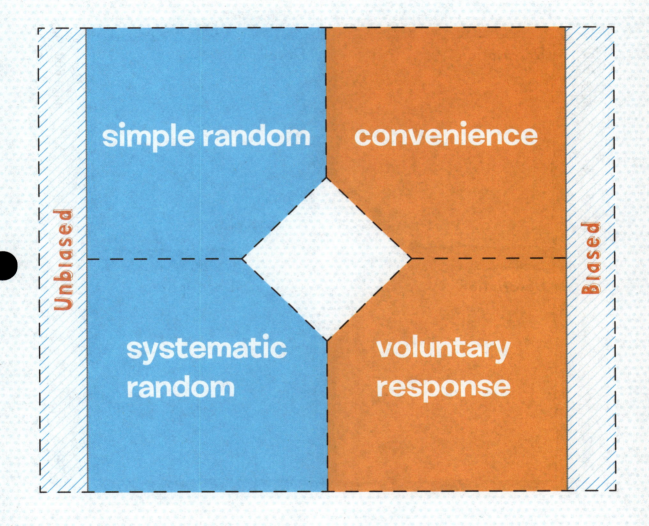

✂ cut on all dashed lines   fold on all solid lines   tape to page 600   **FOLDABLES**

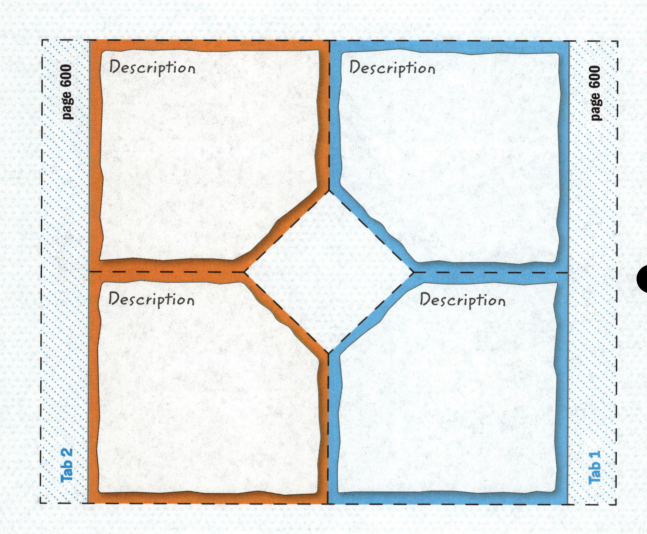

page 600

Description

Description

Description

Description

page 600

Tab 2

Tab 1

Angles

acute	scalene
obtuse	isosceles
right	equilateral

Triangles

✂ cut on all dashed lines   ▭ fold on all solid lines   tape to page 664   **FOLDABLES**

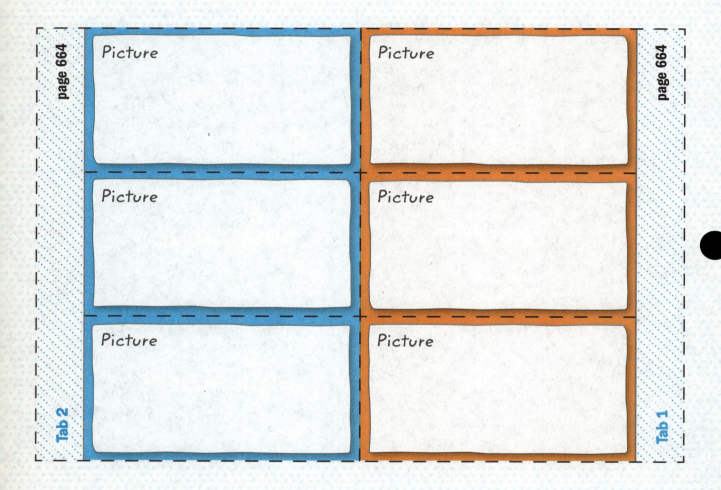

page 664

Picture

Picture

Picture

Picture

Tab 2

Picture

Picture

Tab 1

page 664

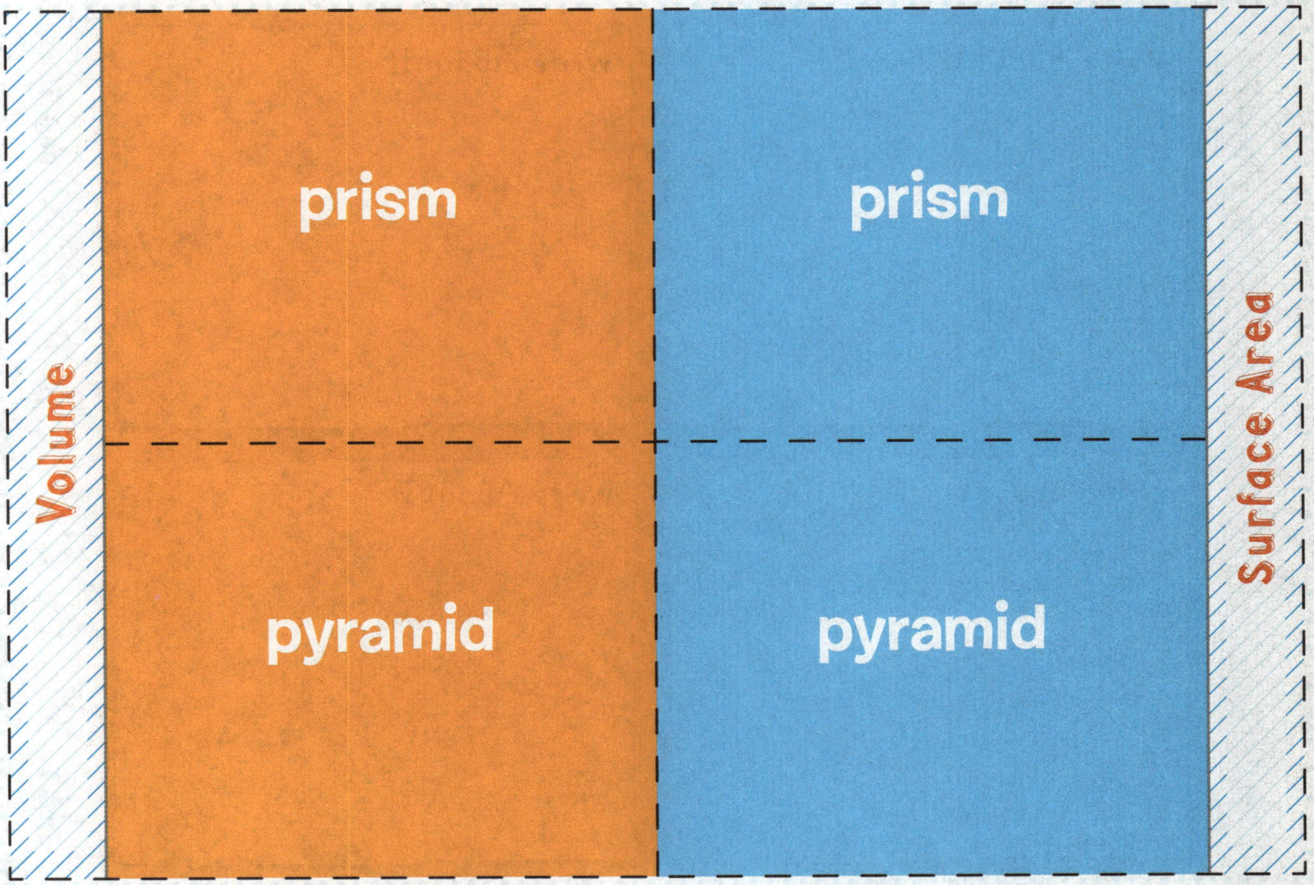

Volume

prism

prism

pyramid

pyramid

Surface Area

cut on all dashed lines   fold on all solid lines   tape to page 760   **FOLDABLES**®

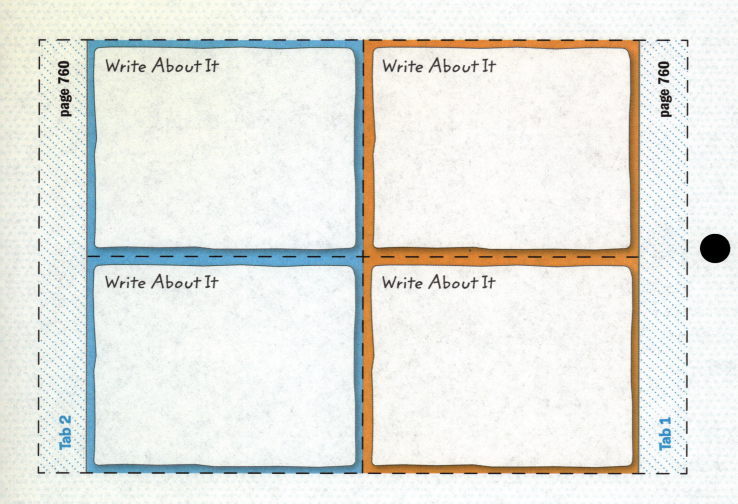

page 760

Write About It

Write About It

page 760

Write About It

Write About It

Tab 2

Tab 1

Probability

simple event	compound event

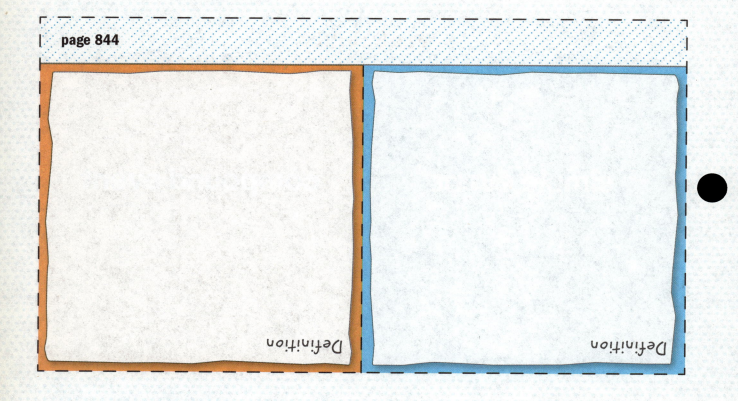

page 844

Definition

Definition

$$\frac{9}{10} \times \frac{5}{3} = \frac{45}{30} \quad \frac{3}{2}$$

$$\frac{1}{8} \times \frac{10}{93} = \frac{2}{3}$$